Carbonate Rocks II: Porosity and Classification of Reservoir Rocks

Selected Papers Reprinted from

AAPG BULLETIN

Published by The American Association of Petroleum Geologists
Tulsa, Oklahoma, U.S.A., 1972

Carbonate Rocks II: Porosity and Classification of Reservoir Rocks: Preface

Carbonate rocks are the host rocks for many of the world's most productive oil and gas fields. Traps in them are generally considered to be more risky to explore for and to develop than those in noncarbonate rocks, largely because of the many variables which affect the occurrence and distribution of reservoir-quality porosity. This volume of the Reprint Series, therefore, is largely devoted to papers concerning porosity in carbonate rocks.

A sufficient number of papers pertaining to carbonate rocks (which have been printed in the *Bulletin*) was judged by the review committee to be worthy of reprinting that they will make up several volumes in the Reprint Series. This one, *Carbonate Rocks II: Porosity and Classification of Reservoir Rocks,* is being published simultaneously with *Carbonate Rocks I: Classifications—Dolomite—Dolomitization* (Reprint Series No. 4). Succeeding volumes will deal with modern and ancient depositional environments; reefs in general and modern reefs; and reefs in late Paleozoic, Devonian, and Silurian rocks.

The papers were selected by Peggy Rice, A. A. Meyerhoff, and R. H. Dott, Sr., with the aid of L. L. Sloss, F. E. Kottlowski, and the writer; they were assembled by Elizabeth Ross.

JULES BRAUNSTEIN
Shell Oil Company
New Orleans, Louisiana
June 12, 1972

Reprinted from:
BULLETIN OF THE AMERICAN ASSOCIATION OF PETROLEUM GEOLOGISTS
VOL. 20, NO. 11 (NOVEMBER, 1936) PP. 1389-1412, 14 FIGS., 1 TABLE

DEVELOPMENT OF POROSITY IN LIMESTONES[1]

W. V. HOWARD[2] AND MAX W. DAVID[3]
Tulsa, Oklahoma, and Midland, Texas

ABSTRACT

The continuous porosity possessed by limestone reservoirs is developed mainly by solution by acids resulting from the bacterial decomposition of organic matter and by carbon dioxide formed during these processes.

Porosity is shown to be of three types, namely, equi-solution, channel, and cellular. In the development of these types of porosity, the composition of the rock and arrangement of mineral grains is important.

Reactions taking place within the reservoir, both prior and subsequent to the entrance of oil, may result in the formation of much secondary calcite. The effect of this material upon the results of acid treatment and also that of the insoluble residues released are touched upon briefly.

INTRODUCTION

Most limestone oil reservoirs owe their porosity to solution performed by meteoric waters, yet little has been published on the mechanics of this process. This investigation on the development of porosity in limestones was carried on by experimental methods, namely, etching and staining. It is hoped that this work may have practical application, not only with reference to the origin of limestone reservoirs, but also to the variable effect of acid treatment of reservoirs.

The limestones and dolomites used in this report were taken, for the most part, by A. N. Murray from outcrops in Illinois, Indiana, Ohio, and Ontario, during the field season of 1927.

---

[1] This paper is based on a thesis submitted by Max W. David in partial fulfillment of the requirements for the degree of Master of Science in Geology, in the Graduate School of the University of Illinois. Manuscript received, July 27, 1936.

[2] J. G. Wray and Company.

[3] Sinclair-Prairie Oil Company.

NATURE OF POROSITY IN LIMESTONES

The one thing which seems certain about the porosity of limestones is that it is modified continuously so long as aqueous solutions are present in the rock, that is, so long as it has any porosity. If the solution is at rest, there will be continuous solution and precipitation of carbonates with the development of larger crystals. Although this process will not increase or decrease porosity, it may bring about changes in permeability. If the solution is circulating, recrystallization, solution, or precipitation of introduced materials will take place either individually or collectively.

Thus, one may refer to the present porosity of a limestone as opposed to the former porosity. The former porosity may in turn consist of original and secondary porosity. There may even be several different stages of former porosity corresponding with changes in conditions affecting the rock. In many places, the rock itself contains indisputable evidence of some of these stages.

Continuous and discontinuous porosity.—Murray[4] states that porosity may be divided into two classes: continuous porosity, suited to the accumulation and commercial production of oil, and discontinuous porosity, unfavorable to the accumulation and production of oil. The continuous type may be made discontinuous by the deposition of secondary minerals at strategic points throughout the reservoir. If they are deposited before oil or source material is introduced, it is naturally impossible for certain parts of the limestone to become a reservoir. Murray found secondary calcite crystals which contained globules of oil in limestone at Monon, Indiana. This dates the calcite deposition to both (a) simultaneous growth with the introduction of oil and (b) subsequent growth after accumulation of oil. If deposition of secondary calcite or other secondary minerals throughout a limestone takes place after accumulation of oil, the oil may be locked up in disconnected channels and cavities. The natural recovery of oil from such a reservoir is limited to the connected area surrounding each well.

Limestone reservoirs.—Howard's[5] original classification of limestone reservoirs may be considered as too complex. Actually, the types of limestone reservoirs now known fall into the following classes.

[4] A. N. Murray, "Limestone Oil Reservoirs of the Northeastern United States and of Ontario, Canada," *Econ. Geol.*, Vol. 25 (1930), pp. 452–59.

[5] W. V. Howard, "A Classification of Limestone Reservoirs," *Bull. Amer. Assoc. Petrol. Geol.*, Vol. 12 (1928), pp. 1153–61.

1. Limestones with secondary porosity associated with former erosion surfaces
   a. Strongly jointed
   b. Not strongly jointed
2. Jointed limestones without secondary porosity

He estimates that 95 per cent of the known limestone oil reservoirs owe their porosity to exposure to weathering. Thus, most limestone reservoirs owe their porosity to solution performed by meteoric waters.

SOLUTION OF LIMESTONES

Meteoric waters.—Although pure water dissolves practically no calcium carbonate, it is important in the development of secondary porosity by solution, in that it carries solvents, such as carbonic acid and organic acids.

There is considerable evidence for the passage of water through limestones. Many joints not normally wide have been observed to be 1–3 inches across. Limestone caverns usually carry considerable water, particularly through the joints. This can be readily seen by observing the ceiling of a wet cave. The intersection points of the joint pattern usually carry the most water; in fact, stalactites usually develop at these points. Also, many joints and fractures are filled with secondary minerals of the types that are deposited from aqueous solutions only.

Carbonic acid.—Because of its abundance, carbonic acid has been considered the most important solvent found in meteoric waters. Common sources of carbonic acid are carbon dioxide gas derived from the respiration of plant roots, the decomposition of organic matter, and the washing of the atmosphere by rain. The annual amount produced will vary in different regions, but it must be a tremendous amount in tropical and temperate regions.

In order to dissolve calcium carbonate from limestone rocks, there must be a circulation sufficiently rapid to remove the calcium bicarbonate as it is formed and to bring fresh carbonic acid into contact with the rock.

By the time the waters have reached the ground-water table, if the pathways are by indirect routes, most of the carbonic acid will have been spent. However, if the passages are direct and movement is rapid, carbonic acid may get down to the ground-water zone. If the ground water is not saturated with carbonates and still contains solvents, such as carbonic acid, solution may be expected in the upper part of the zone, as the water moves laterally to some surface drainage system. Water below the water table is generally alkaline, and there is a normal tendency for calcium carbonate to be precipitated in the zone of lateral flow.

Organic acids.—A study of the action of organic acids upon limestones has been made by Murray and Love;[6] consequently only a summarization of their work is given. They conclude:

1. Soil bacteria possess the ability to generate acids which are capable of dissolving calcium carbonate.
2. Carbon dioxide is generated in large quantities as a result of bacterial decomposition of plant material and also as a result of the reaction between the acids generated and calcium carbonate.
3. The bacteria become dormant when the solutions are made alkaline.
4. The time involved in the bacterial decomposition of plants is sufficient to allow the percolation of solutions containing bacteria to considerable depths before toxic conditions are set up.

Other conclusions arising from their study are:

5. The amount of organic acid carried into limestones can not be measured directly.
6. The solvent action of acids generated by bacteria is probably responsible for much if not most of the solution of limestone taking place in nature, as bacterial action, through formation of organic acids, must be much more effective in making limestones porous than atmospheric carbon dioxide.
7. The solvent action of carbonic acid and organic acids resulting from bacterial action is rendered effective by the intimate spatial relationship between the solvents as they are generated and the rocks which these solvents attack.

EXPERIMENT ON AMOUNT OF SOLUTION PERFORMED BY CARBONIC AND ORGANIC ACIDS ON LIMESTONES

The experiments described by Murray and Love were expanded by the writers in order to determine the relative effect of the following reagents on limestone: (1) acids developed as a result of the bacterial decomposition of plant material; (2) carbonic acid as a result of this reaction; and (3) carbon dioxide (carbonic acid) liberated as a result of the reactions between the acids and limestones.

Description of apparatus.—Elm and maple leaves were placed with water and soil bacteria in flasks. The gases developed in the flasks were allowed to pass upward through a cylinder which contained six limestone samples of known weight and porosity. The samples were separated by glass beads and covered by a constant supply of distilled water. The acid developed in the flasks was tested for normality periodically, drained off, and poured into a second cylinder, which contained in the same order corresponding samples of the limestones in the first. This cylinder was connected by tubing with

[6] A. N. Murray and W. W. Love, "Action of Organic Acids upon Limestones," *Bull. Amer. Assoc. Petrol. Geol.*, Vol. 13 (1929), pp. 1667–75.

TABLE I

RESULTS OF EXPERIMENT SHOWING ACTION OF ACIDS ON LIMESTONE

Number	Composition Percentage Volume			Tube A (CO$_2$ from Leaves)					Tube B (CO$_2$ from Tube C)					Tube C (Acid from Flasks)				
	Calcite	Dolomite	Insoluble	Original Weight in Grams	New Weight	Decrease (Grams)	Original Percentage Porosity	Final Percentage Porosity	Original Weight in Grams	New Weight	Decrease (Grams)	Original Percentage Porosity	Final Percentage Porosity	Original Weight in Grams	New Weight	Decrease (Grams)	Original Percentage Porosity	Final Percentage Porosity
1	34	50	16	137.3	137.1	.2	1.0	1.15	95.2	95.0	.2	2.4	2.6	88.5	87.9	.6	4.2	4.9
2	32	7	61	135.3	135.2	.1	1.2	1.3	143.8	143.7	.1	1.2	1.3	133.1	132.1	1.0	1.2	1.95
3	71	20	9	132.8	131.8	1.0	6.7	7.45	109.4	108.7	.7	7.9	8.5	116.0	115.2	.8	8.1	8.8
4	58	32	10	95.0	94.8	.2	1.5	1.7	101.3	100.9	.4	1.3	1.7	116.7	114.5	2.2	.8	2.7
5	70	8	22	201.5	201.3	.2	1.6	1.7	140.9	140.0	.9	2.0	2.6	132.8	131.7	1.1	1.2	2.0
6				147.4	147.0	.4	1.2	1.5	103.4	103.1	.3	1.3	1.6	101.5	100.4	1.1	1.6	.2.7

7

a third so that the carbon dioxide developed by the reaction of the organic acids on limestone samples could pass through. The third cylinder also contained corresponding limestone samples of known weight and porosity.

A gradual increase in the normality of the acids was noted with time. No peak in the strength was noted in either flask, as was observed by Murray and Love.

The evolution of carbon dioxide gas from the flasks was great during the first 2 months of the experiment, which ran for a total of 11 months. A gradual decrease was noted thereafter. No chemical analyses of the acid or gas were made, but the acids smelled like butyric and propionic.[7] Most of the gas was definitely carbon dioxide.

Effect of acids and gas on limestones.—The limestones in the second cylinder were naturally dissolved the most (Table I). Decreases in weight of the samples ranged from 0.6 to 2.2 grams.

The limestones in the third cylinder were dissolved by the carbonic acid derived from the carbon dioxide, which was given off by the reaction between the organic acid and the limestones in the second. Though the decreases in weight of the samples in this cylinder were not so striking as in the cylinder containing the acid, they were nevertheless substantial. Decreases ranged from 0.1 to 0.9 gram.

Samples in the first cylinder lost weight at about the same rate as those in the third. The decreases ranged from 0.1 to 1.0 gram. The greatest decrease in weight in this cylinder was registered by sample 3, a very porous specimen.

The advisability of considering loss of weight as increase in porosity may be questioned, since most of the solution probably took place on the outside of the samples. However, if solution took place in a limestone in place, it certainly would be considered an increase in porosity. Interpreted in terms of porosity, this experiment shows that the porosity of a limestone can be appreciably increased by solution performed by carbonic and organic acids over relatively short periods of time.

There is no close correlation between the amount of solution developed in the different limestone and the calcite contents. However, none of these samples was notably low in calcite, so that in all cases there was an abundance of easily soluble material available.

Conclusions.—The theoretical conclusions of Murray and Love are thus checked experimentally and the effect of organic acids may be considered to be of the order of 1 to 10 times that of carbonic acid.

[7] Acids formed in the same way were found by Murray to be largely butyric and propionic acids, personal communication.

SOLUBILITY OF CARBONATE MINERALS

The order of solubility of certain naturally occurring carbonates in acid solution is as follows: (1) aragonite, (2) calcite, (3) dolomite, and (4) magnesite. In the case of calcite and dolomite mixtures where the grains are uniform in size, approximately 24 parts of calcite are dissolved for each part of dolomite until all of the calcite has gone into solution.

FIG. 1.—Core showing differential solution of calcite-bearing dolomite.

In the case of rocks, this ratio may be modified by the relative sizes of the crystals present and by the mode of aggregation of the carbonates. When both calcite and dolomite are present on an exposed surface, the dolomite is affected to a negligible extent, while the calcite is strongly attacked. Cores possessing old channels filled with pure secondary calcite crystals exhibit this selective feature very well. While being etched with acid, bubbles of carbon dioxide gas distinctly emerge from the openings, but there is practically no effervescence on the surface of the core; in fact, no appreciable decrease in diameter can be measured after etching in some cases. Figure 1 displays a core in which nodules of calcite have been dissolved very deeply, while the dolomitic part shows minor solution.

Hogbom[8] shows that stalactites from caves in the coral rocks of Bermuda contain only 0.18–0.68 per cent of magnesium carbonate, while the rock from which the waters secured the carbonate minerals are five times as rich in dolomite as calcite. The lime salt was dissolved much more freely than the magnesium compound.

Work by Bischoff, Hunt, Hardman, and Murray and Love points to the fact that calcite dissolves out of rocks much more easily than dolomite, regardless of the solvent.

DEVELOPMENT OF POROSITY IN LIMESTONES BY SOLUTION

The three factors, inherent in the rock, affecting solution to the greatest extent are: (1) the presence of joints and fractures, (2) the nature and frequency of bedding planes, and (3) the nature and arrangement of the grains of the minerals comprising the rock.

Of these, the first can not be studied directly in the laboratory, but the others may be evaluated after treatment of specimens. Most limestones do not give very satisfactory results when studied under the microscope and many large specimens give an illusion of uniformity of texture and composition which is dispelled by etching and staining.

For a study of the development of porosity, rather deep etching with hydrochloric acid was found to give excellent results, and the effects due to variation in composition were accentuated by staining the specimens with potassium ferri-cyanide. As was pointed out by Steidtmann,[9] this reagent stains dolomite blue, leaving calcite white. This, of course, presupposes the presence of some ferrous carbonate in dolomite. The writers found that the method worked excellently, although there were some variations in the blue color, indicating the possibility that its use might not be universally applicable.

Fractures and joints.—Fractures and joints offer the best pathways for meteoric waters to descend to the water table in limestone. In limestones in which there is no interruption in the continuity of the joints to the water table, little more than enlargement or widening of the joints can be expected. To develop secondary porosity by

---

[8] F. W. Clarke, "The Data of Geochemistry," *U.S. Geol. Survey Bull. 770* (1924), p. 574.

[9] Edward Steidtmann, "Origin of Dolomite as Disclosed by Stains and Other Methods," *Bull. Geol. Soc. America*, Vol. 28 (1917), pp. 153-54 (abstract).

solution above the water table, it is believed that the flow of water to the water table must be interrupted, so that other outlets may be formed. Several factors, such as close spacing of joints, or large volume of circulating water, may lead to the development of zones of continuous porosity or even cavernous conditions along some beds. The new outlets may also be porous zones parallel with the bedding planes, or they may be calcite-rich zones, where solution will be rapid and penetrative. The presence of water in zones or horizons above the true ground-water table indicates the presence of a type of perched water table in which the underlying barrier is not necessarily entirely impermeable. The outlets may emerge at the surface as springs, or if the bedding is not horizontal, porous or even cavernous zones may be developed downdip, until the formation dips into the water table.

The amount of solution that will take place in the zone or zones selected depends on the bedding in the limestone, the amount of water available, the amount of carbonate it can dissolve, present porosity, and the arrangement and composition of the mineral grains. A very important influence on the nature and number of porous zones that may develop is the oscillation of the water table as a result of structural or climatic changes and length of time during which the water table remains at any one position.

Weller[10] suggests that the development of different cave levels in Edmonson County, Kentucky, may be caused by changes in the levels of the water tables. He also suggests a correlation between cave levels and corresponding river terraces.

Conclusions.—

1. Fractures and joints offer the best pathways for meteoric waters to reach the ground-water table.

2. Joints are usually best developed in the upper part of a rock section.

3. If joints are continuous to the water table, little more than widening of the cracks can be expected.

4. Interruptions in the continuity of the joints allows solution to take place in porous and calcite-rich zones above the water table in addition to the normal widening.

5. Well developed joints in the upper part of the formation may cause rich calcitic zones to be passed without increasing their porosity.

*Bedding planes.—*One of the important factors that control the development of vertical and lateral solution is the presence of in-

[10] J. M. Weller, "Geology of Edmonson County, Kentucky," *Kentucky Geol. Survey* (1927).

soluble bedding planes in limestones. The nature of the bedding planes varies considerably. Some are just indistinct, straight, or wavy, narrow lines; others are thick, vari-colored clay and shale partings. Several samples after etching and staining revealed that some of the bedding planes were largely dolomite. Figure 2 shows an etched core of this type, in which dolomite is interbedded with the calcite. It suggests that periods of calcite and dolomite deposition took place more or less intermittently.

FIG. 2.—Cores showing effect of bedding planes on solubility of dolomitic limestones.

The bedding planes in the cores that were etched plainly showed their confining or controlling effect on the solution. The solution was greatest in the areas of dolomite and calcite in between insoluble bands. The extent to which the smaller or thin insoluble bedding planes affect solution in a limestone can only be inferred. The thicker and more impermeable or insoluble a parting is, the less likely it is for vertical solution to develop and connect higher and lower stratigraphic units. The presence of impermeable or less soluble bedding planes is probably one of the instrumental causes for the development of porous zones parallel with the bedding.

Arrangement and composition of mineral grains.—If the more soluble minerals, such as calcite, are arranged in a limestone so that they are connected or touching, solution can develop to the extent of these connections. However, if grains of dolomite separate chains or

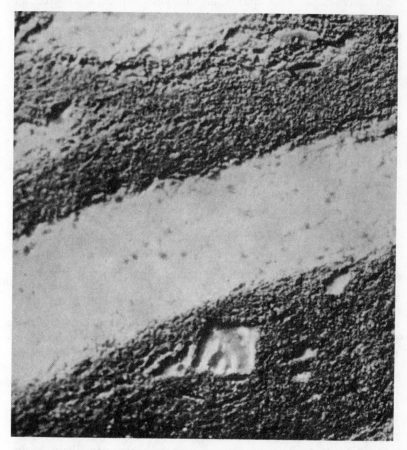

FIG. 3.—Photomicrograph showing alternating calcitic (white) and dolomitic (dark) bands. Magnification, 20 diameters.

sets of calcite grains, the possibility of developing a continuous channel is greatly reduced. Non-carbonate minerals, such as shale or clay particles are even more effective than dolomite in preventing the development of continuous solution channels.

After etching some limestones, it was found that the insoluble residue which collected in the bottom of the beakers often contained some dolomite. These dolomite grains apparently had been completely surrounded by calcite grains. As the calcite grains were dissolved, dolomite grains were released and were not entirely dissolved. Figure 3 shows rather faintly the presence of individual dolomite grains in the rich calcite band.

A microscopic examination of solution cavities after etching, usually reveals many projecting dolomite grains. Apparently, such grains have retained a connection either to a calcite grain which has not been reached by the acid, or to a dolomite grain which was not dissolved.

A limestone possessing heterogeneous carbonate minerals is apt to develop the most penetrative or continuous type of secondary porosity by solution, provided that (a) the more soluble carbonate grains are touching and form continuous chains for some distance, (b) there is enough of the more soluble mineral present to permit an appreciable amount of solution, (c) insoluble mineral grains do not prevent the acidic waters from reaching carbonate grains, and (d) there is sufficient relatively insoluble material present to form a rigid though porous mass on removal of the more soluble material.

ORIGINAL AND PRESENT POROSITY

The primary porosity of a limestone is the percentage of pore space present at or soon after deposition. However, few limestones retain their original porosity.

Chalks, coquinas, and many oölitic limestones have high porosity, and many have continuous porosity to some extent. These limestones may be considered immature and represent early stages of induration. Usually, the porosity of coquinas and other fragmental varieties of carbonate rocks is materially reduced by the infiltration of calcite paste or other minerals into the voids. Probably many old very fossiliferous limestones were originally coquinas.

During induration, the porosity of a limestone is made discontinuous. The extent to which the original porosity is retained may be quite difficult to determine, consequently errors are likely to be made. The terms "original" or "primary" and "secondary" should, therefore, be abandoned in favor of "continuous" and "discontinuous" with definite understanding that "continuous" porosity is almost entirely restricted to immature limestones, which are rarely if ever oil reservoirs, or to limestones with secondary porosity, which are frequently oil reservoirs.

As has been already pointed out, mature limestones, that have

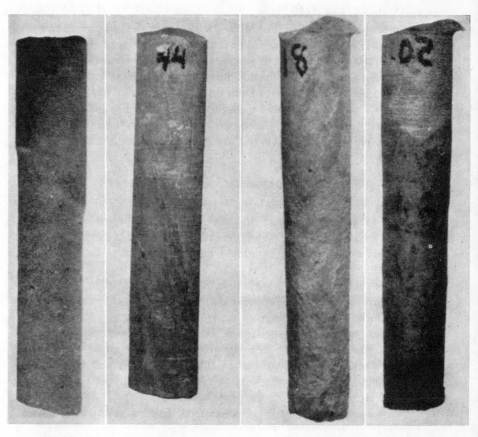

FIG. 4   FIG. 5   FIG. 6

FIG. 4.—Core showing uniform solution of nearly pure dolomitic limestone.
FIG. 5.—Core showing inhibiting effect of uniformly distributed
insoluble material.
FIG. 6.—Cores showing irregularities on equi-solution surface.

not been made porous by solution, possess a discontinuous type of porosity. The voids or cavities are factors in the development of secondary porosity by solution, in that they act as "junctions" for the waters that reach them. The junctions will be surrounded by many carbonate mineral grains, some of which may be calcite. If acidic waters can reach these "junctions," solution will start by the way of the calcite route. All of the cavities may never be reached by solution; consequently, not all of them become a part of the continuous porosity system. If petroliferous material is introduced into the limestone by way of the continuous porosity system, it will not reach cavities that are not a part of this system. Utterback[11] has done considerable work on asphalt-bearing limestones and has found that in the specimens in which the asphalt was definitely not indigenous, cavities containing no asphalt were not a part of the continuous porosity system.

NATURE OF SOLUTION AND TYPES OF PATTERNS

The nature of the solution pattern developed depends on the extent to which the factors that govern the development of continuous porosity are present. The present porosity and the arrangement and composition of the carbonate minerals appear to be the most important factors.

The solution patterns fall into rather distinctive groups, for which the following names are proposed: (a) equi-solution, (b) channel, and (c) cellular.

These names are suggestive descriptions of the solution pattern that is likely to develop in a limestone. In addition to these main types, there are combinations which may be developed in certain limestones. These patterns were obtained in the laboratory as a result of etching many "mature" limestone cores.

Equi-solution type.—The characteristic feature of the equi-solution type of limestones is the evenness with which solution takes place. Either (a) the limestone is pure, or composed of a single carbonate (Fig. 4), or (b) the limestone is impure and the arrangement of the non-carbonate constituents is such that it inhibits solution (Fig. 5).

The arrangement of the minerals is ordinarily so even in rocks possessing an equi-solution pattern, that when the rocks are weathered the solution takes place with the same evenness. Thus, fractures and joints are widened by solution and a fracture or fissure type of potential reservoir is developed.

[11] D. D. Utterback, personal communication.

Channel pattern.—The channel pattern is developed in heterogeneous limestones, consisting mainly of calcite and dolomite. Two types of channel solution were observed in the cores etched. The first type is merely the restoration of old continuous porosity of a channel or tube-like nature.

FIG. 7   FIG. 8

FIG. 7.—Channel type of solution pattern, in which former secondary
continuous porosity is restored.
FIG. 8.—Cores showing development of channel solution pattern.

In this type, secondary minerals have closed off parts of the channels and have made the porosity which was once continuous, discontinuous. In limestones calcite is the most common secondary mineral with dolomite next. The acid readily dissolves the pure calcite crystals and affects the rest of the rock to a much smaller extent. Of the cores of this type treated, the striking feature was the perfect restoration of the old continuous porosity. Where secondary dolomite

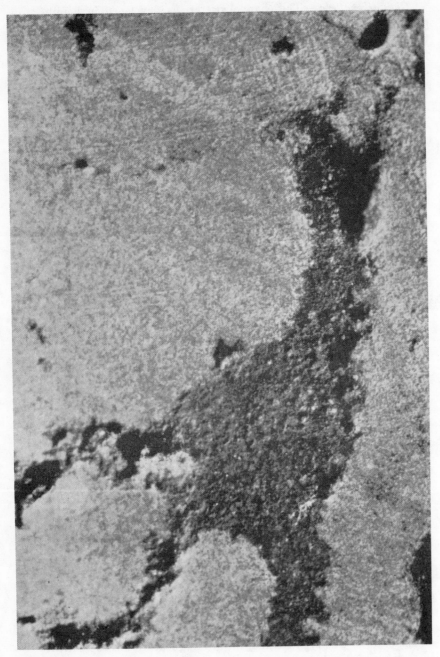

FIG. 9.—Photomicrograph showing incipient development of channel type of porosity around calcite (dark). Magnification, 20 diameters.

is present, it is not dissolved as easily as calcite, and the restoration is not so perfect. These channels are complex. Air blown into one opening of a channel on one side of a core was found to come out of three other openings on the other side. Before etching with acid, this core was impervious to air. Some cores in which secondary minerals

FIG. 10.—Photomicrograph of oölitic limestone showing how channel-porosity **pattern** might develop as result of solution of cement. Magnification, 20 diameters.

had been deposited in the channels revealed by staining that periods of dolomite deposition had taken place with later calcite, or *vice versa*. Figure 7 is a picture of an oil-stained core in which the secondary calcite has been dissolved out in the lower or lighter part of the core. The openings of the channels can be readily seen.

The other type of channel solution is of a similar nature, but represents the development of original solution channels. These channels or tubes are formed, apparently, because calcite grains are arranged in chains. Figure 8 shows small openings leading into deeper

Fig. 11.—Photomicrograph showing in detail development of channel-solution pattern. Magnification, 20 diameters.

channels, while Figures 9, 10 and 11 show types of limestone in which the channel pattern develops.

The channel pattern of solution gives by far the most penetrative kind of porosity. It is, therefore, the commonest type found in oil fields where limestone forms the reservoir.

Cellular type.—The cellular pattern is typified by shallow concavities formed by solution on exposed surfaces. It is apparently due to the presence of scattered soluble grains in a matrix of less soluble material. Figure 12 shows how this pattern is developed, and Figure 13 shows the type of limestone in which this pattern is likely to de-

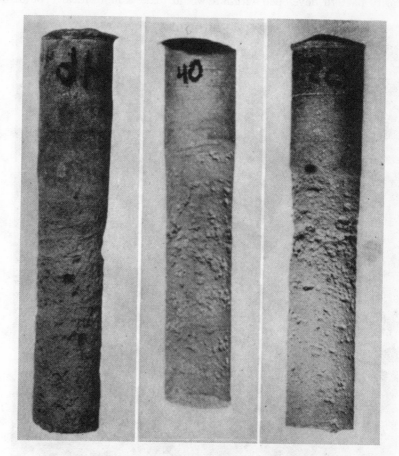

FIG. 12.—Cores showing development of cellular type of solution pattern.

velop. In places small channels are seen leading from one opening to the next, but these are usually so small, that it is questionable whether they would permit the passage of fluids.

Limestones possessing a cellular pattern alone will not develop a penetrative or continuous porosity. In combination with either the equi-solution or channel type, this would, of course, not be the case. If a limestone weathered at the surface, that is, on a horizontal plane, the initial cavities dissolved might be good starting points for further solution, regardless of the less soluble nature of surrounding mineral grains.

Limestone which has a combination of cellular and channel porosity pattern developed within it would make a more ideal type of

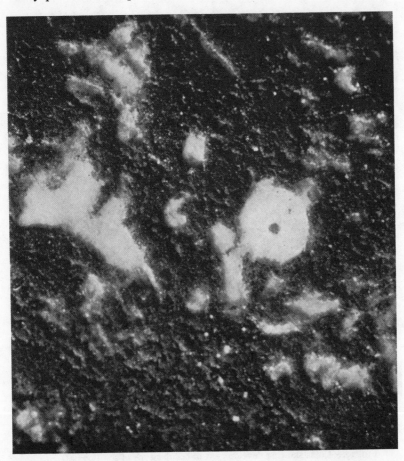

FIG. 13.—Photomicrograph of limestone with disseminated calcite (light) in which cellular type of porosity pattern would develop. Magnification, 20 diameters.

potential reservoir rock, than one possessing only a cellular pattern. The interconnecting channels would have to be sufficiently large to allow the passage of fluids.

ACID TREATMENT

The most important artificial method of increasing the porosity of a limestone reservoir rock is acid treatment. It is impossible to know just what happens in the reservoir during treatment, and only inferences based on indirect evidence can be made. Wells react differently to acid treatment, depending upon the nature of the reservoir and the method of treatment.

At the outset, it may be stated that little if any indigenous oil is released by acid treatment. It would require too great an amount of

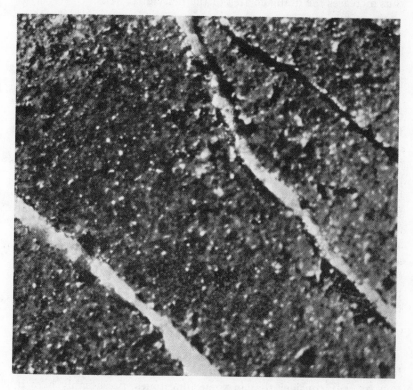

FIG. 14.—Photomicrograph showing partial filling of channel type of solution pattern by precipitation of secondary calcite. Magnification, 20 diameters.

limestone to be dissolved to reach the individual globules of oil to give an appreciable increase in production.

SECONDARY CALCITE

Little attention has been given to the part secondary calcite plays in a reservoir. However, it can not be denied that nearly every limestone reservoir of any consequence possesses considerable secondary calcite.

It is obviously possible for deposition of secondary calcite to take place in such a way that formerly continuous porosity in the reservoir would be broken up into a number of compartments, of irregular size and shape. It is also obvious that some of these compartments might not yield their oil to the nearest well, indeed to any well, unless the wells are very closely spaced. It is believed that acid treatment is in many cases effective in removing barriers formed in this way and thus increases the drainage area of the individual wells.

In certain cases, as production after treatment rises high above the original initial production, it seems highly probable that the acid has eaten its way through secondary calcite and has brought into the area drained by the well new compartments, which were not previously in communication with any well in the field.

In other cases, the acid does not increase production above the original initial production, but does restore an appreciable percentage. Here it seems to operate in cleaning out the well, but this cleaning out may easily include the dissolving of secondary calcite. There is good evidence to believe that secondary calcite is precipitated as the oil is produced. With the development of the field, pressure decreases are likely to result in the deposition of calcium carbonate, which had remained in solution up to that time. Pitzer and West[12] note that appreciable quantities of soft limestone particles are often found in stock tanks of limestone wells. They also note that the obstructions are formed more easily as the field becomes older and the gas pressure drops. Although all the limestone particles found in the stock tanks may not be due to the precipitation of calcium carbonate, many of them are believed to be by the present writers.

RATE OF APPLICATION

Commercial practice invariably involves forcing the acid back into the formation rapidly. Pitzer and West urge speed in application, as they consider that in some limestones, presumably high in calcite, the acid will become neutralized in a very short time. The mere dissolving of the walls of the reservoir rock should not be expected to give any appreciable increases in production. It is believed that the important object is to get the acid back to the secondary calcite as quickly as possible, where it may spend itself on the secondary calcite and open up new compartments, which may contain oil and gas. If the acid is allowed to move along the old channels slowly, it may spend itself before reaching the secondary calcite. Moreover, solution of the secondary calcite gives no insoluble residue.

[12] P. W. Pitzer and C. K. West, "Acid Treatment of Lime Wells Explained and Methods Described," *Oil and Gas Jour.* (November 22, 1934).

Solution of the rest of the reservoir rock may release flocculent clays that may seriously reduce the permeability of the reservoir.

INSOLUBLE RESIDUE

One of the most serious difficulties involved in acid treatment is the release of insoluble residue from the reservoir rock proper. The insoluble residue in limestones may be roughly divided into (a) material of a constant volume and (b) swelling material. The first class consists of sand grains, chert, and other minerals not possessing a colloidal structure. The second class is represented mainly by the clay series.

The residue of a constant volume is not believed greatly to reduce the permeability of the reservoir; however, the piling up of sand and dolomite grains at small openings may seriously retard the passage of fluids. Usually, the material of a constant volume has high enough specific gravity to sink or settle to the bottom of the channels as it is released.

The clays offer the most serious trouble in respect to reduction of permeability. It has been found that the acid clays formed when limestones are dissolved may be altered very rapidly to sodium or calcium clays by base exchange and it is believed that most of the clays found in limestones which have undergone acid treatment will be of the latter type. In some cases, a sodium clay has been found to have a volume of 60 per cent of the equivalent calcium clay. The flocculent nature of the latter is also demonstrated by the fact that some calcium clays have been reduced to one-sixth of their original volume by centrifuging.

NOTE

Although it is not the purpose of the writers to discuss in this paper the origin of petroleum, it is obvious that the formation of hydrocarbons from organic material must involve hydrogenation. Since the only probable supply of hydrogen is water, the oxygen of the water must be eliminated by the evolution of carbon dioxide gas. Buswell[13] and his co-workers have done a great deal of work on the formation of methane from anaerobic fermentation of plant and animal debris, and show that the proportion of carbon dioxide to methane varies from $1:1$ for simpler forms to a theoretical limit of $1:3$ for an acid chain of infinite length. The average methane yield from sewage is approximately 64 per cent.

Although the formation of oil is not completely carried to methane but involves the formation of a large number of hydrocarbons, a considerable

[13] (a) A. M. Buswell, "Production of Fuel Gas by Anaerobic Fermentation," *Indus. and Eng. Chem.*, Vol. 22 (1930), p. 1168.

(b) A. M. Buswell and C. S. Boruff, "The Relation between the Chemical Composition and Quality and Quantity of Gas Produced during Sludge Digestion," *Sewage Works Jour.*, Vol. 4, No. 3 (1930).

quantity of carbon dioxide gas is evolved in excess of that required for the formation of natural gas associated with the oil. Yet, carbon dioxide is found only in very small amounts in natural gas. If it is formed in this way, and is precipitated by the reaction of calcium-bearing waters as calcium carbonate then the effect of this precipitation of calcium carbonate may be roughly estimated.

Let us assume a limestone "pay" 30 feet thick which yields 10,000 barrels of oil per acre and has an average gas-oil ratio of 3,000. The gas content of this "pay" will then be 30 million cubic feet per acre. The equivalent quantity of carbon dioxide would be about $5\frac{1}{2}$ million cubic feet per acre. If it is all precipitated as calcium carbonate, and it appears that it probably would be in a limestone reservoir, about 800 tons per acre-foot would be deposited. This would occupy about 360 cubic feet or about 0.85 per cent of the total volume of an acre-foot. If the original porosity is 20 per cent, the precipitation of this calcium carbonate would fill about 4.2 per cent of the pore space. The extent to which the permeability is effected by this deposition would depend on the places where it was deposited.

Reprinted from:
BULLETIN OF THE AMERICAN ASSOCIATION OF PETROLEUM GEOLOGISTS
VOL. 30, NO. 3 (MARCH, 1946) PP. 305-318, 1 FIG., 1 TABLE

POROSITY THROUGH DOLOMITIZATION[1]

KENNETH K. LANDES[2]
Ann Arbor, Michigan

ABSTRACT

Some oil pools, notably the Trenton field of Ohio and Indiana, and the Adams and Deep River fields in Michigan, produce from locally dolomitized limestones. The porous condition disappears laterally where the dolomite grades into limestone. Obviously this porosity is genetically dependent on the process of dolomitization. The traditional theory of shrinkage of volume through molecular replacement does not fit the facts; neither do the leaching or recrystallization hypotheses. It is suggested that an excess of solution by ground waters over precipitation during the replacement of limestone by dolomite created the porous condition.

INTRODUCTION

Much has been written on the origin of dolomite, and on the origin of cavities of varying sizes in carbonate rocks; considerably less has been contributed on the origin of the porosity that may be present in locally dolomitized limestone. Because this porosity does not extend into the near-by non-dolomitized limestone, it must be genetically related to the process of dolomitization. It is hereafter referred to as "local dolomitization porosity" for it is confined to local dolomites.

Local dolomitization porosity is economically important because a considerable quantity of oil and gas is, or has been, stored in cavities of this type. Oil recoveries of more than 25,000 barrels to the acre are possible. Obviously the search for such reservoirs presents a difficult problem to the geologist, but perhaps a discussion of the occurrence and possible origin of local dolomitization porosity will be of some assistance in this search.

[1] Manuscript received, November 29, 1945.

[2] Department of geology, University of Michigan, and Geological Survey, United States Department of the Interior. Published by permission of the director of the Geological Survey.

The writer is indebted to Joseph Valentin and the Michigan Limestone & Chemical Company of Rogers City for the chemical analyses of well samples; to Carl Addison and the Pure Oil Company for samples and constructive criticism; to Raymond Hunt and the Gordon Oil Company and Fred W. Oudt and the Shell Oil Company for core samples; to Rex Grant and the Michigan Department of Conservation, Geological Survey Division, for well data and a description of the occurrence of oil in the Adams pool; to George Cohee of the Geological Survey, United States Department of the Interior, for a sample of the Trenton "pay" from Indiana and for advice and encouragement; and to Hugh D. Miser, Carle H. Dane, and T. A. Hendricks of the Geological Survey, United States Department of the Interior, for constructive criticism of the manuscript.

Unfortunately, the discovery of a body of locally dolomitized limestone does not insure finding oil or gas. In Arenac County, Michigan, such discoveries as have been made to date have resulted in the opening of new oil fields. Elsewhere it has been found that local dolomites are non-porous, or that they are so situated structurally that no suitable trap for oil accumulation exists and they are therefore non-productive. These facts were recognized by Orton[3] who pointed out nearly 60 years ago that in the Trenton limestone (dolomite) fields of Ohio and Indiana a combination of porosity and favorable structural position was necessary for commercial oil and gas accumulation.

EXAMPLES

The best known example of local dolomitization porosity is in the Lima-Indiana field. There the top of the Trenton limestone lies at depths ranging from 1,000 to 2,000 feet below the surface. The upper 10 to 30 or more feet of the limestone has been altered locally to a porous dolomite from which a large quantity of oil and gas has been obtained. The producing area and the porosity are limited to that relatively small part of the total Trenton area in which the uppermost limestone beds are dolomitized.[4,5]

Local dolomitization porosity has become of considerable economic importance in Michigan, for several of the recently discovered oil fields produce from locally dolomitized limestones. Perhaps the best examples of this are the Adams and Deep River pools in Arenac County, north of Saginaw Bay. Carl C. Addison[6] points out that the Adams and Deep River fields are not *typical* examples of local dolomitization porosity in Michigan. They are exceptional examples because of high recoveries. He names the Sherman, Coldwater, Fork, Evart, Winterfield, and Temple fields as more typical examples.

Concerning the Adams field, Rex Grant[7] writes as follows.

The dolomite area in the Adams field is limited in size as compared to the field, comprising some 300 acres passing N. NE.–S. SW. at the western edge of the field across the northwestern plunging nose of the structure. The maximum width is 1,800 feet, the length as now determined (June, 1945) is $2\frac{1}{4}$ miles, and the average width is about 950 feet.

The first producing well in the dolomite was completed in July, 1940; since then 32 wells have been drilled, 28 of which are now producing. Up to June 1, 1945, 4,760,477 barrels of oil have been produced from the dolomite or nearly 15,000 barrels per acre. Some older leases have produced more than 25,000 barrels of oil per acre.

No well in the area has entirely penetrated the dolomite so we cannot say what the thickness of the dolomite is. Most wells drill only a few feet into the black, very porous dolomite "pay," which is encountered immediately below the base of the Bell shale.

---

[3] Edward Orton, "The Geology of Ohio, Considered in Its Relations to Petroleum and Natural Gas," *Geol. Survey of Ohio*, Vol. 6 (1888), pp. 307–08.

[4] Edward Orton, *op. cit.*

[5] A. J. Phinney, "The Natural Gas Field of Indiana," *U. S. Geol. Survey Ann. Rept. XI* (1889–1890), pp. 657–58.

[6] Letter dated August 23, 1945.

[7] Personal communication, July 3, 1945.

Where dolomite is not penetrated at this horizon, most dry holes encounter only some water in the upper 90 to 177 feet of the limestone that lies below the shale.

Two wells on the west edge of the field drilled through 90 feet of barren limestone before reaching dolomite but pay production was found in the dolomite. One well made 2% water upon completion, the other made water at an early stage. Computed original bottom hole pressures of 1,234 pounds were essentially the same as in the so-called upper dolomite wells. The comparison between bottom hole pressures in the high and low dolomite wells takes into consideration the 80-foot difference in total depths. Considering the recoveries to date and the evidence cited for the two low wells, it seems reasonable to infer that the original oil-water interface was about 90 feet below the base of the Bell shale and that 90 feet is the approximate thickness of the "pay."

Edgewater is nowhere in evidence in the dolomite. Thus the driving force is almost entirely bottom hole water. Gas-oil ratios in the field are now approximately 160 cu. ft. per barrel as compared with the original 170 cu. ft.

The dolomitization of limestones of the Rogers City and Dundee formations by percolating waters along vertical or almost vertical fractures seems the most acceptable hypothesis, to explain the origin of the dolomite, although the lack of evidence is a handicap in working out the geology; the wells have penetrated only a short distance into the dolomite, and no wells have been drilled completely through it. If this hypothesis is tenable then we may believe that the dolomite extends entirely through the Dundee formation. Until a well in the heart of the field is deepened through the dolomite to the underlying Detroit River formation, we will not know whether this condition exists.

The Deep River field lies northeast of the Adams in T. 19 N., R. 4 E. It was discovered in December, 1943, by the Werblo well in the S. $\frac{1}{2}$ of the NW. $\frac{1}{4}$, NW. $\frac{1}{4}$ of Sec. 8. To the present time (June 19, 1945) 32 producing wells and 23 dry holes have been drilled in the field. The successful wells ranged up to 7,000 barrels per day in initial production. As shown by the accompanying map (Fig. 1) the Deep River pool is long and narrow. It lies on the northeastern flank of a structural dome. Higher parts of the dome contain gas in commercial quantities in the Berea sandstone (Mississippian), but are dry in the Rogers City and Dundee formations (Devonian).

It is obvious from Figure 1 that the distribution of oil in the Deep River pool must be controlled entirely by porosity. Some successful wells are structurally higher than dry holes, but others are at the same level as, or lower than, dry holes. Likewise some wells with the greatest daily production are higher and others lower, structurally, than the lesser producers. For example, a 6,000-barrel well near the NE. corner of the NW. $\frac{1}{4}$ of Sec. 16 is 18 feet lower than its west offset, a 3,000-barrel well, and 10 feet lower than a 1,000-barrel well at the east. It is 6 feet higher, however, than a 5,000-barrel well three locations east.

The structure contours show exceptional irregularity over much of the Deep River field. There is little or no evidence of structural displacement, either horizontal or vertical. It is more likely that some settling took place along the belt of greatest solution in the upper part of the Rogers City limestone. Such settling would produce structurally low zones of high porosity located near the axis of the field, which would account for the greater production from some wells in those zones than from structurally higher wells in the outer zone.

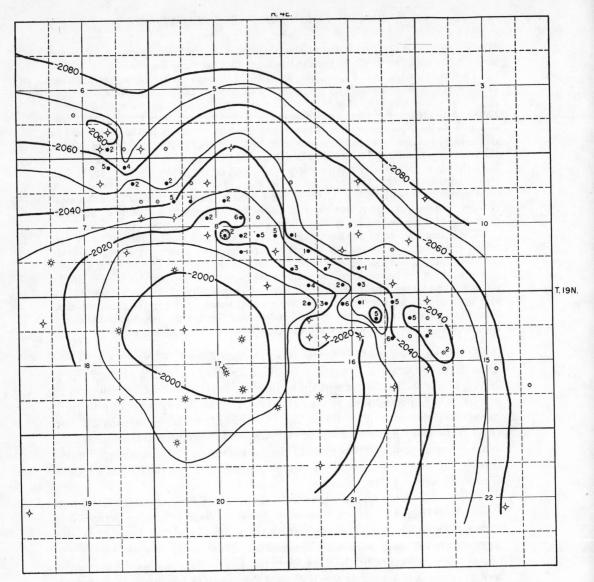

FIGURE I. STRUCTURE CONTOUR MAP OF THE DEEP RIVER OIL POOL,
ARENAC COUNTY, MICHIGAN

DATUM IS BASE OF TRAVERSE
CONTOUR INTERVAL 10 FEET

SCALE

0 ⌐————————————⌐ MILE

EXPLANATION

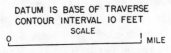 2 OIL WELL. FIGURE DESIGNATES NUMBER OF
THOUSAND BARRELS (TO NEAREST THOUSAND) INITIAL
PRODUCTION. FIGURE −I DENOTES PRODUCTION OF
LESS THAN 500 BARRELS; I AN INITIAL PRODUCTION
BETWEEN 500 AND 1500 BARRELS, ETC.

✳ GAS WELL

✧ DRY HOLE

○ DRILLING WELL (JUNE 20,1945)

MOST WELLS IN AND AROUND THE GAS FIELD STOPPED IN THE
BEREA SANDSTONE. CONTROL POINTS FOR CONTOURING WERE
OBTAINED BY ADDING 1314 FEET TO THE NEGATIVE ELEVATION
OF THE TOP OF THE BEREA

The reservoir rock in the Deep River oil field is the Rogers City limestone which underlies the Traverse group and overlies the Dundee formation. Before the Rogers City limestone was named[8] these rocks were placed in the uppermost Dundee formation and still are so classified in oil-field terminology. Normally the Rogers City is a limestone, but in the Deep River pool, *where productive of oil*, it is dolomite. The unsuccessful wells failed to find either dolomite or sufficient porosity for storage of oil in commercial volume. Therefore, the map of the Deep River field not only shows the approximate area of the buried oil "pool," but it also shows the distribution of porous dolomite and impervious limestone in the Rogers City limestone beneath the Traverse rocks.

The top of the "pay" in the Rogers City limestone lies in almost all wells within 20 feet of the base of the overlying Traverse group. A few wells struck oil at the very top of the Rogers City limestone. All wells finding the top of the "pay" within 3 feet of the top of the formation are on or close to the axis of the field. The converse, however, is not everywhere true. It is 16 feet to the top of the oil zone in one well on the axis. The Deep River pool does not have any evidence of a hade to the dolomitized (porous) zone, which would result in its being struck by wells on one side or the other of the field at a lower depth. As many of the deeper (6 to 29 feet) "pays" appear to be on the northwest as on the southeast side of the field. An exception is a small well on the southwest side of the field, the Neidwecki well in Section 8, which struck its first and only oil 149 feet below the base of the Traverse. At least 10 other wells have drilled this section on the same side of the field, some of them equally close to the axis, without success.

There is but little correlation between depth of the oil zone below the Traverse group and amount of initial production. The two best wells drilled into oil in the top 3 feet of the Rogers City limestone, but some poor wells did the same. On the other hand, a 5,000-barrel well was drilled where the "pay" was 16 feet below the base of the Traverse. This well, like most of the better wells, lies close to the field axis.

The thickness of the dolomitized zone is not yet known for most wells, because drilling ceased at the top of the pay zone. The logs of a very few wells show rock, supposedly unproductive, below a pay zone from 2 to 6 feet in thickness. Other wells, however, record pay zones up to 11 feet in thickness.

CHEMICAL ANALYSES OF OIL-FIELD CARBONATE ROCKS

Through the kindness of the Michigan Limestone & Chemical Company, Paul V. Thornley, chief chemist, made nine analyses of samples obtained from wells drilled in Michigan and Indiana. The purpose of the analyses was to determine the $MgCO_3$ content necessary for commercial production. The wells in the Deep River pool flow as soon as the reservoir rock is struck by the drill, so samples of the "pay" itself can only be obtained by coring. No cores were available from a Deep River producer, but one was obtained from the Pinconning well in Bay

[8] George M. Ehlers and Robert E. Radabaugh, "The Rogers City Limestone, a New Middle Devonian Formation in Michigan," *Michigan Acad. Arts, Science, and Letters*, Vol. 23 (1938), pp. 441–46.

County where production comes from similar local dolomitization porosity. A sample of the Trenton "pay" was also analyzed. The analyses are shown in Table I.

TABLE I

Sample No.	Location	CaCO₃	CaO	SiO₂	Fe₂O₃ Al₂O₃	MgO	MgCO₃	Remarks
1	Basin Oil Co., Sterling Bank 2, NW ¼, NE ¼, SE ¼ Sec. 8, T. 19 N., R. 4 E., Arenac County, Mich.	56.77	31.79	8.96	5.66	12.94	27.17	Sample from 2797–2804 ft. Well had "show" at 2797 ft., 800 ft. of oil in hole at 2804 ft., and a flow of 200 bbls./hr. at 2806 ft.
2	Basin & Rayburn, Klenk 3, SE ¼, SE ¼, NW ¼, Sec. 8, T. 19 N., R. 4 E.	89.27	50.00	2.74	1.54	2.97	6.23	Sample from 2754 to 2762 ft. Pay is at 2765–67 ft.
3	Wicklund Development Co., State-Deep River A-1, C, S ½, SW ¼, SE ¼ Sec. 6, T. 19 N., R. 4 E.	80.36	45.00	2.64	3.28	6.58	13.81	Sample from 2800–2834 ft. ¾ bbl. oil at 2813–2825 ft. 2000-bbl. well 330 ft. east
4	Basin Oil Co., Sherman 1, SE ¼, NE ¼, SW ¼ Sec. 9, T. 19 N., R. 4 E.	95.11	53.26	1.40	.92	1.11	2.33	Dry hole, no water. 7000-bbl. well 1000 ft. southwest
5	Walton & Stewart, S. Koziak 1, NW ¼, NW ¼, SW ¼ Sec. 15, T. 19 N., R. 4 E.	94.82	53.10	1.48	1.20	1.11	2.33	Dry hole, 2000-bbl. well 1000 ft. southwest
6	Basin & Rayburn, Neidwecki 1, SE ¼, NW ¼, SE ¼ Sec. 8, T. 19 N., R. 4 E.	89.55	50.15	5.28	2.40	1.26	2.64	Samples from 2779–2810 ft. (Base Traverse at 2779 ft.) 8 bbl./hr. after acidizing from 2927–2942 ft.
7	Shell Oil Co., Kath 1, SW ¼, NE ¼, NW ¼ Sec. 2, T. 16 N., R. 4 E., Bay Co., Mich.	56.20	31.47	.1.04	2.26	19.19	40.30	Saturated core from 2922–2927 ft. Flowed 340 bbls./8 hrs. from 2898–2900 ft.
8	Gordon Oil Co. Weber 3, NW ¼, NW ¼, NE ¼ Sec. 7, T. 19 N., R. 4 E., Arenac Co., Mich.	97.68	54.70	.30	.16	.85	1.79	Core from 2869 ft. Dry hole, with top of Dundee (Rogers City) at 2848 ft. 5000-bbl. well from 2855–2863 ft., 660 ft. east
9	NE ¼, SE ¼ Sec. 36, T. 24 N., R. 12 E., Blackford Co., Ind.	55.61	31.14	1.14	2.08	19.65	41.27	Samples from "pay" zone in Trenton

Comments on analyses.—Where the MgCO₃ is 1 to 3 per cent the limestone has insufficient porosity for oil or water production. The well from which sample No. 6 was obtained did not produce in the limestone at the top of the Rogers City limestone but did produce a small quantity in rock of unknown character from 149 to 163 feet below. On the other hand, MgCO₃ percentages of 40 or more in areas of local dolomitization porosity insure ample porisity for oil storage. Carman and Stout[9] have noted that magnesium carbonate percentages of 20 or more are necessary for oil production in the Trenton reservoirs of Ohio. Percentages between 3 and 40 may or may not indicate nearness to production. The rock with 27 per cent MgCO₃ (analysis No. 1) was oil-bearing, but the big flow came 2 feet below the base of the sample. The analysis of Sample 2 shows 6 per cent MgCO₃ and the rock contained no oil, but oil was produced 3 feet below. It is probable that in both wells the partially dolomitic limestone becomes true dolomite at the level from which the oil flows to the surface. The samples from the Wicklund well (analysis No. 3) contained nearly 14 per cent MgCO₃ but only a showing of oil was found. However, only 330 feet east a well with an initial production of approximately 2000 barrels daily was drilled to the same

[9] J. Ernest Carman and Wilber Stout, "Relationship of Accumulation of Oil to Structure and Porosity in the Lima-Indiana Field," *Problems of Petroleum Geology*, Amer. Assoc. Petrol. Geol. (1934), p. 528.

level. Presumably this well found true dolomite whereas the well on the west penetrated only dolomitic limestone.

CONCLUSIONS ON OCCURRENCE OF LOCAL DOLOMITIZATION POROSITY

Some generalizations can be made from the examples of peculiar dolomite porosity described in the preceding section. In the first place, there can be no doubt but that this porosity was produced during, and as a result of, dolomitization. Its delimitation to that part of a limestone that has been locally dolomitized is proof of this relationship. Secondly, the dolomite bodies containing this porosity are of local rather than regional extent. To be sure, the area of dolomitized Trenton limestone covers several hundred square miles, but is small compared with the total extent of this formation. In the Deep River pool the dolomite is in a narrow elongate body and the total area is small. Delimitation of the dolomite within the limestone may be vertical as well as horizontal. The top of the dolomitized zone lies at or close to the top of the limestone, and beneath a thick shale in both the Lima-Indiana and Arenac County fields. There may also be a more than accidental relationship between the position of the dolomite body and the rock structure. The dolomitized Trenton limestone in Ohio and Indiana is high on the flanks of the Cincinnati arch and its branches and in part extends over the top of the arch. The dolomite in the Deep River field is within 30 to 60 feet of the highest point of the Deep River dome.

Apparently the cavities in the local dolomites are similar in type. They may vary considerably in size, but are interconnecting and make ideal voids for the passage and accumulation of liquids and gas. Core and chip samples show that the cavities are definitely not interstices between crystals or grains. They transect bedding planes and single crystals. Their relationship to the dolomite is the same as that of caverns in limestone, although the scale is much smaller. Phinney[10] suggested a solution cause for the cavities in the dolomitized Trenton limestone 55 years ago

It should be noted that the porosity of the dolomitic portion of the Trenton limestone is not due wholly to coarseness of grain, for chips and larger masses thrown out of the wells by the force of the gas show that even when the rock is hard and compact, small cavities are scattered throughout it in such a manner as to suggest that a part of its substance had been removed by solution.

It should be pointed out, however, that in the Indiana specimens at least, the texture indicates that in any alteration which may have taken place the porosity is the result of loss of substance and not of substitution, as the rock is commonly hard and uniform in texture and moderately compact between the irregularly ramified cavities and pores interspersed through it.

Furthermore, these cavities may show some alignment:[11]

It is also of interest to observe that most of the openings show a rough alignment, or are confined to a well-defined zone, as if they were the result of solution by waters traveling along a seam, joint, or bedding plane. This fact strongly suggests the presence generally throughout the limestone of enlarged open spaces along induced joints and cracks.

[10] A. J. Phinney, *op. cit.*

[11] A. W. Lauer, "Petrology of Reservoir Rocks," *Econ. Geol.*, Vol. 12 (1917), p. 455.

The shape of the dolomite body at Deep River suggests that both the location of the dolomite and of the contained cavities was controlled by a crack or fissure cutting through the Rogers City limestone on the north flank of the Deep River dome.

A core of dolomitized limestone from the Evart field in Osceola County, Michigan, shows not only interconnecting cavities, but also drusy crystals (unit rhombohedra) of dolomite. An exceptional case of crystal-lined cavities in pebbles derived from Carboniferous limestone has been described by Kendall.[12]

At the last two localities the pebbles have been very extensively dolomitised subsequently to deposition, for they have in many cases been reduced to a mere shell, usually lined with crystals of dolomite.

Skeats[13] noted dolomite crystals lining cavities in limestone in cores from Funafuti.

PREVIOUS EXPLANATIONS

The presence of exceptional porosity in dolomite has been recognized for more than a century, and much has been written on this subject. At least four theories have been advanced, but the writer does not believe any of them to be adequate. These theories are described and discussed briefly in the following paragraphs.

The classic theory, proposed by Elie de Beaumont[14] in 1836, is that molecular replacement of limestone by dolomite would result in a volume shrinkage of between 12 and 13 per cent. In spite of its many flaws this theory still appears in articles and textbooks. It should have ceased to receive serious consideration after 1912 when Lindgren[15] in his well known paper on replacement pointed out that replacement is on a volume for volume, and not molecule for molecule, basis. Five years later Steidtmann[16] described field evidence for replacement of limestone by dolomite without volume change.

The sharp borders between calcite and dolomite grains and knife-edged contacts of dolomite invaders in casts prove that certain replacements of calcite by dolomite were accomplished without volume change. No evidence could be found to show that it ever takes place with volume change.

Twenhofel[17] wrote in a similar vein in 1926.

It has been commonly assumed that in the formation of dolomite by replacement, there is an increase in the porosity of the rock formed. Many dolomites are porous and cavernous, and this characteristic has been assumed to be typical of all dolomites and to

[12] P. F. Kendall, "On the Brockrams of the Vale of Eden *etc.*," Rept. of the *British Assoc. for the Advancement of Science* (1902), p. 605.

[13] E. W. Skeats, "The Formation of Dolomite and Its Bearing on the Coral Reef Problem," *Amer. Jour. Science*, Vol. 45 (March, 1918), pp. 188–89.

[14] Francis M. Van Tuyl, "The Origin of Dolomite," *Iowa Geol. Survey*, Vol. 25 (1914), p. 286.

[15] Waldemar Lindgren, "The Nature of Replacement," *Econ. Geol.*, Vol. 7 (1912), pp. 521–35.

[16] E. Steidtmann, "Origin of Dolomite," *Bull. Geol. Soc. America*, Vol. 28 (June, 1917), p. 449.

[17] William H. Twenhofel, *Treatise on Sedimentation* (1926), p. 261.

have arisen through replacement after solidification. However, many dolomites have more than the required pore space, while others in essentially horizontal positions have less than 1 per cent. It is difficult to explain these variations as due to replacement alone. Shells which have undergone partial or complete replacement by dolomite in numerous instances show no decrease in volume, and it is obvious that field observations do not support the view that dolomitization involves a decrease in volume.

The most detailed attack on the de Beaumont theory was made by Murray[18] in 1930. He called attention to the fact that no evidence has been advanced to support the concept of cavity development through molecular replacement, other than the fact that some dolomites are porous and that a single sample of dolomite collected from the Austrian Tyrol more than 100 years ago had a porosity percentage approximately equivalent to the theoretical volume loss which would be produced by the molecular replacement of limestone by dolomite. Murray further reminds us that other types of rock shrinkage, such as that caused by cooling or dessication, produces cracks instead of cavities. Lastly, Murray notes that a bed of dolomite may be very porous at one point and quite dense and impervious a short distance away. Obviously, if dolomite porosity has been produced by shrinkage of volume during replacement, the dolomite rock resulting from replacement would have to be consistently porous.

The theory that the cavities in porous dolomite are produced by differential leaching of carbonate rocks has a number of adherents. There are three divisions to this theory, depending on whether the material leached is calcite, dolomite, or fossils. The concept of the formation of cavities through the leaching of calcite is a by-product of one of the theories of the origin of dolomite. According to this idea the original carbonate rock was a mixture of calcite and dolomite crystals, and it became dolomite through the solution and removal of the more soluble calcite.[19] Such selective solution would produce cavities, but not local dolomitization porosity, for the non-dolomitized parts of the carbonate rock are not rich enough in dolomite crystals. The *volume* of dolomite crystals would have to be just as great in the non-dolomitized rock as in the dolomite; only the *percentage* would be less.

The unusual idea that the leaching of some of the dolomite from a dolomitic limestone ooze has produced porosity has been expressed by R. H. Fash.[20]

In limestone or dolomite-forming sediments, the acids liberated by the fermentation will be neutralized by the sediments. The carbon dioxide formed will dissolve calcium and

[18] A. N. Murray, "Limestone Oil Reservoirs," *Econ. Geol.*, Vol. 25, No. 5 (August, 1930), pp. 167–98.

[19] Edward T. Hardman, "On the Carboniferous Dolomites of Ireland," *Proc. Royal Irish Academy*, Vol. II, Science (1875–1877), p. 730.
C. W. Hall and F. W. Sardeson, "Origin of the Dolomites," *Bull. Geol. Soc. America*, Vol. 6 (January, 1895), p. 198.
Francis M. Van Tuyl, "The Origin of Dolomite," *Iowa Geol. Survey*, Vol. 25 (1914), p. 385.
A. J. Goodman, "Limestone Reservoir Conditions in Turner Valley Oil Field, Alberta Canada," *Bull. Amer. Assoc. Petrol. Geol.*, Vol. 29, No. 8 (August, 1945), p. 1167.

[20] F. M. Van Tuyl, B. H. Parker, and W. W. Skeeters, "The Migration and Accumulation of Petroleum and Natural Gas," *Colorado School Mines Quart.*, Vol. 40, No. 1 (January, 1945), p. 34.

magnesium carbonates, causing porosity. Calcium bicarbonate is less soluble than magnesium bicarbonate, and, therefore, in dolomitic limestone, the porosity will be greater than in nondolomitic limestone.

Assuming that Fash is correct in ascribing greater solubility to magnesium carbonate, although there is disagreement on this point, one still finds it difficult to comprehend how porosity established in sediments would survive burial and lithifaction. This theory can not be applied to local dolomitization porosity, for the same reasons as given under calcite leaching.

The vulnerability of dolomite-enclosed fossil shells, especially where calcitic, to leaching by ground waters is well known.[21] The result of this differential leaching is a highly porous rock in the zone of weathering. Some of the porosity below unconformities in regional dolomites is no doubt of this type. But such porosity should not be confined to the locally dolomitized parts of limestones.

Dolomites, in addition to becoming porous through the dissolving of fossils, can become porous, and even cavernous, through ground-water solution in the same manner as limestones. Murray[22] and Howard and David[23] have pointed out the importance of ground water leaching of carbonate rocks above the water table. Davis[24] and Rich[25] emphasize the possibilities of solution below the water table, either by free or confined water. Without doubt ground-water solution, either above or below the water table, is of utmost importance in producing porosity in carbonate rocks. However, this type of porosity should extend across the boundary between limestone and dolomitized limestone and would thus not be local dolomitization porosity.

Lastly, there is the theory that dolomite porosity is produced by recrystallization. This was Orton's[26] but not Phinney's[27] conclusion for the porous Trenton dolomite.

The fact remains in either case that the oil rock is a dolomite, and that its porosity results from its highly crystalline character. Interlocking crystalline growths have empty spaces between them, and thus furnish adequate storage, as the result has proved, for high-pressure gas and great stocks of oil.

[21] F. H. Hatch, R. H. Rastall, and M. Black, *The Petrology of the Sedimentary Rocks* (1938), p. 193.

[22] A. N. Murray, "Limestone Oil Reservoirs," *Econ. Geol.*, Vol. 25, No. 5 (August, 1930), pp. 452–69.

[23] W. V. Howard and Max W. David, "Development of Porosity in Limestones," *Bull. Amer. Assoc. Petrol. Geol.*, Vol. 20, No. 11 (November, 1936), pp. 1389–1412.

[24] W. M. Davis, "Origin of Limestone Caverns," *Bull. Geol. Soc. America*, Vol. 41 No. 3 (1930), pp. 475–628.

[25] John L. Rich, Discussion, *Bull. Amer. Assoc. Petrol. Geol.*, Vol. 22, No. 7 (July, 1938), p. 918.

[26] Edward Orton, "The Geology of Ohio, Considered in Its Relations to Petroleum and Natural Gas," *Geol. Survey of Ohio Report*, Vol. 6 (1888), pp. 307–08.
———, "The Trenton Limestone as a Source of Petroleum and Natural Gas in Ohio and Indiana," *U. S. Geol. Survey Ann. Rept. VIII*, Vol. 2 (1886–1887), p. 584.

[27] A. J. Phinney, "The Natural Gas Field of Indiana," *ibid.*, XI (1889–1890), pp. 657–58.

Hanna[28] ascribes the porosity of the Texas Comanche carbonate rocks to recrystallization, but does not confine his theory to dolomitization: " . . . porosity is not a function of dolomitization or faunal content, but rather a function of recrystallization either with or without dolomitization." Adams[29] believes that:

Recrystallization may also be responsible for some enlargement of porosity and increase of permeability. It is especially noted in dolomites, but may also be present in limestones.

However, recrystallization can not be the answer to the origin of local dolomitization porosity. The pores seen in cores and chips have the irregular rounded walls of solution cavities rather than the angular faces of intercrystal voids.

SUGGESTED THEORY

The thesis of this study is that local dolomitization porosity results from an excess of solution over precipitation during the process of local replacement of limestone by circulating ground waters.

Origin of dolomite.—The voluminous literature that has appeared on the subject of dolomite origin is concerned mainly with the process or processes which produce dolomites of *regional* extent. Nevertheless, a number of papers have been written in which *local* dolomitization has been ascribed to either circulating ground waters or magmatic waters. Among these is the paper by Kendall[30] to which previous reference has been made, in which the dolomitization of limestone pebbles in a conglomerate is described. Obviously this dolomite was produced by a process of replacement which took place not only after the limestone was deposited, but also after the limestone had been broken up by erosion processes and redeposited as clastic sediment. The importance of fissures or joint cracks in supplying channelways for dolomitizing ground waters has been pointed out by several, including Geikie.[31]

Dolomite has been produced both on a small and on a great scale. In the north of England and elsewhere, the Carboniferous limestone has been altered for a few feet or yards on either side of its joints into a dull yellow dolomite, locally termed "dunstone." Similar vertical zones of dolomite occur also in the Carboniferous limestone of Ireland.

Fault planes are stressed by Hatch, Rastall and Black.[32]

Subsequent Dolomitization.—Dolomites of this type are most easily recognized in formations which are not completely metasomatized, but still contain relics of unaltered

[28] Marcus A. Hanna, "Alteration of Comanchean Limestones of South-Central Texas," *Jour. Sed. Petrology*, Vol. I, No. 1 (April, 1931), p. 47.

[29] John Emery Adams, "Origin, Migration and Accumulation of Petroleum in Limestone Reservoirs in Western United States and Canada," *Problems of Petroleum Geology*, Amer. Assoc. Petrol. Geol. (1934), p. 359.

[30] P. F. Kendall, *op. cit.*

[31] Sir Archibald Geikie, *Textbook of Geology*, Vol. I (1903), p. 426.

[32] F. H. Hatch, R. H. Rastall, and M. Black, *The Petrology of the Sedimentary Rocks* (1938), p. 193.

limestone. In the most characteristic occurrences, the secondary dolomite is clearly related to the planes of weakness normally found in solid rocks, the commonest channels of dolomitization being fault planes, joints, and minor fractures. At certain places where the Carboniferous limestone of the Pennines is cut by the Craven Faults, for example, the fault plane is bordered by dolomite, which also invades the adjacent limestone along joints and bedding planes; the less altered limestone is frequently veined by strings of dolomite-crystals arranged along irregular cracks, or may contain minute perfectly formed rhombs scattered throughout the rock. Away from the faults, dolomite becomes less abundant and the altered rock gives way to purer undolomitised limestone.

Van Hise[33] considered the problem of whether the dolomitizing solutions were descending or ascending, and concluded that the latter was probable, at least in many instances.

As to whether dolomitization takes place more rapidly while the solutions are descending or ascending no definite answer can be given without further experimental work. It is believed that the process probably occurs throughout the journey of the underground water, as explained on pages 636–639. Doubtless in many cases where there is local dolomitization adjacent to the main underground circulation channels, the process has taken place while the waters were ascending, for, as shown on page 583, the trunk channels of underground waters are more often ascending than descending.

Local dolomitization of limestones by the same solutions that carry the ore minerals has been reported in several mining districts, especially Joplin.[34]

Both the megascopic and microscopic character of the ore and gangue shows that the ores, the jasperoid, and the dolomite, were deposited from the same solution, for the most part simultaneously and in the main as by replacement of limestone.

Earlier Spur[35] had called attention to fracture controlled local dolomitization in the Aspen district.

In Aspen there is evidence of two distinct periods at which dolomite was formed. The main body of dolomite, consisting of the whole of the Silurian beds and the lower part of the Leadville formation, existed previous to the deformation of the rocks by faulting and folding, since the dolomite beds are faulted in the same proportion as the rest of the strata. Along these main faults and fractures, however, the blue limestone at the top of the Leadville formation has been altered irregularly for varying distances on each side of the fractures into dolomite, microscopically identical with that formed at the earlier period. This later dolomite forms wherever the rock has been open to circulating waters. Thus it follows faults and fractures which cut directly across stratification, and also slip planes and porous zones conforming with the stratification. As before, the microscopic structure shows that the rock was produced by the action of solutions which exchanged carbonate of magnesia for part of the original carbonate of lime, but in this case the solutions have been comparatively scanty and short-lived, for they have not affected the whole rock, but only zones along watercourses. On the other hand, analyses of the locally dolomitized zones which traverse the blue limestone, show all transitions from a pure dolomite into a pure limestone, the dolomitization growing less as the distance from the fracture along which the dolomitizing solutions apparently flowed increases.

[33] Charles R. Van Hise, "A Treatise on Metamorphism," *U. S. Geol. Survey Mon. 47* (1904), p. 807.

[34] C. E. Siebenthal, "Origin of the Zinc and Lead Deposits of the Joplin Region," *U. S. Geol. Survey Bull. 606* (1915), p. 192.

[35] Josiah E. Spurr, "Geology of the Aspen Mining District, Colorado," *U. S. Geol. Survey Mon. 31* (1898), pp. 208–09.

According to Hewett[36] magmatic solutions have caused the alteration of lime-stones to dolomite in southern Nevada.

Limestones of the upper Paleozoic section are extensively altered to dolomite in the southern end of Spring Mountain Range.

Dolomitization was largely effected without appreciable shrinkage in volume. The solutions that accomplished it were probably related to the intrusions of orthoclase por-phyry. It is clearly of hydrothermal alteration.

Bernauer[37] ascribes the origin of the banded dolomite of Burs, Vorarlberg, Austria, to leaching of the more soluble limestone layers followed by the deposition of dolomite in the cavities and in the immediately contiguous limestone.

The writer believes that the local dolomitization which has produced local dolomite porosity has been caused by circulating ground waters. These were moving in an artesian system and were probably ascending at the time of dolomitization. At lower depths the waters had passed through older, regional dolomites and had picked up magnesium from those rocks. In the Adams and Deep River pools the circulating solutions were confined to a single master fracture. The Trenton limestone in the Lima-Indiana field is apparently traversed by many fractures, so that the dolomitization was more widespread. The answer to why the dolomitization is largely confined to the upper part of the limestones may be the presence of an overlying thick shale which might partially dam the ascending solutions so that they spread out and moved laterally in the upper part of the limestone.

Origin of cavities.—The voids in the dolomite have all the characteristics of solution cavities. They are irregular in shape, and possess cross-cutting relation-ships to the minerals and laminae in the rock. Yet they can not have been formed by ground water leaching or the neighboring limestone would be similarly honey-combed.

The replacement process, as demonstrated by Lindgren and others, is in reality two processes: solution and precipitation. Ordinarily the second process keeps up with the first, so that volume for volume replacement results. But this is not necessarily so. According to Lindgren:[38]

Solution and precipitation go on practically simultaneously dependent upon the constantly changing equilibrium, the supply of solvent and the facility of escape for the dissolved material. Two or several minerals may be dissolved at the same time to make room for the new as in the replacement of shale by a pyrite crystal. The volume of the rock remains constant, held by pressure. The moment a place is available some mineral will separate out from the concentrated solution. *This law fails to apply* in free crystals or when rock pressure can be overcome by the force of crystallization, or when a solid is replaced by a gel, or *when the solutions circulate so rapidly that there is a strong balance in favor of solution.* (Italics by present writer.)

[36] D. F. Hewett, "Dolomitization in Southern Nevada," *Bull. Geol. Soc. America*, Vol. 35, No. 1 (March, 1924), pp. 124–25.

[37] Ferdinand Bernauer, "Gebänderte Carbonatgesteine und ihre Umwandlung," *Neues Jahrbuch*, *Beil.-Bd. 66* (1933), Abt. A, H.3, pp. 362–80.

[38] Waldemar Lindgren, *Mineral Deposits* (1933), p. 174.

A footnote on an earlier page (page 93) in Lindgren's text contains the following.

When a rock is permeated by strong, rapidly moving liquids, solution may overtake deposition and a drusy structure may result. But even in this case the bulk volume is likely to remain about constant, except under very heavy pressure.

The writer[39] has elsewhere developed the theory of excess solution over precipitation to explain cavities in pegmatites and ore deposits where replacement processes have been operative. Although magmatic rather than meteoric solutions were there involved, the mechanics of replacement should be the same. Incidentally, the cavities thus formed in pegmatites and ore deposits are lined with crystals brought in by the replacing solutions in the same way that the dolomite cavities are lined with dolomite crystals.

This theory would explain the presence of "tight" dolomite surrounded by porous dolomite. In the zones of impervious dolomite, precipitation kept pace with solution, which is the general rule except where circulation was most active.

CONCLUSIONS

The theories advanced heretofore to explain the porosity that is confined to locally dolomitized zones in limestones are inadequate. The writer believes that local diastrophism has produced master fissures in the limestone-containing section; that an artesian circulation has been developed which has carried waters through deeper dolomites and up into the limestone; and that these waters have replaced some of the limestone by dolomite that is locally porous where there was an excess of solution over precipitation during the replacement process.

One wonders how much undiscovered oil is locked up in the earth's crust in reservoirs of this type. Allegedly "dry" domes, tested by one or two wells near the top, may contain oil in a belt of local dolomitization porosity on the flanks. It is suggested that, in regions where oil is known to occur in reservoirs of this type, (1) exploration be not confined to the tops of anticlines, and (2) samples be analyzed for magnesium carbonate content. A dry hole in which the limestone samples contained more than average in $MgCO_3$ would encourage exploration laterally in the hope of finding true dolomite.

[39] K. K. Landes, "The Paragenesis of the Granite Pegmatites of Central Maine," *Amer. Mineralogist*, Vol. 10 (1925), No. 11, pp. 363–66.
———, "Criteria of Age Relations of Minerals," *Econ. Geol.* Vol. 27 (1932), No. 2, p. 211.

Reprinted from:
BULLETIN OF THE AMERICAN ASSOCIATION OF PETROLEUM GEOLOGISTS
VOL. 36, NO. 2 (FEBRUARY, 1952) PP. 278-298, 15 FIGS.

CLASSIFICATION OF CARBONATE RESERVOIR ROCKS AND PETROPHYSICAL CONSIDERATIONS*

G. E. ARCHIE†
Houston, Texas

ABSTRACT

Limestone reservoirs found at increasingly greater depths, with accompanying higher per well cost of production, have made the problem of determining net pay thickness of limestone reservoirs more exacting. In discussing the petrophysics of limestones, it is necessary first to classify them in a manner to portray as much as possible the essential pore characteristics of a reservoir.

A skeleton classification with symbols is presented and coordinated with petrophysical data, such as porosity, permeability, capillary pressure, and electrical resistivity of water-bearing and oil-bearing limestones.

Petrophysical relationships of some limestones are discussed. The application of these relationships to field practice is much more difficult than for sandstones because of the heterogeneity and great amount of dense limestone generally encountered in the gross reservoir interval. This increases the so-called "geometrical" variables, making well-logging interpretation difficult.

The usefulness of the electrical resistivity curve in detecting productive parts of a limestone reservoir will vary, for it is shown that the resistivity of the productive part of a limestone formation may be greater than, less than, or the same as, the resistivity of the dense, non-productive parts. This is due mainly to the variation of porosity (or permeability) with water saturation, i.e., pore-size distribution.

INTRODUCTION

Recent limestone drilling at increasingly greater depths with accompanying higher per well cost has made the problem of determining net pay thickness of limestone reservoirs more exacting. Limestone, being heterogeneous, ranges from dense to porous limestone within a few feet or even fractions of an inch. As much as we would like to get the basic reservoir data (porosity, permeability, connate water, and thickness) directly from cores and production data, rather than indirectly from drill cuttings, electrical and other well logs, it is not always possible. Coring is costly because the gross section is commonly large. Further, a small amount of lost recovery can not generally be tolerated because the thin productive intervals normally encountered might constitute the lost part.

Irregularities inherent in drilling operations, the personal equation, and economic considerations place certain limitations on obtaining all the desirable information. Therefore, it is necessary to use other rock characteristics, i.e., resistivity, S.P., neutron, gamma ray, examination of drill cuttings for porosity and permeability, and residual oil and gas in cuttings, in order to get a basis for reserve estimates. To intrepret these more or less "indirect" data, it is necessary to investigate the relations that exist between these characteristics and the basic or desired factors. The relation between the basic factors themselves also needs investigation, i.e., the interrelationship of porosity, permeability, capillary pressure, and connate water. Of fundamental interest, of course, is the pore structure which is determined by the type of carbonate reservoir rock.

* Read before the Association at St. Louis, April 25, 1951. Manuscript received, May 10, 1951.

† Shell Oil Company. The writer thanks the Shell Oil Company for permission to publish this report and is particularly grateful to C. G. Cooper, R. C. Spivey, and O. Wilhelm for their contributions in the classification of carbonate rocks within the Shell Oil Company.

DISCUSSION

GENERAL

In discussing the petrophysics of limestones, it is desirable first to classify them in a manner to portray as much as possible the essential pore characteristics of a reservoir. When correlating drill cuttings with so-called "indirect" methods more quantitatively, it is necessary to study the pore structure in detail.

For example, pore structure is indicated in a qualitative way by the relation between porosity and permeability. Low porosity accompanied by high permeability means larger pores and, generally, low connate water because of the low capillary pull. High porosity and low permeability suggest smaller pores and generally higher connate water. A limestone of the former type would be the compact or dense crystalline limestone with secondary development of porosity. See, for example, Figure 2, specimens labeled I-B and I-C. Most of the porosity is secondary and, therefore, of relatively large size. Little of the total porosity exists in the matrix (as minute pores between the tightly bound crystals). An example of the latter would be an earthy or chalky limestone. See, for example, Figure 2, specimens II-A and II-B. An intermediate type would be a sucrose dolomite with so-called intergranular porosity.

It can be seen that a limestone classification emphasizing pore structure is quite practical. Such a classification places emphasis on the flow of fluids (permeability and relative permeability), fluid distribution (capillary pressure), and flow of electricity (resistivity), rather than the mineral content or any terminology that implies a particular origin of the effective porosity. A consideration of the latter is, of course, of great importance in geological subsurface studies.

The following classification is, therefore, presented before discussing other properties. Symbols are given for easy reference. The following points are given consideration in setting up the classification.

1. It is desirable to retain present lithological descriptions insofar as it is possible (6, 3, 4).

2. Emphasis is placed on pore-size distribution and related fluid distribution.

3. The system is kept as general as possible in order to be applicable to all carbonate rocks and to allow expanding to greater detail for special subsurface studies.

4. The effects of the personal equation should be at a minimum so that field data collected by different individuals may be reliably correlated.

5. Descriptions should be applicable to drill cuttings.

CLASSIFICATION

The classification consists of two parts:

A. The texture of the matrix, and

B. The character of the visible pore structure.

The former fulfills in part the lithological description and also gives information on the minute pore structure between the crystals, granules, or fossils. This minute pore structure can not be readily seen or investigated, even under the microscope at ordinary magnification, yet it is important in the fluid distribution within reservoirs.

The texture of the matrix may be classified as follows.

Texture of Matrix	Appearance of Hand Sample	Appearance under Microscope 10× to 15×
Type I Compact Crystalline	Crystalline, hard, dense, sharp edges and smooth faces on breaking. Resinous	Matrix made up of crystals tightly interlocking, allowing no visible pore space between crystals, commonly producing "feather edge" on breaking due to fracturing of clusters of crystals in thin flakes
Type II Chalky	Dull, earthy or "chalky." Crystalline appearance absent because small crystals are less tightly interlocked, thus reflecting light in different directions, or made up of extremely fine granules or sea organisms. May be siliceous or argillaceous	Crystals, less effectively interlocking than the foregoing, joining at different angles. Extremely fine texture may still appear "chalky" under this power, but others may begin to appear crystalline Grain size for this type is less than about 0.05 mm. Coarser textures classed as Type III
Type III Granular or Saccharoidal	Sandy or sugary appearing (Sucrose). Size of crystals or granules classed as: Very fine = 0.05 mm. Fine = 0.1 mm. Medium = 0.2 mm. Coarse = 0.4 mm.	Crystals interlocking at different angles, generally allowing space for considerable porosity between crystals. Oölitic and other granular textures fall in this class

The visible pore size may be classed as follows.

Class A: No visible porosity under about 10-power microscope or where pore size is less than about 0.01 mm. in diameter
Class B: Visible porosity, greater than 0.01 but less than 0.1 mm.
Class C: Visible porosity, greater than 0.1 mm., but less than size of cuttings
Class D: Visible porosity as evidenced by secondary crystal growth on faces of cuttings or "weathered-appearing" faces showing evidence of fracturing or solution channels; where pore size is greater than size of cutting

The frequency of the visible pores can be classed as:

Description	Frequency—Percentage of Surface Covered by Pores
Excellent	20
Good	15
Fair	10
Poor	5

Other descriptive terms may be added, particularly for subsurface geological studies, such as oölitic, fossiliferous, dolomitic, siliceous, or argillaceous.

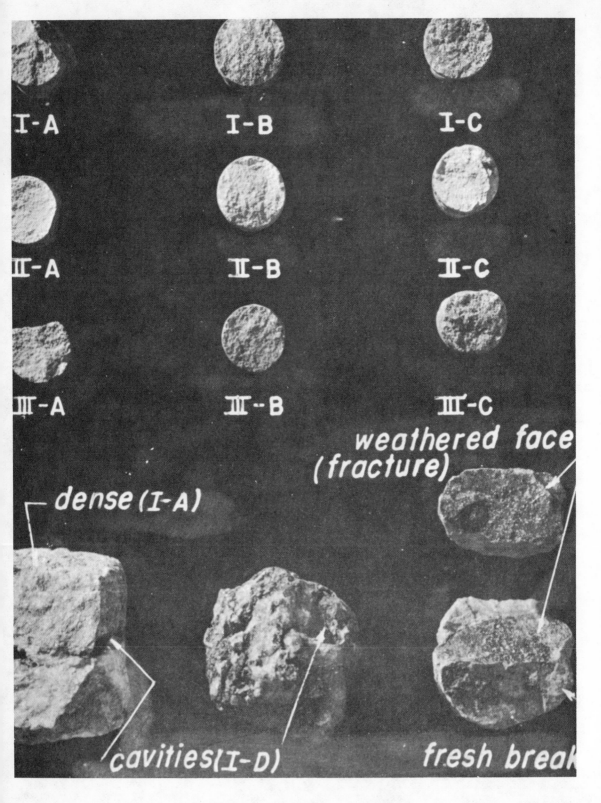

FIG 1.—Examples of types of limestone. Full size.

G. E. ARCHIE

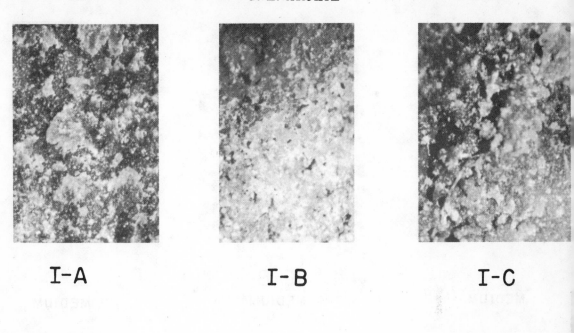

I-A   I-B   I-C

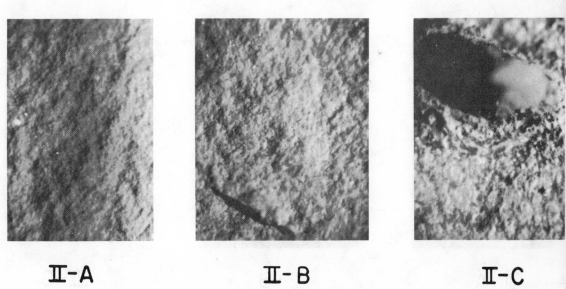

II-A   II-B   II-C

Fig. 2.—Photomicrographs of types of limestone. 10✕.

III-A
MEDIUM

III-B
MEDIUM

III-C
MEDIUM

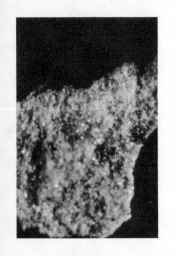

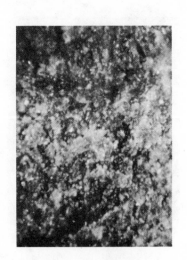

III-A
FINE

I-B

III-C
OOLITIC
COARSE

FIG. 3.—Photomicrographs of types of limestone. 10✕.

Photographs of examples of the different types of limestones are given in Figure 1. The small cylindrical cores are "permeability plugs" drilled out of cores sent to the laboratory for analysis. The large specimens are pieces of cores obtained by reverse circulation while coring the Ellenburger formation, Ordovician system, of West Texas. The two specimens in the lower right corner fit together to form one piece of core. The indicated dark "weathered" surfaces fit together forming a fracture plane.

Photomicrographs of examples of the various classifications are shown in Figures 2 and 3. Samples labeled Type I-A, I-B, I-C, II-A, II-B, II-C, III-A (med.), III-B (med.), and III-C (med.) are the same "plugs" shown in Figure 1.

As a matter of interest, the porosities and permeabilities of the samples shown in Figures 2 and 3 are shown in the following table.

Type	Porosity (Per Cent)	Permeability (Millidarcys)
I-A	4.1	<0.1
I-B	10.1	7.7
I-C	8.1	7.1
II-A	29.5	37.8
II-B	25.0	13.0
II-C	18.1	0.4
III-A (medium)	—	
III-B (medium)	21.6	339.0
III-C (medium)	17.3	478.0

It is believed that a classification of this type keeps the effects of the personal equation at a minimum and yet is general enough to be applicable to all limestones.

Further amplification of the reasons for including two main subdivisions (first, matrix, and second, visible pore distribution) may be given:

"PRIMARY" POROSITY

The texture of the matrix or crystal structure is a broad indication of the minute pore structure between the crystals; for instance, in the I-A type the crystals are tightly interlocking and the porosity is seldom more than 5 per cent; whereas in the "chalky" type, II-A, the porosity between the crystals may be as high as about 25 per cent, yet it is not readily visible. Generally, this minute pore space is considered to be "primary."

Varying amounts of the minute pore space contain connate water even within a hydrocarbon reservoir. This minute pore space makes up part of the "total" porosity measured in the laboratory, and, although it is not available space for hydrocarbons, it comes into play in electrical and neutron measurements. For instance, in Type I-A (whose porosity ranges from about 1 to 5 per cent) all of the porosity is of this kind and seldom, if ever, contains hydrocarbons.

"SECONDARY" POROSITY

Visible pore distribution, i.e., Class B, C, and D, describes the larger pore structure. This is generally considered to be "secondary" porosity and is, of course, more important with respect to the permeability to fluid.

Porosity analyses of drill cuttings, if the cuttings are of reasonable size, are reliable on Types I-A, II-A, III-A, I-B, II-B, and III-B (8). Porosity determinations on I-C, II-C, and III-C are generally low when the cuttings have large holes, unless special precautions are taken to obtain the true bulk volume. The usefulness of laboratory reports are greatly enhanced by including photomicrographs of typical cuttings in each interval studied. This aids in correlations between drill cuttings, logging surveys, and general subsurface features for an estimate of reserves.

Porosity measurements can not be made on Type I-D (except occasional tests to determine the porosity of the matrix) because the pore size is larger than the size of the cutting. This type may be examined under the microscope to determine the number of faces on the cuttings having secondary crystal growth or other evidence of being the lining of a solution cavity or fracture. The total sample can be carefully "parted down" to a small representative portion in order that this count may be made on as few cuttings as possible. The frequency of the number of "weathered" or "solution channel" faces can be correlated with the electrical log and the net section approximated more closely.

Drill cuttings from Type I-D formations often appear entirely dense on casual examination. Also, the loosely held secondary crystals within the cavities may break away while drilling and not be recovered unless the cuttings are carefully removed from the mud stream. In oil-bearing sections a fluoroscope is useful, for the faces of fractures and cavities of oil-bearing layers will fluoresce.

All limestones do not, of course, fall exactly within the classifications given. There are gradations from one type to another. For example, a sample may appear slightly "earthy" to the naked eye, but under the microscope appear to be of the crystalline type. These samples have more than 1 to 5 per cent porosity, typical of I-A type, running up possibly to 10 per cent porosity. They may be designated as I-A(II-A) or I/II A. Another example would be a limestone of predominant I-B type, but some of the pores are C-size. It could be designated as I-B(C) or IB/C. The generalized chart at the top of the next page shows the symbols and approximate porosities that may be expected for each type.

PETROPHYSICAL CONSIDERATIONS
GENERAL

In any petrophysical consideration it is important first to type the rock (1). The foregoing classification is an attempt to orient limestone petrophysical relationships.

We are just beginning to understand the properties of rock pore structure and recent work on capillary pressure has contributed greatly (2). Even with a good

GENERALIZED CLASSIFICATION AND SYMBOLS (LIMESTONE)

Class	Crystal or Grain Size (mm.)		Usual Appearance (Luster)	Approximate Matrix Porosity % Not Visible (12×–18×) A	Visible Porosity (% of Cutting Surface) Size of Pore—mm.			Approximate Total Porosity Per Cent	
					−0.1 B	0.1–2.0 C	+2.0 D	A+B	A+C
I Compact	L* M F	0.4+ 0.2 0.1	Resinous to	2	e.g. 10	e.g. 15	‡	12	17
	VF	0.05	Vitreous†	5	e.g. 10	e.g. 15		15	20
II Chalky	VF	0.05−	Chalky†	15	e.g. 10	e.g. 15		25	30
III Sucrose	F	0.1	Finely sucrose	10	e.g. 10	e.g. 15		20	25
	M	0.2							
	L	0.4	Coarsely sucrose	5	e.g. 10	e.g. 15		15	20

* L = large (coarse); M = medium; F = fine; VF = very fine.
† Where cuttings are between vitreous and chalky in appearance, designate as I-II or II-I. Samples are considered in VF group when grain or crystal size is difficult to distinguish (12X–18X). Place in F group if grains are easily distinguished.
‡ When pores are greater than about 2.0 mm. and therefore occur at edge of cuttings (e.g., sub-cavernous pores), amount of such porosity is indicated by % of cuttings in an interval showing evidence of large pores.
Symbols:
III F-B_{10} = Finely sucrose (therefore, matrix porosity about 10%), visible porosity about 10%, total porosity about 20%.
(II-I)VF-A = Chalky to vitreous, very fine texture (therefore, matrix porosity about 8%), no visible porosity, total porosity about 8%.

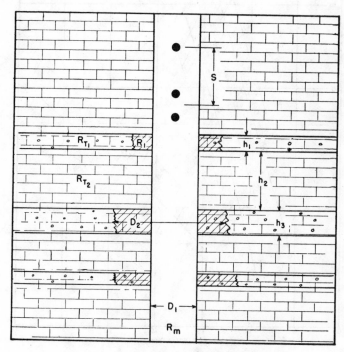

FIG. 4.—Geometrical variables (macroscopic).

understanding of pore structure, additional problems exist in the field application.

One of the most difficult problems involves an analysis of thin, porous layers imbedded between layers of low porosity. This condition is the rule rather than the exception for limestone since few limestones are known where the porosity is uniform over a vertical interval of a few feet or more. This complicates the interpretation of drill cuttings and core analyses, as well as electrical, radioactivity, and other well logs. Regarding well logging in general, this may be defined as the "geometrical" problem, i.e., the combination of layer thickness, existence of the bore hole, electrode spacing, and mud filtrate invasion near the bore hole.

The "geometrical" problem is not as difficult where shale is the interbedded impermeable formation as where the impermeable rock is of the same lithologic type as the porous layers (impermeable limestone or sandstone). Figure 4 illustrates the large number of variables in a limestone reservoir: D_1 (diameter of

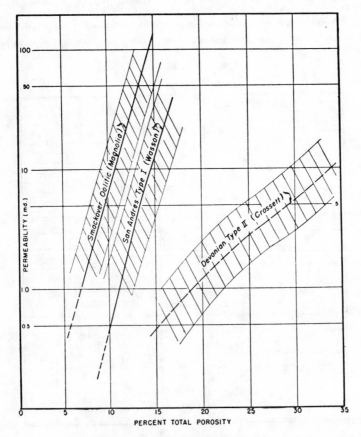

FIG. 5.—Limestone trends.

bore hole), D_2 (diameter of "invaded" zone), S (electrode spacing), h_1 and h_3 (permeable layers), h_2 (impermeable layer), resistivity variables R_m (mud), R_I ("invaded" zone), R_{T_1} (true formation, permeable), R_{T_2} (true formation, impermeable), and other rock properties.

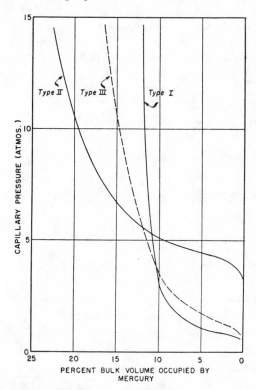

FIG. 6.—Typical capillary pressure curves for different types of carbonate reservoir rock.

POROSITY AND PERMEABILITY

Figure 5 shows the relation between porosity and permeability for three limestone reservoirs: compact, granular (oölitic), and chalky. (The Wasson reservoir is predominantly Type I; however, parts are Type III.) It can be seen from the figures that porosity alone is not indicative of productive thickness. A chalky type of limestone requires a considerably greater porosity to be productive. Therefore, the type of void structure for any porosity must be known before the permeability, and therefore the net pay, can be determined in even a qualitative way from porosity measurements alone.

CONNATE WATER AND CAPILLARY PRESSURE

The capillary-pressure curve allows us to predict, in a qualitative way at least, the effective pore-size distribution and the amount of connate water that a producing reservoir may contain. Families of capillary-pressure curves of compact, granular, and chalky are shown in Figure 6. The plateau of the San Andres limestone, of Permian age (predominantly Type I), is flat and the steep slope is at a high angle, indicating that there are mainly two types of pores: the larger or secondary porosity, and the finer or matrix porosity. Further, it can be seen that the connate water would be relatively low for the productive part of the reservoir, less than about 10%. Actually, this reservoir was cored with oil and the connate water was found to be low. Figure 7 shows the water saturation plotted

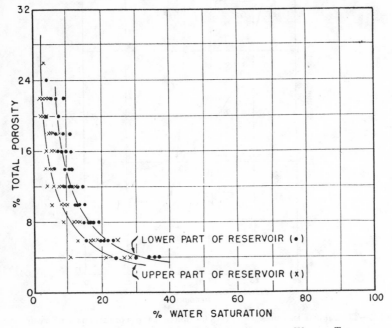

Fig. 7.—Average water saturation, San Andres limestone, Wasson, Texas.

against porosity. (Permeability could have been used as well for this general graph, but low permeabilities, <0.1, are difficult to measure with reasonable accuracy.) Each point represents an average of all cores having the same porosity from one well; five wells are represented.

In contrast, the Devonian lime has a high displacement pressure and the plateau is not marked, indicating that most of the pores are small, grading to very small, and that the connate water would be expected to be high.

ELECTRICAL RESISTIVITY

Electrical logs are one of our greatest sources of information, and, therefore, it is important to know how the resistivity is related to pore and fluid distribution.

RELATIONSHIP BETWEEN RESISTIVITY AND POROSITY

A relation exists between resistivity and porosity of a limestone when its pores are entirely filled with water (Figure 8). It may be noted that fundamentally this relation is no different from that for sandstones (1). Greater variation from the average exists, but this is to be expected because of greater heterogeneity of limestone pore structure.

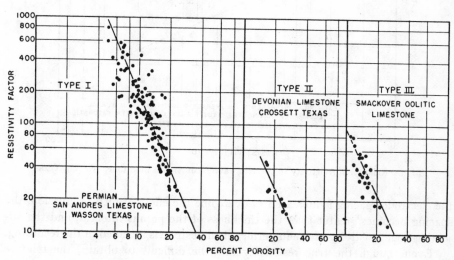

FIG. 8.—Relation of porosity to formation resistivity factor.

RELATIONSHIP BETWEEN RESISTIVITY AND CONNATE WATER

The general relation between resistivity and connate water for limestones tested thus far appears to be of the same type as sandstones. An example of the compact Type I is shown in Figure 9, where the resistivity ratio is the resistivity of the oil-bearing rock divided by the resistivity of the same rock when 100% water-bearing. The data were obtained from cores cut with oil flush. The cores were canned immediately at the well and sent to the laboratory where the "natural resistivities" (as received) were measured. Immediately following this measurement, routine core analyses were made for oil and water saturation, chloride content of the connate water, porosity, and permeability.

RELATIONSHIP OF RESISTIVITY, POROSITY, PERMEABILITY, CONNATE WATER

The foregoing data indicate that the resistivity curve recorded opposite a limestone reservoir can be used to estimate the connate water, or conversely, oil and gas saturation, in the same manner as is done for sandstone reservoirs. A practical difficulty, the "geometrical problem," generally arises because thick, porous limestone intervals are rare. Therefore, it is difficult to obtain the true resistivity of the porous interval underground from the electrical log (Fig. 4). As

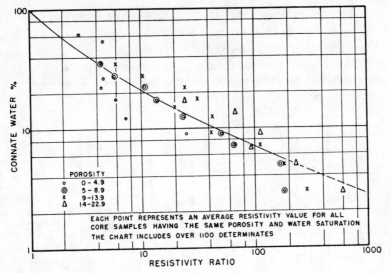

Fig. 9.—Relation of resistivity to connate water, San Andres limestone, Wasson, Texas.

the electrode spacing is increased to overcome the effect of filtrate invasion, the spacing becomes greater than the thickness of the porous interval, and the adjoining high resistivity of the impermeable limestone is included in the recording.

Even though the true resistivity may be difficult to obtain, the relative changes in resistivity may be significant, such that the curve can be used in a qualitative way. To determine this, however, the interrelation of all rock properties must be studied. For example, assume that a broad relationship or trend ex-

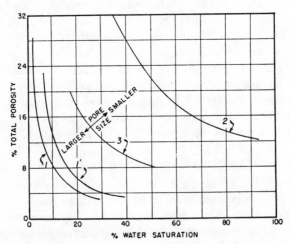

Fig. 10.—Possible average relationship of connate water and porosity for different types of limestone.

ists between porosity and permeability, resistivity factor and porosity (Figs. 5 and 8). Now, the usefulness of the resistivity curve in outlining the net pay section, within a gross limestone interval, will depend on how the water saturation varies with porosity (or permeability). Assume, for instance, that this relationship is as shown in Figure 10. Line 1 could represent a Type I limestone, low con-

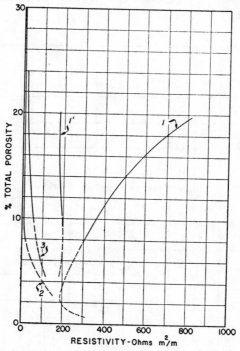

FIG. 11.—Possible generalized relations between resistivity of an oil and gas reservoir and porosity.

nate water for a given porosity; line 2 could represent a Type II limestone, high connate water; while line 3 could be intermediate, say Type III, fine-grained. Line 1' could represent Type I nearer the water table, or considered intermediate between 1 and 3.

The manner in which the resistivity curve varies with porosity (or permeability for a particular type of rock) for 1, 1', 2, and 3 is shown in Figure 11. Note that the net pay of 1 is indicated by increases in resistivity, 2 and 3 by decreases or depressions in the resistivity curve, while in the case of 1' the resistivity curve does not aid in outlining the pay.

Another variable, capillarity, enters when attempting to use the foregoing analysis in an actual interpretation. The connate water increases as the water table is approached; therefore, if condition 1 exists well above the water table, condition 1' or even 3 might exist respectively as the water table is approached.

The San Andres limestone is an example. The upper interval of the reservoir is actually condition 1, and the lower interval is condition 1'. Compare the average lines in Figure 7 with lines 1 and 1' of Figure 10. As a cross check of measurements on cores, the resistivity of the core as withdrawn from the well is plotted directly against porosity in Figure 12. The trend of the points is similar to the average lines 1 and 1' in Figure 11.

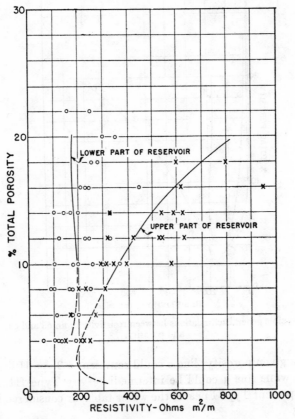

FIG. 12.—San Andres limestone. Resistivity of cores as extracted from well versus porosity.

Further, in an actual interpretation, invasion of filtrate changes the resistivity curve, and the qualitative relations discussed (variation of resistivity to indicate net pay thickness) may be controlled by other considerations—resistivity of the filtrate, depth of invasion, and electrode spacing. It is generally necessary to use a combination of relations and various well surveys to evaluate a limestone reservoir. The micro-resistivity log (5) and neutron log (7) are useful.

EXAMPLES

COMPACT, CRYSTALLINE—TYPE I-B, I-C RESERVOIR

WICHITA FORMATION OF PERMIAN AGE, UNION DISTRICT, WEST TEXAS

Figure 13 shows the cutting analysis plotted beside the electrical log. The interval from 7,300 to 7,400 feet was drilled, with reverse circulation, and the drill cuttings analyzed for porosity. Three main types of limestone were encountered in this 100 feet: crystalline limestone with no visible porosity (I-A), crystalline limestone containing visible pores greater than 0.1 mm. in diameter (I-C), and earthy appearing limestone (II-A). There were sufficient pieces of crystalline limestone (I-A) in each 2-foot interval for analysis.

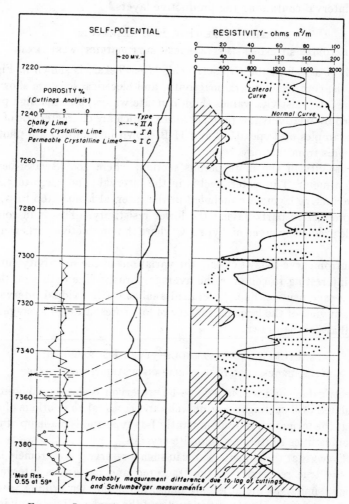

FIG. 13.—Log of Permian limestone, Union district, West Texas.

Earthy appearing limestone (non-productive) was encountered at 7,314, 7,340, and 7,350 feet (electrical-log depths). These intervals have low resistivity values accompanied by increases in S.P. This is indicative of high connate water, which is to be expected from the fine structure, even though the layers are within the producing reservoir.

Dense I-A limestone intervals, such as 7,316–7,330 feet, are highly resistive with somewhat depressed S.P.

The productive section, Type I-C, is highly resistive. The interval from 7,364 feet to total depth consists of about 40% I-C and 60% I-A, as indicated by drill cuttings.

Using both the drill cuttings and the electrical log allows a better understanding of the interval containing the productive layers.

EARTHY—TYPE II-A, II-B RESERVOIR
DEVONIAN SILICEOUS LIMESTONE, CROSSETT DISTRICT, WEST TEXAS

A graph of a well in the Crossett field, West Texas, is shown in Figure 14. Core analysis, core recovery, radioactivity, and electrical logs are shown.

Note the low resistivity values (high connate water), and the high porosities accompanied by relatively low permeabilities, which are characteristic of Type II pay. The examples of Types II-A and II-B shown in Figure 2 are photomicrographs of cores from this pay.

The resistivity of the more porous section, where 100% water-bearing, is about 1 ohm-meter. The water level is in the interval from 5,420 to 5,440 feet, and the productive layers are included in the interval from 5,360 to 5,420 feet, the more productive parts having the lower resistivity. (This is in contrast to the example previously given of Type I-C where the productive parts were highly resistive.)

The neutron curve follows closely the variations of the resistivity curve. Further, it is interesting to compare the average porosity line drawn on the graph with the average neutron line. A detailed analysis of individual intervals is not warranted, in view of the large percentage of lost cores; a rough average porosity line is all that can be drawn.

FRACTURED AND CAVERNOUS—TYPE I-D RESERVOIR
ELLENBURGER LIMESTONE, MONAHANS DISTRICT, WEST TEXAS

The electrical log of a well in a Type I-D reservoir is shown in Figure 15. Reverse circulated drill cuttings on some wells and cores taken in others of this field showed that the formation is predominantly I-D type and is made up of fractures and solution cavities containing dolomite crystals.

It is believed that the connate water in such a reservoir is extremely low, and, therefore, the true resistivity of the fractured and cavernous intervals is extremely high, similar to the adjoining dense limestone. On drilling with water-base mud, however, the filtrate of the mud and the mud itself, in many instances,

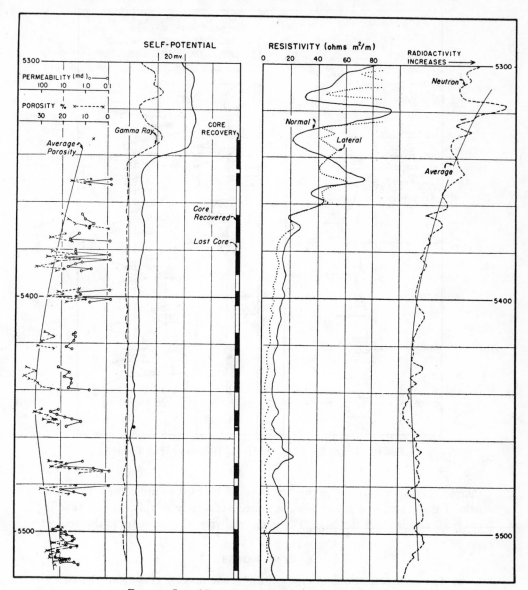

Fig. 14.—Log of Devonian limestone, Crossett, West Texas.

flow into these crevices and reduce the resistivity of these breaks near the bore hole. Therefore, sharp decreases in resistivity are recorded opposite these beds in contrast to the adjoining highly resistive dense limestone. An increase in S.P. is recorded opposite the cavity or creviced zone if thick enough.

All the curves shown in the graph were exactly duplicated on resurveying;

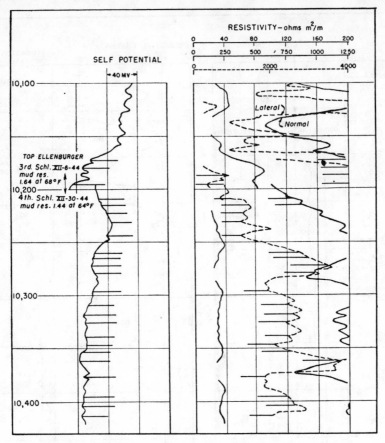

FIG. 15.—Log of Ellenburger limestone, Monahans, West Texas.

therefore, small variations in the curves could be used as indicators. The thickness of these breaks can not be determined accurately in this case because the electrode spacing was too large. The micro-resistivity log is useful in this respect.

CONCLUSIONS

1. The great variations in types of limestone make a classification based on pore structure necessary for the interpretation of various well data. This is particularly true in attempting an evaluation of a stratum on penetrating it in the exploratory drill hole. A skeleton classification is presented, together with symbols. This is coordinated with petrophysical data, such as porosity, permeability, capillary pressure, and electrical resistivity of water-bearing and oil-bearing limestones.

2. Petrophysical relationships or trends of limestone are of the same general

type as found for sandstones. Greater variations from the average may be expected because of the heterogeneity of limestone pore structure.

3. The application of these relationships to field practice is much more difficult than for sandstones because of the great amount of dense limestone generally found in the reservoir. This increases the so-called "geometrical" variables, making well-logging interpretation difficult.

4. Factors causing variations in resistivity within the limestone reservoir are discussed in relation to the qualitative use of the resistivity curve to outline net pay intervals. It is shown that the productive part of a limestone formation may be indicated by increases or decreases (or, in some cases, no variation at all) in resistivity, depending mainly on the variation of porosity (or permeability) with water saturation, i.e., pore-size distribution.

REFERENCES

1. ARCHIE, G. E. (1950), "Introduction to Petrophysics of Reservoir Rocks," *Bull. Amer. Assoc. Petrol. Geol.*, Vol. 34, No. 5.
2. BROWN, H. W. (1951), "Capillary Pressure Investigations," *Jour. Petrol. Tech.*
3. BULNES, A. C., AND FITTING, R. U., JR. (1945), "An Introductory Discussion of the Reservoir Performance of Limestone Formations," *Trans. A.I.M.E.*, Vol. 160.
4. COOPER, C. G., SPIVEY, R. C., AND WILHELM, O., Discussions of standardization of description of carbonate rocks.
5. DOLL, H. G. (1950), "The MicroLog—A New Electrical Logging Method for Detailed Determination of Permeable Beds," *Trans. A.I.M.E.*, Vol. 189.
6. HILLS, J. M. (1949), "Sampling and Examination of Well Cuttings," *Bull. Amer. Assoc. Petrol. Geol.*, Vol. 33, No. 1.
7. MARDOCK, E. S., AND FEARON, R. E. (1951), "The Quantitative Interpretation of Radioactivity Logs," given at Third World Petroleum Congress, The Hague.
8. PURCELL, W. R. (1949), "Capillary Pressures—Their Measurement Using Mercury and the Calculation of Permeability Therefrom," *Trans. A.I.M.E.*, Vol. 186.
9. WESTBROOK, M. A., AND REDMOND, J. F. (1946), "A New Technique for Determining the Porosity of Drill Cuttings," *Trans. A.I.M.E.*, Vol. 165.

Reprinted from:
BULLETIN OF THE AMERICAN ASSOCIATION OF PETROLEUM GEOLOGISTS
VOL. 44, NO. 5 (MAY, 1960) PP. 569-588, 9 FIGS. 5 PLATES

FACIES AND POROSITY RELATIONSHIPS IN SOME MISSISSIPPIAN CARBONATE CYCLES OF WESTERN CANADA BASIN[1]

G. E. THOMAS[2] AND R. P. GLAISTER[2]
Calgary, Alberta, Canada

ABSTRACT

Case histories of textural and reservoir analyses of two Mississippian carbonate cycles of the Western Canada basin are presented to illustrate the relationships of grain, matrix, and cement variants of carbonate rocks to porosity and permeability determinations.

Large stratigraphic oil pools have been discovered, at or near the Paleozoic subcrop of the Mississippian "Midale" carbonate cycle, in southeastern Saskatchewan. Apart from scattered, vuggy, algal-encrusted strand line deposits, most of the carbonates of the "Midale" producing zone consist of skeletal and oölitic limestones which have a finely comminuted, commonly dolomitized, limestone matrix with intergranular and chalky porosity. Effective reservoir porosity is controlled by the relative distribution and grain size of this matrix.

Major hydrocarbon (oil and gas) reserves have been found in the Mississippian "Elkton" carbonate cycle, both in the Foothills Belt and along the subcrop, in southwestern Alberta. Effective reservoir material of this cycle was found to consist mainly of the dolomitized equivalent of an originally coarse skeletal limestone, with a variable amount of generally porous, finely comminuted (granular) skeletal matrix. Primary porosity was very important in the control of dolomitization which probably began with the replacement of this matrix by euhedral rhombohedrons and finally affected the coarse skeletal material (now generally indicated by leached fossil cast outlines). These porous dolomites grade laterally in a predictable way into tight, relatively non-dolomitized, well sorted, coarse skeletal limestones with original high interfragmental porosity now completely infilled with clear crystalline calcite. This lithification by cementation took place early in the history of carbonate sedimentation of this area and before secondary dolomitization processes took effect.

INTRODUCTION

During the past 10 years there has been an increasing demand from industry, national geological organizations, and universities to organize the classification of carbonate rocks into a single, moderately detailed system of nomenclature which will be understood and used by all concerned. Unfortunately, it now appears that this demand will soon be met by not one but by a plethora of carbonate rock breakdowns.

Any proposed carbonate rock classification which does not attempt to give an explanation for the variances in reservoir void space in limestone or dolomite sequences will not satisfy the requirements of an oil geologist or reservoir engineer. Effective porosity isopach and allied carbonate textural maps will be essential to future exploration and exploitation programs in the Western Canada basin, because most hydrocarbons discovered to date are contained in carbonate stratigraphic traps of organic reef or clastic origin.

It is fortunate that carbonate sedimentation is so sensitive to environmental conditions that widely various textures and structures result, each of which records the stamp of the depositional conditions which produced it. The full significance of carbonate rock textures in environmental interpretation and in evaluation of potential reservoir zones is becoming more and more apparent.

In this report, case histories of textural and reservoir analyses of two Mississippian carbonate cycles of the Western Canada basin are presented to illustrate the relation between the occurrence and petrographic nature of what constitutes an effective carbonate reservoir rock and the framework of carbonate sedimentation. Various types of carbonate rock pores, which are known to be characteristic of many limestone and dolomite sections, are described and evaluated with respect to effective porosity. These associations of textural type and porosity development are not found exclusively in one area. The descriptions here should be helpful in the recognition and mapping of such associations in other places. Figure 1 is an index map of the areas of study in Saskatchewan and Alberta, Canada. A generalized Mississippian correlation chart of these two areas is shown in Figure 2.

[1] Manuscript received, August 6, 1959.

[2] Geologists with Imperial Oil Limited. Thanks are due to Imperial Oil Limited for permission to publish this paper.

The valuable assistance rendered by J. W. Young of Imperial's Regina Division in the "Midale" carbonate study is gratefully acknowledged.

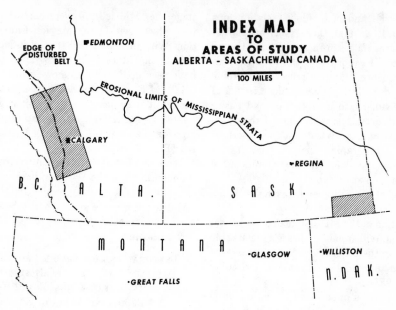

FIG. 1

DEPOSITIONAL HISTORY OF MISSISSIPPIAN SEDIMENTS IN WILLISTON BASIN

Accumulation of Mississippian oil in this area is strongly influenced by stratigraphy, and it is imperative to have an accurate understanding of the character and distribution of the formational subdivisions of the Mississippian system. A sche-matic table of Mississippian formations in the area is shown in Figure 3. The division of the Mis-sissippian into Lodgepole, Mission Canyon, and Charles formations is as much a controversial is-sue as ever, if one judges by current literature.

An analysis of carefully selected Mississippian time lithological units will demonstrate persistent

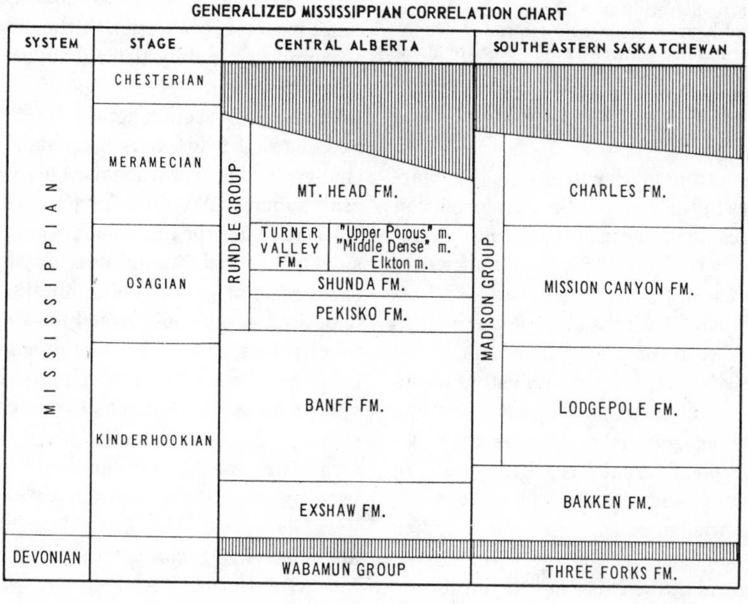

GENERALIZED MISSISSIPPIAN CORRELATION CHART

SYSTEM	STAGE	CENTRAL ALBERTA		SOUTHEASTERN SASKATCHEWAN	
MISSISSIPPIAN	CHESTERIAN	RUNDLE GROUP		MADISON GROUP	
	MERAMECIAN		MT. HEAD FM.		CHARLES FM.
	OSAGIAN		TURNER VALLEY FM. "Upper Porous" m. "Middle Dense" m. Elkton m.		MISSION CANYON FM.
			SHUNDA FM.		
			PEKISKO FM.		
	KINDERHOOKIAN		BANFF FM.		LODGEPOLE FM.
			EXSHAW FM.		BAKKEN FM.
DEVONIAN		WABAMUN GROUP		THREE FORKS FM.	

FIG. 2

basin, stable shelf, and unstable shelf relationships over the area. In general, there is a clear relation between the gross facies of these units and known oil occurrences. Evaporites in the Mississippian carbonate sequence definitely reflect the tectonic conditions under which they were deposited, and have been divided into intra-basinal and basin-margin occurrences. The separation of these two evaporitic environments was deemed so important for regional stratigraphic analysis that it was found necessary to redefine the lower limits of the Charles formation at its type locality.

Correlation of Mississippian rocks in the Williston basin is shown in Figure 3.

The evolution of the Mississippian depositional patterns in the Williston basin bears a remarkable resemblance to the sequence of West Texas-New Mexico Permian sedimentation as summarized by L. L. Sloss (1953).

The basic pattern of successive environmental and tectonic influences on sedimentation suggests the following sequence.

1. Establishment of a fully differentiated tectonic framework in the earliest Mississippian (Kinderhookian) with restricted, euxinic environments in the basins (formation of black shales and bituminous, micrograined limestones), normal marine conditions on the surrounding shelves, and brackish and terrestrial deposition at the margins of the sea.

2. Continuation of the initial pattern into the Osagian but with the establishment of saline (evaporitic) environments at the distal margins of the sea. Maximum carbonate development on the shelves as a result of an over-all, basinward migration of a shallow epeiric sea.

3. Formation of a single, markedly restricted evaporitic basin (Meramecian). Concentration of halite along the negative axis of the basin.

4. Tectonic stabilization of the entire area and deposition of a veneer of terrestrial redbeds (basal Chesterian).

The transition from marine limestone into marginal evaporites in the Mission Canyon formation has led to widespread confusion and miscorrelation. In a paper written in 1954, the senior writer advocated the use of persistent silt, sand, and argillaceous carbonate horizons as time boundaries in subdividing a carbonate, evaporite sequence in the northeastern parts of the Williston basin. These silt and mud incursions which terminate thin, carbonate depositional cycles were the products of epeirogenic fluctuations of the area. In that early paper, as a result of lack of well control, incomplete knowledge of the type Mississippian sections, and bad judgment on the writer's part only five members of the Mission Canyon formation were recognized. However, even at that early stage, the "Midale" and overlying carbonate cycle were placed within the Mission Canyon formation. With increased well control it soon became obvious that at least nine cartographic units could have been used. Industry now includes the "Midale" (M.C. 7) pay in the Charles formation, although it is evident that this unit is genetically related to the interplay of transgression and regression of an over-all, retreating Mission Canyon sea (Fig. 3).

With this broad introduction to Mississippian sedimentation in the Williston basin, some highlights of the facies and porosity relations of the "Midale" carbonate cycle on the Souris Valley shelf feature of southeastern Saskatchewan are now presented.

TEXTURAL AND RESERVOIR PROPERTIES OF "MIDALE" CARBONATES (MISSION CANYON FORMATION) IN KINGSFORD-FLORENCE PRODUCING AREAS OF SOUTH-EASTERN SASKATCHEWAN

Large stratigraphic oil pools have been discovered at or near the Paleozoic subcrop of the "Midale" carbonate cycle in southeastern Saskatchewan (Fig. 4a). However, it was found that, though mechanical logs indicated fairly constant porosity up to the subcrop area, the character and distribution of carbonate lithosomes in the cycle controls the quality of production in these pools. There is a wealth of core information along this trend, because reservoir evaluation of the different pools is accomplished mainly through an extensive coring program.

Figure 4b, a section across the East Kingsford-Steelman oil fields, illustrates some of the facies changes of this depositional cycle toward the Paleozoic subcrop. Attempts have been made by some workers to use the marginal evaporite in the cycle as a time-stratigraphic unit, but local patch or shoal reefs of porous algal limestone were being deposited amidst submerged shoals of calcareous fossil debris and oölites at the same time when evaporites were being precipitated in back lagoonal areas. A thin, chalky to earthy, locally silty, argillaceous dolomite bed (M.C. 6) which terminates the M.C. 5 carbonate cycle has been used by the writers to delineate the base of the "Midale" cycle. This bed retains its lithological and electric-log characteristics over the Souris Valley platform.

The "Midale" carbonates are overlain by an-

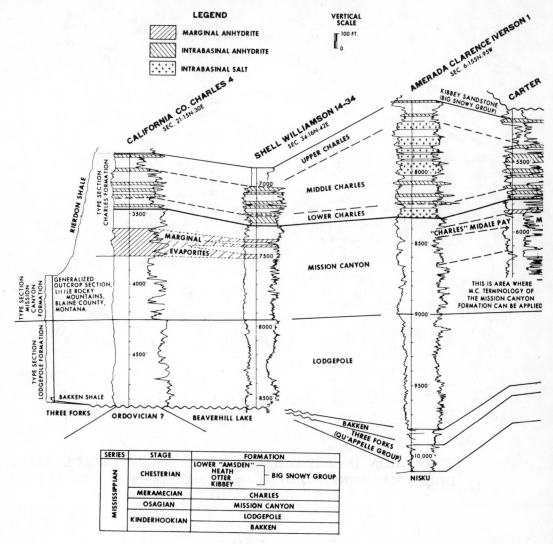

FIG. 3

hydrite and underlain throughout most of the area by an anhydrite floor. At the Paleozoic subcrop there is considerable secondary anhydrite infilling of primary carbonate porosity accompanied by dolomitization. The topographic highs on the Paleozoic erosional surface in parts of the Florence field, for example, are locally much brecciated, veined with gray or white anhydrite, and contain inclusions of the overlying Watrous redbeds. Completely dolomitized sections at the subcrop are very interesting because of the preservation of relict fossil structures.

Following the termination of deposition of the

M.C. 5 carbonate cycle by a veneer of chalky to earthy argillaceous dolomite, continued withdrawal of a shallow sea over the Souris Valley shelf resulted in the development of relict shoreline areas in which evaporites were deposited. Small patch or shoal reefs of vuggy, algal encrusted, bar-like material are found in juxtaposition to the marginal anhydrite sheet in the "Midale" beds (Kingsford area). These reefs could have acted as minor silling features necessary for the restriction and subsequent evaporation of the back lagoonal areas.

Calcareous algae played an important role in

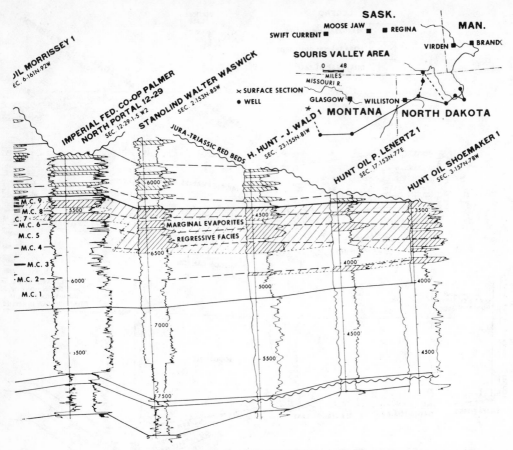

CORRELATION OF MISSISSIPPIAN ROCKS IN WILLISTON BASIN
LITTLE ROCKY MTNS. MONTANA - HUNT SHOEMAKER 1 N. DAKOTA
DECEMBER 1955

limestone building on the interior of the Souris Valley shelf area of southeastern Saskatchewan. J. Harlan Johnson (1956) has described in detail several genera of calcareous algae from thin sections of Saskatchewan material sent to him by one of the writers. Some stages in stabilization and encrustation of submerged, drifting shoals of calcareous, skeletal, and non-skeletal debris to form vuggy, algal, reef-like bodies are shown in Plate 1. Some of the strandline deposits have the appearance of oölite sand bars which have been stabilized by sediment-binding, encrusting calcareous algae. According to published reports, blue-green algae are commonly the earliest colonizers of sediment newly deposited on tidal flats. It is well known that such algae exert a strong stabilizing effect upon the sediment they colonize, largely because they bind it together with their growing filaments and ultimately cover it with a mass of felted tubes. The stabilization of drifting sand-like material is really incipient reef growth. Photochemical removal of carbon dioxide from sea water by sea plants causes a decrease in bicarbonate ions and thus promotes the precipitation of calcium carbonate. Calcium carbonate is precipitated as a colloidal gel encrusting the leaves and

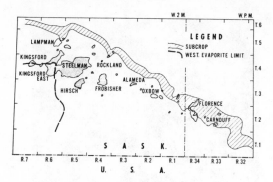

FIG. 4a.—"Midale" oil fields.

stems of these plants. The end-result is the production of cryptograined limestone which contains "syneresis" cracks and associated primary contraction vugs. The algal "knolls" of the Kingsford area generally have excellent horizontal as opposed to vertical permeability because of thin, cryptograined layers of encrusting algal limestone which separates partly encrusted, vuggy, pisolitic, and oölitic sections. From a reservoir point of view these carbonates are difficult to analyze because of anhydrite and calcite infilling of vugs and irregular, algal carbonate mud encrustation of original intergranular porosity. One has to resort to recording the percentage of effective void space.

Screened lenses of porous, finely comminuted carbonates are found draped over the wave resistant algal "knolls" of the West and East Kingsford area (Fig. 4b). Porosity, permeability, and oil saturation properties of these carbonates could be directly related to quantitative, textural (including grain size) carbonate measurements. The chart of Figure 5 shows that carbonate-matrix textural studies were the key to effective reservoir distribution in the upper "Midale" carbonates. Most of these carbonates consist of skeletal and oölitic limestones which have a finely comminuted, commonly dolomitized, limestone matrix with intergranular and chalky porosity. Effective reservoir porosity is controlled by the relative distribution and grain size of this matrix. Similar matrix grain size and effective reservoir relations have been found in the Triassic Boundary Lake lithosome in British Columbia and the Swan Hills member of the Beaverhill Lake formation in Alberta.

Bar-like trends of frequently current-bedded, skeletal, or non-skeletal material of very fine silt dimensions can be mapped in the Steelman and Oxbow areas of southeastern Saskatchewan. These deposits are usually extremely well sorted and are thought to have been developed by the attrition of crinoidal, algal, and oölitic material in

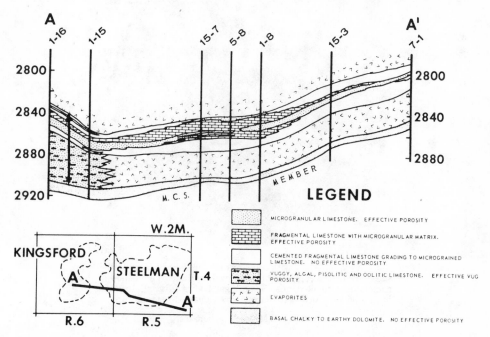

FIG. 4b.—"Midale" beds, Kingsford-Steelman area.

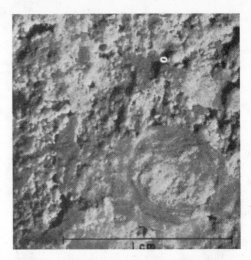

a.—Reefal algal limestone. Oölitic and pisolitic bodies encrusted and bound together by layers of originally gelatinous calcareous mud precipitated by algal action. Drying of this material has produced primary contraction vugs. Excellent reservoir rock with much greater horizontal than vertical permeability. Vertical core.

b.—Fine-grained, well sorted, oölitic, and accretionary composite lump limestone (Bahama sands type), partly encrusted by large algal, pisolitic, and "biscuit" bodies. Horizontal core.

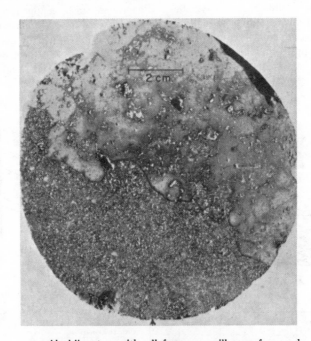

c.—Algal limestone with colloform mammillary surfaces and shrinkage cracks encrusting fine-grained, well sorted oölite and comminuted fossil debris. Some algal bodies in groundmass have been identified as Codiacean green algae. Horizontal core.

PLATE 1.—"Midale" carbonates.

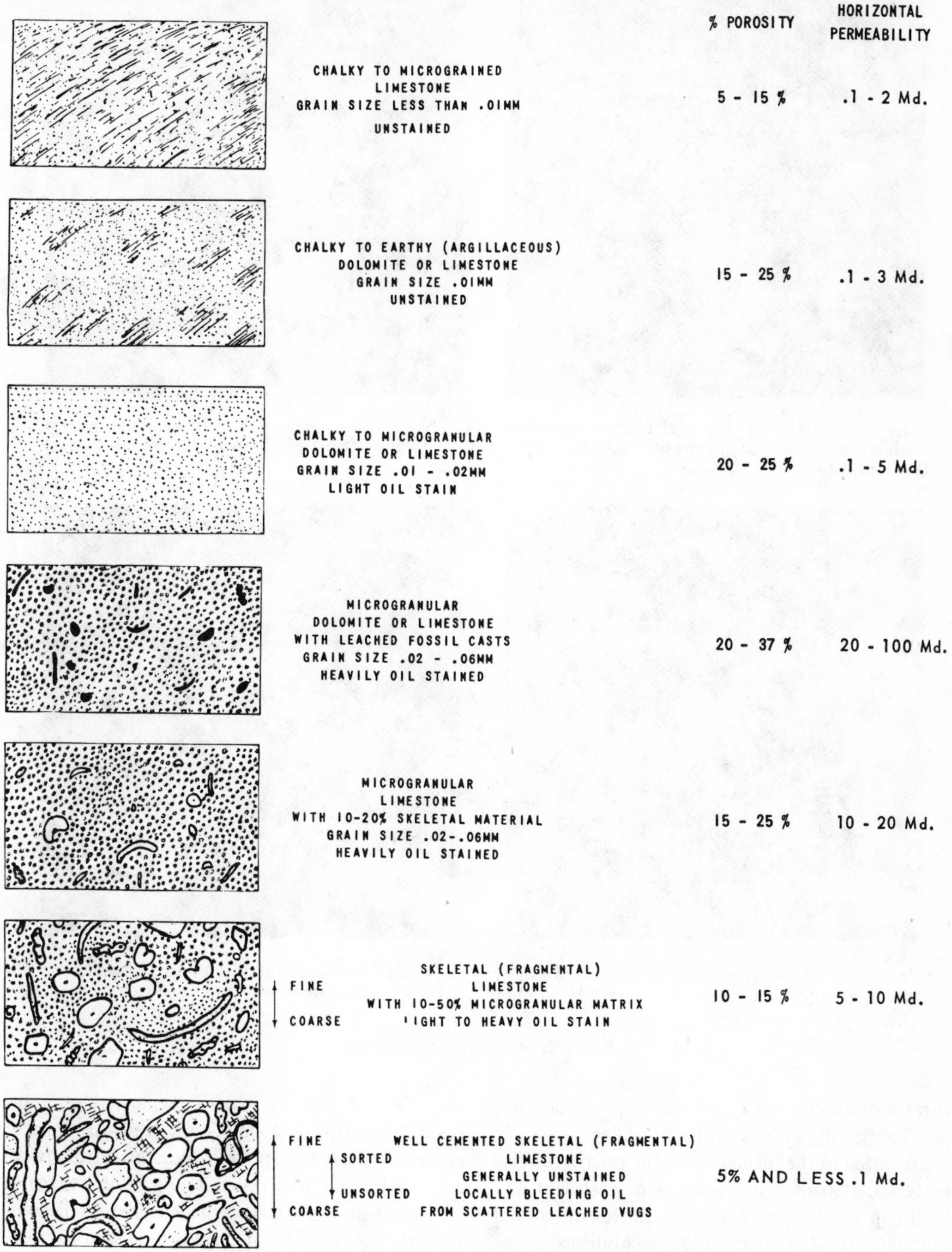

	% POROSITY	HORIZONTAL PERMEABILITY
CHALKY TO MICROGRAINED LIMESTONE GRAIN SIZE LESS THAN .01MM UNSTAINED	5 - 15 %	.1 - 2 Md.
CHALKY TO EARTHY (ARGILLACEOUS) DOLOMITE OR LIMESTONE GRAIN SIZE .01MM UNSTAINED	15 - 25 %	.1 - 3 Md.
CHALKY TO MICROGRANULAR DOLOMITE OR LIMESTONE GRAIN SIZE .01 - .02MM LIGHT OIL STAIN	20 - 25 %	.1 - 5 Md.
MICROGRANULAR DOLOMITE OR LIMESTONE WITH LEACHED FOSSIL CASTS GRAIN SIZE .02 - .06MM HEAVILY OIL STAINED	20 - 37 %	20 - 100 Md.
MICROGRANULAR LIMESTONE WITH 10-20% SKELETAL MATERIAL GRAIN SIZE .02-.06MM HEAVILY OIL STAINED	15 - 25 %	10 - 20 Md.
FINE ↕ COARSE SKELETAL (FRAGMENTAL) LIMESTONE WITH 10-50% MICROGRANULAR MATRIX LIGHT TO HEAVY OIL STAIN	10 - 15 %	5 - 10 Md.
FINE ↕ COARSE SORTED ↕ UNSORTED WELL CEMENTED SKELETAL (FRAGMENTAL) LIMESTONE GENERALLY UNSTAINED LOCALLY BLEEDING OIL FROM SCATTERED LEACHED VUGS	5% AND LESS	.1 Md.

Fig. 5.—Relation of textural variations, "Midale" carbonates with oil-saturation and porosity-permeability determinations.

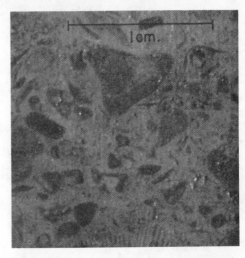

a.—Dolomitized microgranular limestone with leached fossil casts. 28% Porosity. 60 Millidarcys. Horizontal core.

b.—Skeletal limestone with microgranular matrix. 12% Porosity. 5 Millidarcys. Horizontal core.

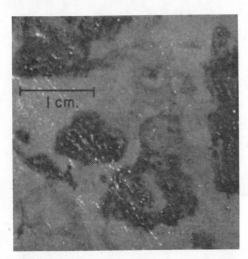

c.—Chalky to microgranular limestone with algal "cabbages" enclosing fine pellet material. Horizontal core.

d. Spiriferids in chalky to earthy dolomitic limestone. Horizontal core.

PLATE 2.—"Midale" carbonates.

current-agitated areas. Floating, calcareous, planktonic algae (Coccolithophoridae) possibly contributed to the formation of the microgranular material. Porosity in this class of carbonates is high (up to 37%, with permeabilities up to 120 millidarcys). The highest permeabilities occur where fossil (usually ostracod) casts supplement the pore space between the packed granules (Pl. 2a). This permeability is proportionately reduced when unleached skeletal material remains in the rock (Fig. 5 and Pl. 2b). The packed granules (usually in the 0.02–0.06 mm.-grain-size range) are particularly susceptible to dolomitization processes giving rise to a crystalline-granular texture.

All transitions to a rhombic (saccharoidal) dolomite with leached fossil casts can be seen particularly near the subcrop, although in this area the textures are partly masked by secondary anhydrite permeation. The pellicles of dolomite around the granules have a deterring effect on acid treatment results in the Kingsford-Steelman fields. In these fields the microgranular carbonate lenses are fairly continuous and should respond favorably to water injection processes (Fig. 4b).

These microgranular carbonates grade vertically and laterally into chalky to micrograined carbonates, which are partly of chemical origin but probably represent the "flour" formed by disintegration and abrasion of fossil debris and algal growths developed on the Souris Valley shelf. This "flour" or fine suspension material settled in the quiet-water environments of shelf-lagoons and around shoal areas during periods of relative quiescence in current activity. With decrease in grain size and increase in the amount of fine, chalky to clay-like material, the microtextured carbonates lose their oil-wetting ability and have high connate water saturation. The writers include the chalky to microgranular carbonates (grain size 0.01–0.02 mm.) in the effective reservoir material because they usually have some oil saturation. The chalky carbonate sections generally contain abundant ostracod remains. In the Florence-Oxbow areas scattered algal cabbages and fine pellet material are commonly observed (Pl. 2c). Well preserved brachiopods and articulate crinoid stems are usually found in the relatively thin beds of chalky to earthy, slightly argillaceous carbonates which can be traced over large areas of the shelf by their mechanical-log and lithological characteristics (Pl. 2d).

Lithographic, cryptograined to micrograined carbonates and skeletal to non-skeletal carbonates with a variable, lithified, carbonate-mud matrix are also well developed in the intershoal areas. All gradations from cryptograined limestone to skeletal or non-skeletal limestone with, for example, 5–10 per cent cryptograined matrix can be seen. All of this heterogeneous material appears to be genetically related and can be mapped and classed as belonging to the same group of carbonates. Even though this group locally contains a considerable amount of skeletal or non-skeletal grains, the sea currents during deposition were not strong enough or persistent enough to winnow away the carbonate ooze which remains as a matrix. Calcite cement is very subordinate or lacking simply because no pore space was available.

In the Alameda-Oxbow and Florence areas there is a thin development of algal lump and pellet limestone at the base of the "Midale" carbonate cycle. Plate 3a illustrates a relatively unce-

a.—Uncemented pellet limestone. 21% Porosity. 225 Millidarcys. Horizontal core.

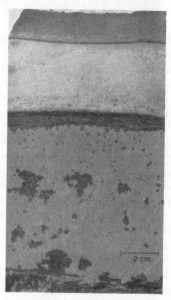

b.—Brown anhydrite development at porosity permeability differences in "Midale" carbonates. Vertical core.

Description from top to bottom of core:

Inches

1   Chalky to microgranular dolomitic limestone (.01–.02 mm.). Light oil staining.

$\frac{1}{16}$ Brown anhydrite layer.

2   Chalky to earthy dolomite (.01 mm.). Scattered brown anhydrite crystals at base. No oil staining.

$\frac{1}{2}$ Brown anhydrite with carbonaceous laminae.

$\frac{5}{}$ Cryptograined limestone with abundant vague pisolitic bodies partly replaced by brown anhydrite porphyroblasts.

PLATE 3.—"Midale" carbonates.

mented pellet limestone (Florence-Glen Ewen area) which was probably produced by the fragmentation of algal colonies. Thin stringers of this highly permeable pellet, locally oölitic material contribute mainly to the high initial flow potential of some of the Florence-Glen Ewen wells. This pellet material is associated with, and grades toward the west into, cryptograined limestones containing abundant algal "cabbages," lumps, and scattered leached ostracod casts. Due to the erratic nature of the pin-point vugs in the algal material and the development of leached ostracod casts, it is difficult to analyze the effectiveness of this type of limestone which has a bleeding type of oil staining. This basal, generally carbonate-mud rich unit could possibly have been laid down contemporaneously with the upper parts of the algal pisolite facies of East Kingsford.

Of particular interest are the brown porphyroblasts of "metasomatic," euhedral, anhydritic crystals, which are found scattered through the "Midale" carbonate sections. The crystals are brown because of hydrocarbon inclusions and commonly replace different types of carbonates. Oölites, for example, are commonly included in these brown anhydrites. Preliminary work suggested that since the "Midale" carbonates are sandwiched between primary anhydrite sheets over most of the area, a "wave" of metasomatism from the top anhydrite has contributed to the oil-trapping mechanism for the "Midale" cycle. The writers now think that even though some irregular anhydrite replacement of carbonates has taken place, this "metasomatism" has not materially altered their reservoir characteristics. Thin layers and scattered brown anhydrite crystals are usually found at porosity and permeability breaks within the "Midale" carbonate sections (Pl. 3b). This suggests that a salt-filtration mechanism affecting calcium sulphate-rich, circulating waters could be an explanation for this anhydrite formation. The distribution of these "metasomatic" anhydrite crystals bears no relation to the position of the overlying primary anhydrite or the basal, marginal anhydrite sheet of the "Midale" cycle.

When a clasticity index approach is applied to "Midale" carbonates, the final textural results can easily be contoured into linear patterns which appear to fit oil-production behavior of the various wells. The topographical expression of the algal banks west of the evaporite strandline must have had an important influence on current refraction patterns during later "Midale" carbonate deposition. These current patterns sifted the carbonates with effective matrix porosity into linear belts or shoals which run transverse to the Paleozoic subcrop trend of the "Midale" beds. The bar-like trends of carbonates with effective porosity are separated by quiet water, intershoal areas in which are found higher percentages of shelf-lagoonal carbonate muds, chalky carbonates, and fragmentals with a mud matrix, which have no effective porosity. With the use of effective porosity isopachs, isoporosity feet, and facies maps, one can be selective about development and wildcat acreage in an area formerly thought to be one huge stratigraphic pool.

TEXTURAL AND RESERVOIR PROPERTIES OF "ELKTON" CARBONATE CYCLE (TURNER VALLEY FORMATION) IN SOUTHWESTERN ALBERTA

Official nomenclature of well defined Upper Mississippian (Rundle group) shelf-carbonate cycles in southwestern Alberta is still burdened with old Turner Valley field names, such as "Upper Porous" and "Middle Dense" zones. Widespread transgressive sheets of coarse, generally dolomitized, fragmental (skeletal) limestones are separated by shallow-water depositional units of silty, locally cherty, lithified carbonate muds which can be established as time-stratigraphic boundaries for correlation purposes. However, it is not the purpose of this report to condemn present Mississippian nomenclature or to rename some of the carbonate cycles as has been done in southeastern Saskatchewan.

Major hydrocarbon (oil and gas) reserves have already been discovered in the Mississippian "Elkton" carbonate cycle, both in the Foothills Belt and along the subcrop in southwestern Alberta. The "Elkton" carbonate cycle generally consists of coarse skeletal (predominantly crinoidal) carbonates, ranging in thickness from 80 to 150 feet and of variable porosity and permeability. These carbonates are overlain and underlain by tight, lithified, silty carbonate mud deposits up to the subcrop area, where the eroded reservoir material is covered by generally impermeable Mesozoic shales and silty sandstones. Porosity and permeability properties of the producing intervals in the Sundre, Westward Ho, and Harmattan-Elkton fields, situated at or near the "Elkton" subcrop, can be directly related to quantitative, carbonate textural measurements. In this area, as opposed to the "Midale" cycle, mechanical logs (neutron, microlog, and microlaterolog) can be used to differentiate effective and non-effective reservoir types. Effective reservoir material of this cycle was found to consist mainly of the dolomitized equivalent of an originally coarse skeletal limestone with a variable amount of porous, finely comminuted (granular) skeletal matrix. Primary porosity was very important in the control of dolomitization, which began with the replacement of this matrix by euhedral rhombohedrons and finally affected the coarse, skeletal material (now generally indicated by leached, fossil cast outlines). These porous dolomites grade laterally in a predictable way into tight, relatively non-dolomitized, well sorted, coarse skeletal limetones, with original high interfragmental porosity now completely infilled with clear crystalline calcite. This lithification by cementation took place early in the history of carbonate sedimentation of this area and before secondary dolomitization processes took effect. Present hydrocarbon accumulation along the subcrop is controlled largely by updip truncation of the "Elkton" member. However, it is also strongly influenced by primary porosity pinchouts caused by lateral facies changes from dolomitized, leached, skeletal limestones with matrix into tight, cemented skeletal limestones. Similar facies changes exist in the Turner Valley oil field, suggesting primary hydrocarbon accumulation in the "Elkton" member before the Laramide structural movements took place.

At the Jasper Conference of the American Association of Petroleum Geologists, in September, 1955, D. G. Penner introduced the name "Elkton" member for the lower bioclastic or skeletal rich unit of the Turner Valley formation. In 1957 the proposed nomenclature was further refined by Penner. The type section of this member was designated as that penetrated in the Great Plains et al. Elkton No. 16-13 well (Lsd. 16, Sec. 13, T. 31, R. 4, W. 5th Meridian) between the depths of 8,705 and 8,845 feet. Development drilling in the Harmattan-Elkton field showed that it was possible to subdivide the "Elkton" member into three sub-members (Penner, 1957). The "Elkton" member, 140 feet thick, was equated to the combined "Lower Porous" and "Crystalline Zone" of the Turner Valley field.

Penner's published cross section from Elkton No. 16-13 to the Pine Creek well (Lsd. 12, Sec. 12, T. 20, R. 2, W. 5th Meridian) and intervening locations is shown in the upper half of Figure 6. While commending Penner's clarification of the relation of the Sundre-Harmattan producing intervals to those of the Turner Valley oil field, for regional correlation purposes, the writers have had to redefine the upper limits of his "Elkton" member.

The "A" sub-member in the Harmattan-Elkton field was found to consist generally of a microcrystalline dolomite with scattered relict skeletal material and abundant inclusions of milky white chert. Rock photograph of Plate 4a is fairly typical of this sub-member and shows it to be the dolomitized equivalent of washes of micro-finely comminuted, skeletal material deposited in a carbonate mud environment. Chert nodules, quartz silt partings, and scattered plant fragment traces are common, suggesting muddy, shallow-water deposition which was unfavorable for much skeletal carbonate or good reservoir development. Microcrystalline (anhedral to subhedral) calcareous dolomites are generally the rule, with fairly high porosity (commonly more than 10%) and low permeability. These dolomites commonly give rise to substantial blows of gas on drill-stem test. Locally within the field, the "A" sub-member has good porosity and permeability, due to an increase in the amount of coarser-textured, more rhombic dolomite whose intercrystalline porosity has been supplemented by the presence of scattered, leached, coarse skeletal material. Within and away from the Harmattan-Elkton field these coarser-textured, rhombic dolomites with effective porosity grade laterally and vertically into cherty, silty, and argillaceous, microcrystalline dolomites that are texturally indistinguishable from Penner's middle sub-member.

On the basis of carbonate texture, chert and silt content, depositional environment, time-stratigraphic correlation, and general reservoir properties, Penner's middle and upper "Elkton" sub-members are considered to be lateral equivalents of the cherty, "Middle-Hard" or "Middle-Dense" zone of the Turner Valley oil field. For convenience the writers have designated Penner's lower sub-member, or main prospective zone, as the "Elkton" carbonate cycle.

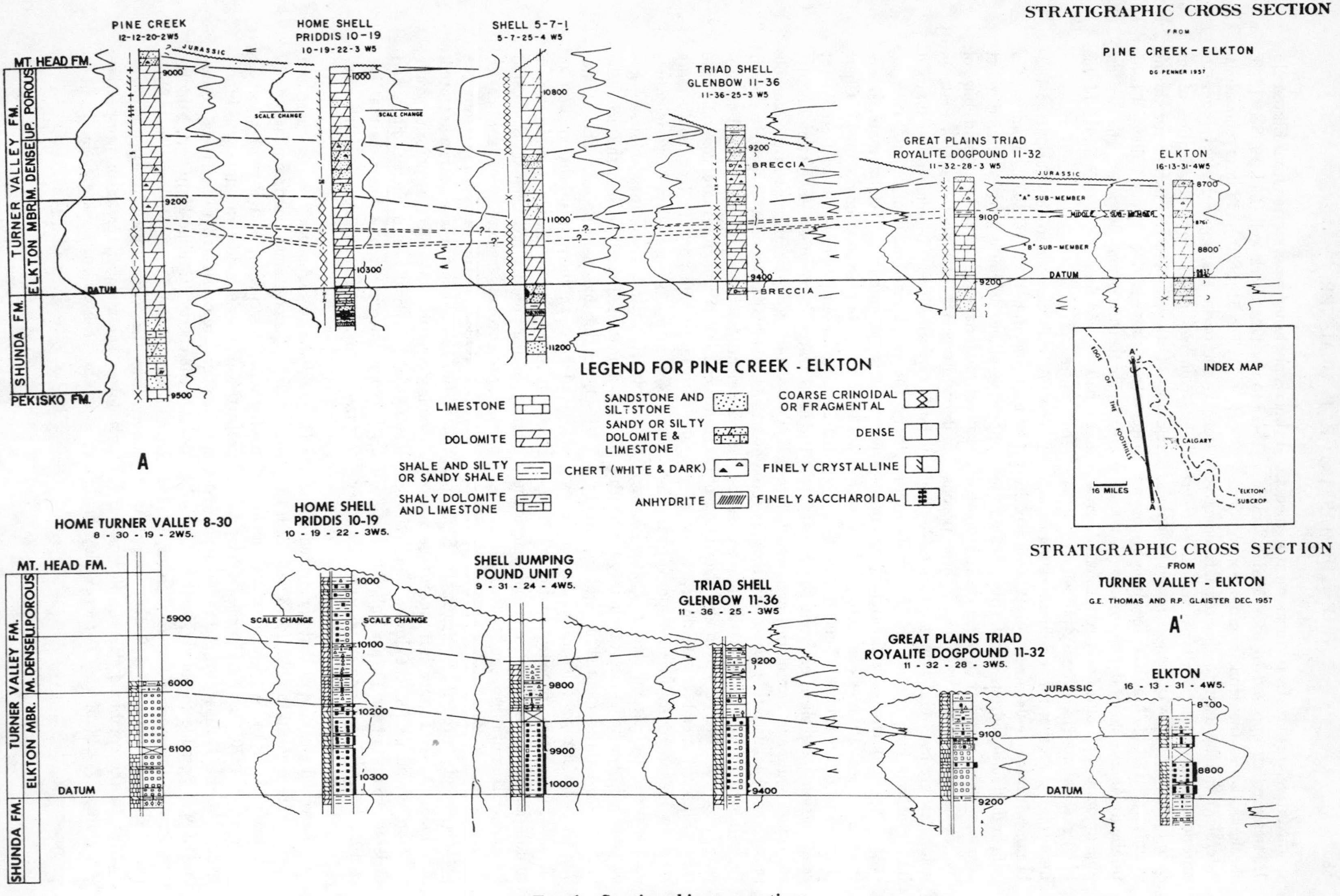

FIG. 6.—Stratigraphic cross sections.

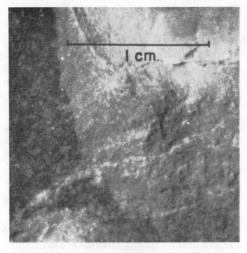

a.—Cherty microcrystalline dolomite.

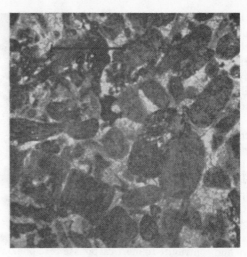

b.—Cemented skeletal (crinoid-bryozoa) limestone.

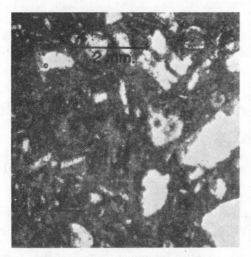

c.—Dolomitized leached skeletal limestone with porous matrix.

d.—Micro-rhombic dolomite with leached fossil casts.

PLATE 4.—"Elkton" carbonates.

"ELKTON" CARBONATES WITH NO EFFECTIVE POROSITY

For mapping purposes, "Elkton" carbonates can be broken down into effective and non-effective porosity units.

CEMENTED SKELETAL AND NON-SKELETAL CARBONATES

Of great interest is the widespread occurrence in the "Elkton" cycle of thick deposits of generally coarse, cemented skeletal limestones ("crystalline" limestones of former workers). These are composed predominantly of the calcareous remains of disarticulated echinoderm ossicles and plates. Although space between crinoid fragments in rocks of this type consists largely of clear crystalline calcite, few samples lack some organic remains of non-crinoidal origin. Most commonly the "foreign" material consists of bryozoan fragments. These tight, coarse, skeletal limestones, with high original interfragmental porosity, now completely infilled with clear crystalline calcite, usually analyze less than 5 per cent porosity and 0.1 MDS. Apparently, earlier workers did not recognize echinoderm plates and ossicles as rock-builders in the lower "crystalline" zone of the Turner Valley oil field and referred to them as calcite crystals. Even in recent excellent papers (e.g., Hemphill, 1957) occur statements such as "in the No. 9-22 well the section consisted of limestone, medium-grey, medium to coarsely crystalline, and slightly fossiliferous."

The thin-section photograph of Plate 4b should clarify concepts of what constitutes a "crystalline" or cemented skeletal limestone. Even though cemented skeletal or non-skeletal limestones are found from the Cambrian to Quaternary and contribute to most carbonate text-book photographs, extremely few authors have committed themselves in mode of origin discussions. The clear crystalline calcite cement of the sorted skeletal or non-skeletal limestones might be interpreted as reorganized carbonate mud matrix or as primary calcite cement. The writers concur with R. C. Moore's observations on the Mississippian of the Ozarks and believe it to be a primary chemical precipitate for the following reasons.

1. The crystalline cement is present in considerable amounts only in skeletal or non-skeletal limestones that have a relatively high degree of sorting and rounding. This suggests that much of the interstitial fine material was winnowed out by strong currents or shoaling water where wave action was effective. This winnowing process would create interstitial voids favorable for the formation of primary crystalline cement.

2. Prominent crystalline calcite overgrowths on many grains, especially on crinoid columnals, are in optical continuity. According to Pettijohn, this continuity is a characteristic of primary cement.

3. There are no relict structures of grains or comminuted fossils in the crystalline cement as would be expected if the cement was the product of a reorganized or replaced matrix. The cement was probably introduced into open pores in the course of diagenesis, being precipitated as crystal growths derived from carbonate-saturated waters.

4. Edges of the fossils or non-skeletal material are not corroded or altered in a manner suggesting effects of recrystallization.

This lithification by cementation took place early in the carbonate sedimentation history of this area, and before secondary dolomitization processes took effect. The very nature of the clear crystalline calcite cement infilling of primary interfragmental porosity inhibited dolomitization. Dolomitization of these limestones could develop along cleavage cracks in the calcite cement or along incipient fractures. Cemented skeletal or non-skeletal limestones in Devonian or Mississippian sections of the Rockies or Foothills Belt, usually show effects of dolomitization processes as a result of stresses induced by mountain-building.

Oölitic and associated surficially coated grains occur locally in cemented skeletal limestones of the "Elkton" member. Localities where these fringing shoal deposits have been found include the center part of the Turner Valley oil field, and the Blackie, Brant, Dogpound, and Sundre areas. For mapping purposes, these generally cemented, well sorted, oölitic limestones can be grouped with cemented skeletal limestones, with which they are closely associated. Oölites are rare in unsorted skeletal limestones.

SKELETAL OR NON-SKELETAL LIMESTONES WITH CHALKY TO MICROGRAINED MATRIX

Of local interest are the skeletal or non-skeletal limestones containing a chalky matrix which are found in the Brant and Blackie areas, south of Calgary. Poor grain-sorting, presence of delicate bryozoan fronds, and chalky to micrograined matrix, all suggest sheltered, quiet-water conditions of deposition. The chalky matrix material has high connate water content and virtually no oil saturation because of the fine capillary pores. These were the only areas where the microlog curve gave unreliable estimates of effective porosity in the "Elkton" reservoir.

DOLOMITIZED CARBONATE MUDS AND NON-LEACHED SKELETAL TO NON-SKELETAL CARBONATES WITH TIGHT, ORIGINALLY CARBONATE MUD MATRIX

All gradations from original cryptograined limestone to relict skeletal or non-skeletal limestone (e.g., with 5–10% cryptograined matrix) can be seen. The carbonate mud was apparently easily dolomitized to produce a cryptocrystalline to microcrystalline, anhedral, interlocking type of dolomite with no effective porosity.

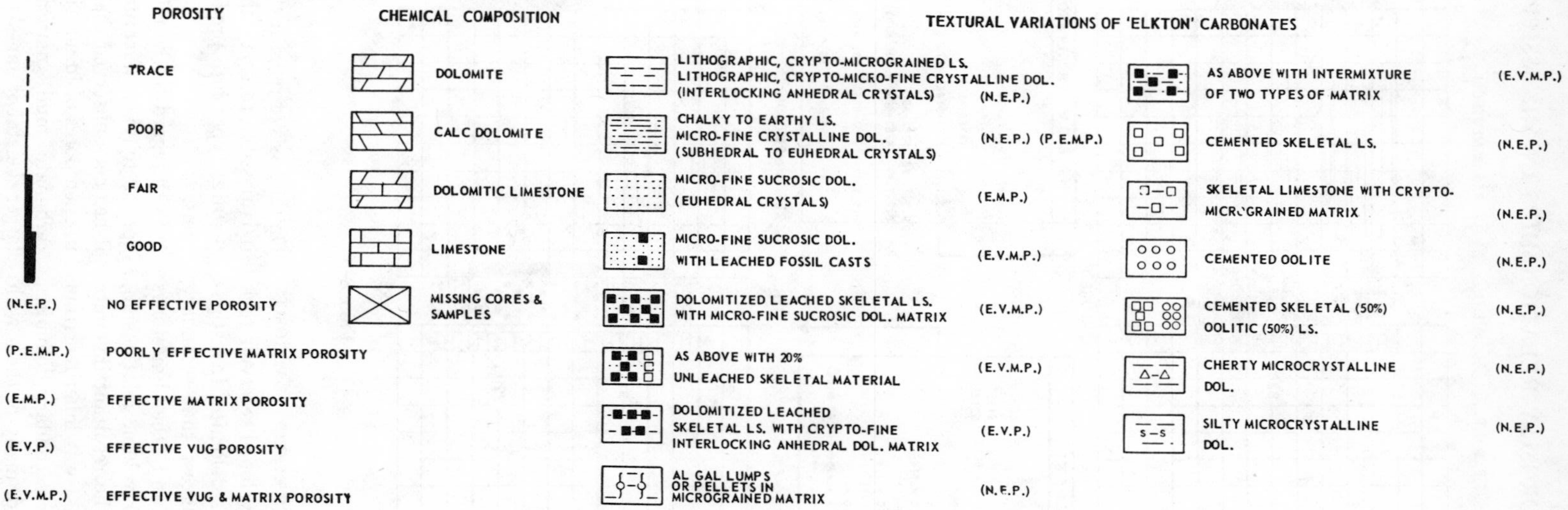

POROSITY

TRACE

POOR

FAIR

GOOD

NO EFFECTIVE POROSITY (N.E.P.)

POORLY EFFECTIVE MATRIX POROSITY (P.E.M.P.)

EFFECTIVE MATRIX POROSITY (E.M.P.)

EFFECTIVE VUG POROSITY (E.V.P.)

EFFECTIVE VUG & MATRIX POROSITY (E.V.M.P.)

CHEMICAL COMPOSITION

DOLOMITE

CALC DOLOMITE

DOLOMITIC LIMESTONE

LIMESTONE

MISSING CORES & SAMPLES

TEXTURAL VARIATIONS OF 'ELKTON' CARBONATES

LITHOGRAPHIC, CRYPTO-MICROGRAINED LS. LITHOGRAPHIC, CRYPTO-MICRO-FINE CRYSTALLINE DOL. (INTERLOCKING ANHEDRAL CRYSTALS) (N.E.P.)

CHALKY TO EARTHY LS. MICRO-FINE CRYSTALLINE DOL. (SUBHEDRAL TO EUHEDRAL CRYSTALS) (N.E.P.) (P.E.M.P.)

MICRO-FINE SUCROSIC DOL. (EUHEDRAL CRYSTALS) (E.M.P.)

MICRO-FINE SUCROSIC DOL. WITH LEACHED FOSSIL CASTS (E.V.M.P.)

DOLOMITIZED LEACHED SKELETAL LS. WITH MICRO-FINE SUCROSIC DOL. MATRIX (E.V.M.P.)

AS ABOVE WITH 20% UNLEACHED SKELETAL MATERIAL (E.V.M.P.)

DOLOMITIZED LEACHED SKELETAL L.S. WITH CRYPTO-FINE INTERLOCKING ANHEDRAL DOL. MATRIX (E.V.P.)

AL GAL LUMPS & PELLETS IN MICROGRAINED MATRIX (N.E.P.)

AS ABOVE WITH INTERMIXTURE OF TWO TYPES OF MATRIX (E.V.M.P.)

CEMENTED SKELETAL LS. (N.E.P.)

SKELETAL LIMESTONE WITH CRYPTO-MICROGRAINED MATRIX (N.E.P.)

CEMENTED OOLITE (N.E.P.)

CEMENTED SKELETAL (50%) OOLITIC (50%) LS. (N.E.P.)

CHERTY MICROCRYSTALLINE DOL. (N.E.P.)

SILTY MICROCRYSTALLINE DOL. (N.E.P.)

FIG. 7.—Legend for Figures 6, 8, and 9.

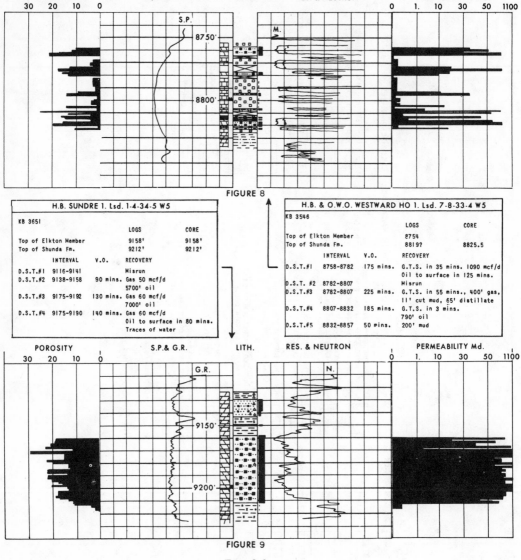

FIGURE 8

H.B. SUNDRE 1. Lsd. 1-4-34-5 W5		
KB 3651		
	LOGS	CORE
Top of Elkton Member	9158'	9158'
Top of Shunda Fm.	9212'	9212'
INTERVAL	V.O.	RECOVERY
D.S.T.#1 9116-9141		Misrun
D.S.T.#2 9138-9158	90 mins.	Gas 50 mcf/d 5700' oil
D.S.T.#3 9175-9192	130 mins.	Gas 60 mcf/d 7000' oil
D.S.T.#4 9175-9190	140 mins.	Gas 60 mcf/d Oil to surface in 80 mins. Traces of water

H.B. & O.W.O. WESTWARD HO 1. Lsd. 7-8-33-4 W5		
KB 3546		
	LOGS	CORE
Top of Elkton Member	8754	
Top of Shunda Fm.	8819?	8825.5
INTERVAL	V.O.	RECOVERY
D.S.T.#1 8758-8782	175 mins.	G.T.S. in 35 mins. 1090 mcf/d Oil to surface in 125 mins.
D.S.T.#2 8782-8807		Misrun
D.S.T.#3 8782-8807	225 mins.	G.T.S. in 55 mins., 400' gas, 11' cut mud, 65' distillate
D.S.T.#4 8807-8832	185 mins.	G.T.S. in 3 mins. 790' oil
D.S.T.#5 8832-8857	50 mins.	200' mud

FIGURE 9

FIGS. 8–9

"ELKTON" CARBONATES WITH EFFECTIVE POROSITY

The only extensively developed reservoir rock in the "Elkton" member is dolomite. Investigations so far completed suggest that secondary dolomitization of skeletal and other limestones took place on a volume-for-volume relationship, and that the porosity of the resultant dolomite (apart from leaching effects) was inherited from the original limestone. The secondary dolomites are generally coarse-grained, many of them with relict limestone textures or casts of fossil debris.

On the basis of relict textures in these dolomites, it is possible to carry the zonation of limestone textural types into predominantly dolomite sections.

With regard to the relation of dolomite development to textural features of original limestones, it has been observed that it preferentially occurs in open pores or in matrix (chalky, granular, and carbonate mud) material that surrounds the larger skeletal or non-skeletal grains. These larger grains are generally the last to show conversion to dolomite. Many skeletal fragments remain as calcite even when the remainder of the rock may be dolomite. The final type in this sequence is a dolomite with fossil casts. This preferential development of dolomite in certain textural components of the original limestone suggests that dolomitization processes are strongly controlled by the presence of fluids in interfragmental or intergranular porosity or by carbonate mud material that had a high fluid content.

It is possible to designate the composition of the original matrix material through studies of the grain-size and shape of the resultant dolomite (Fig. 7). An interlocking or anhedral type of crypto-microcrystalline dolomite matrix is interpreted as derived from carbonate mud. The comminuted or pulverized, generally porous, granular and chalky material, either of skeletal or non-skeletal origin, commonly contributes to matrix or intergranular porosity in carbonate reservoirs. On dolomitization, this porous material gives rise to subhedral or euhedral (rhombic) dolomites with intercrystalline porosity, unless the enlargement of the granules has continued too far to produce "mosaic" textural types.

DOLOMITIZED LEACHED SKELETAL LIMESTONES
WITH POROUS MATRIX

The most effective reservoir material of the "Elkton" carbonate cycle was found to consist mainly of the dolomitized equivalent of an originally coarse, skeletal limestone with a variable amount of generally porous, finely comminuted (granular) skeletal matrix. Primary porosity was very important in the control of dolomitization and much of the dolomite replacement occurred very shortly after the limestone was laid down. Dolomitization probably began with the replacement of the porous granular matrix by sub-euhedral rhombohedrons and finally affected the coarse, skeletal grain material (now generally indicated by leached fossil cast outlines). Highest permeabilities occur where fossil casts supplement the pore space between the packed dolomite rhombs (Pl. 4c). This permeability is proportionately reduced when relict unleached skeletal material remains in the rock.

The highest porosities and permeabilities are found in the relatively poorly sorted, dolomitized, leached skeletal limestones with porous matrix (up to 30% porosity and 1,000+ MDS.) These porous dolomites grade laterally in a predictable

way into tight, well sorted, cemented, skeletal limestones. Figures 8 and 9 illustrate that porosity logs readily distinguish these markedly different facies types in the Sundre-Westward Ho fields. The cemented skeletal limestones were probably laid down under initial high wave energy or shoal conditions in which the comminuted, microgranular to finely granular material, which contributes to matrix porosity, was winnowed out and deposited under lower energy conditions.

The rock photograph sequence of Plate 5 demonstrates that locally there is a progressive destruction of skeletal grain outlines during the process of dolomitization. The end-result of such dolomitization is the production of medium to coarse crystalline dolomite, the generic implications of which are in doubt. This type of material is common in the stratigraphic column of the Western Canada basin (e.g., the Devonian Nisku formation). When definite skeletal outlines have been destroyed and replaced by medium to coarse dolomite crystals, a crystallinity (dolomite grain size) ratio map would be of great value in differentiating dolomitized fragmentals and dolomitized carbonate mud areas.

MICRO TO FINE RHOMBIC DOLOMITES WITH
LEACHED FOSSIL CASTS

The rock photograph of Plate 4d is representative of this locally developed group of "Elkton" carbonates with effective porosity. These carbonates are considered to be the dolomitized equivalents of comminuted, skeletal, or non-skeletal grains in current-agitated areas. Porosity in this class of carbonates is high, but permeability is high only where fossil casts supplement the pore space between the packed granules. Complex intermixtures of this group of carbonates with effective matrix and vug porosity and chalky to earthy carbonates with no effective porosity are usually found at the top of the "Elkton" member.

DOLOMITIZED CARBONATE MUDS WITH LEACHED
FOSSIL CASTS AND LEACHED SKELETAL TO
NON-SKELETAL CARBONATES WITH TIGHT,
ORIGINALLY CARBONATE MUD MATRIX

Carbonate muds, probably because of an original high fluid content, alter easily to a crypto-microcrystalline, anhedral to subhedral, interlocking type of dolomite with little or no effective

a.—Dolomitized unleached skeletal limestone with porous matrix.

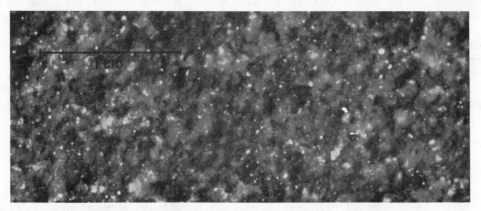

b.—Dolomitized partly leached skeletal limestone with porous matrix.

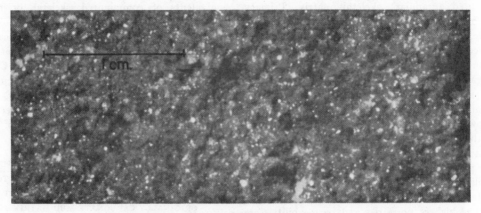

c.—Dolomitized partly leached skeletal limestone with porous matrix.
(Medium to coarse sub-euhedral dolomite)

PLATE 5.—"Elkton" carbonates. Demonstration series illustrating progressive destruction
of skeletal grain outlines during dolomitization.

porosity. However, the skeletal or non-skeletal grains embedded in this original carbonate mud material are locally leached to produce generally poorly effective vug porosity.

Conclusions

It is hoped that these observations on the relations of grain, matrix, and cement variants of carbonate rocks to porosity and permeability determinations will be helpful in the recognition and mapping of such associations in other places.

With regard to exploration philosophy on unconformity, "porosity-wedge" plays, these studies again reveal the necessity for reconstruction of the sedimentation history of the prospective, eroded unit. The mapping of dissected, primary permeability barriers (cemented skeletal limestones) at or near the "Elkton" subcrop is just as important to oil and gas exploration as is the recognition of impermeable, marginal anhydrites at or near the subcrop of the Mississippian shelf carbonate cycles in the Souris Valley area of southeastern Saskatchewan.

References

HEMPHILL, C. R., 1957, "History and Development of the Sundre, Westward Ho and Harmattan Oil Fields," *Jour. Alberta Soc. Petrol. Geol.*, Vol. 5, No. 10, pp. 232–47.

JOHNSON, J. H., 1956, "Studies on Mississippian Algae," *Quar. Colorado School Mines*, Vol. 54, No. 4 (October).

MOORE, R. C., 1957, "Mississippian Carbonate Deposits of the Ozark Region," *Soc. Econ. Paleon. and Mineral. Spec. Pub. 5.*

PENNER, D. G., 1957, "The Elkton Member," *Jour. Alberta Soc. Petrol. Geol.*, Vol. 5, No. 5 (May), pp. 101–04.

SLOSS, L. L., 1953, "The Significance of Evaporites," *Jour. Sed. Petrology*, Vol. 23, No. 3 (September), pp. 143–61.

THOMAS, G. E., 1954, "The Mississippian of the Northeastern Williston Basin," *Canadian Inst. Min. Met. Bull. 503* (March), pp. 136–42.

Reprinted from:
BULLETIN OF THE AMERICAN ASSOCIATION OF PETROLEUM GEOLOGISTS
VOL. 44, NO. 8 (AUGUST, 1960) PP. 1421-1424, 6 TABLES

TEODOROVICH'S METHOD FOR DETERMINING PERMEABILITY FROM PORE-SPACE CHARACTERISTICS OF CARBONATE ROCKS[1]

BERT C. ASCHENBRENNER[2] AND GEORGE V. CHILINGAR[3]
New York, N. Y., and Los Angeles, California

INTRODUCTION

As one of the outstanding carbonate specialists in U.S.S.R., G. I. Teodorovich has analyzed extensively the character of different pore-space configurations in carbonate rocks. After studying numerous thin sections prepared from cores whose permeability had been tested prior to sectioning them, Teodorovich (1943, pp. 231–34) concluded that a quantitative relation between the permeability and pore-space characteristics could be worked out for carbonate rocks. Therefore, after a detailed analysis of more than 400 thin sections of Paleozoic carbonate reservoir rocks, Teodorovich (1949, pp. 281–92) prepared tables of empirically derived values as well as certain computational procedures for determining permeability from thin sections.

The present writers have prepared this review and discussion for the following reasons.

1. To acquaint both geologists and engineers with Teodorovich's method which relates petrographic characteristics (pore-space configuration) with criteria of fluid flow (permeability). Aside from the obvious possibility of using this method for calculating permeabilities when they can not be measured, it is thought that wise use of Teodorovich's technique may help clarify the poorly understood problems of fluid flow through heterogeneous media.
2. To discuss Teodorovich's method in the light of their own experience and results.
3. To stimulate an exchange of ideas, experiences, and results among those who are or have been concerned with defining and evaluating quantitatively the pore space characteristics of reservoir rocks.

In the first part of this paper, material published by Teodorovich is briefly reviewed and his method for calculating permeability from thin sections is described. In the second part, the present writers describe their experience with Teodorovich's method and compare their calculated permeabilities with previously measured permeability values. The conclusions and some suggestions by the present writers form the third part of this note.

[1] Manuscript received, March 14, 1960.

[2] Autometric Corporation.

[3] University of Southern California, Petroleum Engineering Department.

TEODOROVICH'S METHOD

According to Teodorovich the principal factors which determine the quality of carbonate reservoir rocks as far as permeability is concerned are the following.

A. The character of the pores and pore interconnections (pore-space type) as well as the width and number of the passages between pores (pore space sub-types). The classification of pore space developed by Teodorovich was previously described by Chilingar (1957) and Aschenbrenner and Achauer (1960, p. 237).

B. The effective porosity.

C. The average size of the pores.

D_1. The shape (elongation) of the pores.

D_2. The type and amount of cement.

D_3. The degree of aggregation of the pores.

E. The shape (smoothness?) of the surfaces which form the walls of the pores and of the passages between pores.

An important factor governing permeability is the presence and amount of fracturing. Depending on the degree of fracturing, the permeabilities calculated from thin section analysis may be much too small.

The influence of the foregoing factors on permeability can be expressed as

$$K = A \times B \times C \times D_1 \times D_2 \times D_3 \times E$$

and this relationship usually reduces to

$$K = A \times B \times C \times D_1$$

where K is the permeability in millidarcys and factors A through D are represented by empirically derived numbers. These empirical coefficients are obtained from Tables I–IV, whereas the petrographic criteria for which the empirical values stand are determined by thin-section analysis.

From the tables it can be seen that even for the same pore space type the permeabilities can vary considerably. These variations in permeability are mainly due to differences in the width and abundance of the pore interconnections. The range of empirical coefficients for different types and sub-types is from 2 to 64. Carbonate rocks whose pore space configuration is classified as type II are in

TABLE I. EMPIRICAL COEFFICIENT A FOR PORE-SPACE TYPE

Pore Space Type	Characteristic of Subtype (As Seen in Thin Sections)	Empirical Coefficient A
I	With very narrow conveying canals (avg. diameter ≈0.01 mm.), usually not visible in thin section under the petrographic microscope using normal range of magnification	2
	With rare relatively wide canals (avg. diameter ≈0.02 mm.) visible in thin sections	4
	With few relatively wide canals, visible in thin section	8
	With many relatively wide canals, visible in thin section, or with few wide canals (avg. diameter ≥0.04 mm.)	16
	With abundant wide canals or few to many very wide conveying canals	32
II	With poor porosity, the pores being relatively homogeneous in size and distribution	8
	With good porosity and (or) porosity ranging from poor to good: pores being of different size	16–32
	pores being vuggy and irregular in outline	32–64
III	With very poor porosity inside the conveying canals	6
	With poor porosity inside the conveying canals	12
	Conveying canals finely porous	24
IV	With interconnected pore space between rhombohedral grains	10
	With interconnected pore space between subangular-subrounded grains	20
	With interconnected pore space between rounded to well rounded grains	30

general better reservoir rocks than those of other types.

Effective porosity normally ranges in carbonates from 2 to 25 per cent and the empirical values have very nearly the same range, i.e., from 0 to 30.

Table III shows the size of the pores to range from less than 0.01 mm. to more than 2 mm. in diameter. Thus this range involves two orders of magnitude. The empirical coefficients range from 0.0625 to 16; hence, their range involves three orders of magnitude.

TABLE II. EMPIRICAL COEFFICIENT B FOR POROSITY

	Effective Porosity	Empirical Coefficient B
Descriptive Term	Limits in Per Cent	
Very porous	>25	25–30
Porous	15–25	17
Moderately porous	10–15	10
Pores abundant	5–10	2–5
Pores present	2–5	0.5–1.0
Some pores present	<2	0

TABLE III. EMPIRICAL COEFFICIENT C FOR PORE SIZE

Descriptive Term	Maximum Size of Pore (mm.)	Empirical Coefficient C
Large vugs	>2.00	16
Medium to large vugs	0.50–2.00	4
Medium pores	0.25–1.00	2
Fine to medium pores	0.10–0.50	1
Very fine to fine pores	0.05–0.25	0.5
Very fine pores	0.01–0.10	0.25
Pinpoint to very fine pores	<0.10 and in part <0.01	0.125
Mostly pinpoint porosity	<0.03 and in part <0.01	0.0625

The influence of the pore shape (elongation) is expressed by empirical coefficients which vary from 1 to 4. Inasmuch as these empirical values stay within the same order of magnitude, factor D is probably somewhat less significant than the other factors.

Table V shows both the measured and the calculated permeabilities for 19 samples. The present writers added to Teodorovich's original tabulation by computing the difference between these values

TABLE IV. EMPIRICAL COEFFICIENT D
FOR PORE SHAPE

Descriptive Term	Empirical Coefficient D
More or less isometric pores	1
Elongate pores	2
Very elongate pores or pores arranged in bands with emanating conveying canals	4

TABLE V

Pore Space Type	Measured Permeability md.	Calcultd Permeability md.	Differ- ence md.	% Deviation
I	62.3	91.0	28.7	46
I	8.6	10.0	1.4	16
I	8.7	10.5	1.8	21
I	7.4	8.0	0.6	8
II	61.9	90.0	28.1	45
II	51.3	62.5	11.2	22
I	13.1	12.7	0.4	− 3
II	88.7	120.0	31.3	35
I	14.5	15.0	0.5	3
II	50.5	60.0	9.5	19
II	33.7	40.0	6.3	19
I	104.6	120.0	15.4	15
II	50.54	61.1	10.56	21
II	163.9	150.0	13.9	− 8
I	101.9	110.0	8.1	8
I	52.87	34.0	18.87	−36
I	15.8	15.0	0.8	− 5
II	115.0	156.0	41.0	36
I	795.7	800.0	4.3	1

Arithmetic mean of all per cent deviations: +13.8 per cent.

in millidarcys and by expressing this difference as a per cent deviation from the measured permeability values. The arithmetic mean of the per cent deviations is +13.8 per cent for the data given by Teodorovich.

APPLICATION OF METHOD

Having been interested in Teodorovich's method and in the general problem of analyzing pore space configurations in carbonate rocks, the writers decided to go beyond a mere review of Teodorovich's method. In an effort to gain an appreciation for the problems involved in calculating permeabilities from thin sections, the writers analyzed ten thin sections available to them according to Teodorovich's method previously reviewed here. Table VI shows the results of this analysis. These results are in good agreement with those published by Teodorovich as far as the differences between measured and calculated permeability values are concerned.

The writers noticed the following in connection with the analysis of the ten thin sections.

1. When the average diameter of the conveying canals is about 0.01 mm., the calculated permeability ranged from 2 md. to 16 md.

2. With an average diameter of the pore interconnections of approximately 0.02 mm., the permeability values vary between 30 md. and 75 md.

3. If a large number of the canals have an average diameter of about 0.03 mm., the permeability increases by an order of magnitude to a range from 600 md. to 800 md.

4. An abundance of wide interconnecting canals (≈0.04 mm. in diameter) is associated with permeabilities between 1,200 md. and 1,300 md.

These observed ranges are again in good agreement with conclusions reached by Teodorovich.

Teodorovich has pointed out that carbonate

TABLE VI. APPLICATION OF TEODOROVICH'S METHOD
(Results of Calculations by Present Writers)

Sample No.	Pore Space Type	Measured Permeability md.	Calculated Permeability md.	Difference md.	Per Cent Deviation
1	I	2	2	0	0
2	I	4	4	0	0
3	I	16	10	− 6	−37.5
4	I	75	80	5	6.7
5	I	605	640	35	5.8
6	I	800	800	0	0
7	I	1,190	1,088	− 2	− 0.2
8	I	1,300	1,280	−20	− 1.5
9	II	1,006	960	−46	− 4.6
10	IV	13.1	8.8	− 4.3	−32.8

Arithmetic mean of all per cent deviations: −6.4 per cent.

rocks of type I and type II pore space configurations may have their permeabilities related to effective porosity in a manner similar to that established by Trebin (1945) for certain sandstones. Trebin has derived the following expressions for sandstones of (a) less than 12 per cent porosity and (b) more than 12 per cent porosity.

(a) $K = 2.00 \times e^{0.316\ P}$
(b) $K = 4.94\ P^2 - 763$

where

K = permeability in millidarcys
P = effective porosity in per cent
e = 2.71828 . . . (Napierian base)

The writers are inclined to agree with Teodorovich, especially regarding the similarity between carbonate rocks with type I pore space configurations and sandstones of less than 12 per cent porosity. The relationship (a) derived by Trebin seems to be a fairly good approximation for low porosity reservoir rocks, carbonates as well as sandstones.

CONCLUSIONS AND SUGGESTIONS

The writers of this note feel that Teodorovich's method for calculating the permeability of carbonate reservoir rocks is a tool worthy of the attention and scrutiny of all explorationists. Examples given by Teodorovich as well as the results obtained by the writers when they applied Teodorovich's method suggest an average discrepancy of approximately 10 per cent between calculated and measured permeability values.

It is thought possible that permeability can be expressed as a geomathematical function of petrologic and geometric parameters. The writers suggest that a pooling of experience, resources, and data may be necessary in order to find the proper relations between petrographic characteristics and criteria of fluid flow. It is hoped that this review and discussion of Teodorovich's pioneer efforts may stimulate and encourage those who through their own or cooperative efforts could contribute to the solution of these complex problems.

REFERENCES

ASCHENBRENNER, B. C., AND ACHAUER, C. W., 1960, "Minimum Conditions for Migration of Oil in Water-Wet Carbonate Rocks," *Bull. Amer. Assoc. Petrol. Geol.*, Vol. 44, No. 2, pp. 235–43.
CHILINGAR, G. V., 1957, "A Short Note on Types of Porosity in Carbonate Rocks," *Compass*, Vol. 35, No. 1, pp. 69–74.
STRAKHOV, N. M., BUSHINSKIY, G. I., PUSTOVALOV, L. V., KHABAKOV, A. V., AND KHVOROVA, I. V., 1957, *Methods of Studying Sedimentary Rocks*, Vol. I. 611 pp. Gosgeoltekhizdat, Moscow.
TEODOROVICH, G. I., 1943, "Structure of the Pore Space of Carbonate Oil Reservoir Rocks and Their Permeability as Illustrated by Paleozoic Reservoirs of Bashkiriya," *Doklady Akad. Nauk SSSR*, Vol. 39, No. 6, pp. 231–34.
———, 1949, *Carbonate Facies, Lower Permian—Upper Carboniferous of Ural-Volga Region*, Issue 13 (17). 304 pp. Izdat. Moskov. Obshch. Ispyt. Prirody, Moscow.
———, 1958, *Study of Sedimentary Rocks*. 572 pp. Gostoptekhizdat, Leningrad.
TREBIN, F. A., 1945, *Permeability to Oil of Sandstone Reservoirs*. Gostoptekhizdat, Moscow.
(The references listed here are available from George V. Chilingar.)

Reprinted from:
BULLETIN OF THE AMERICAN ASSOCIATION OF PETROLEUM GEOLOGISTS
VOL. 48, NO. 3 (MARCH, 1964) PP. 329-337, 11 FIGS.

PORE GEOMETRY AS RELATED TO CARBONATE STRATIGRAPHIC TRAPS[1]

JOHN L. STOUT[2]
Denver, Colorado

ABSTRACT

Stratigraphic entrapment of oil in carbonate is a function of petrophysics of the reservoir and trap rock. These petrophysical characteristics can be observed from sample examination without extensive laboratory measurements.

Petrophysics is an essential addition to the physical measurements of total porosity and permeability routinely collected from reservoir rock samples. Total porosity is a ratio of the rock's void space to its bulk volume. Under subsurface reservoir conditions, this porosity is occupied by fluid of two phases. Commonly the non-wetting oil phase occupies this porosity according to the size and distribution of the rock's pore system. The displacement of interstitial water by oil depends on the size of pore throats. That part not effectively displaced by oil remains as irreducible water saturation within the reservoir. These reservoir properties can be determined from capillary pressure measurements conducted in the laboratory. The capillary pressure curves may be investigated by the same statistical methods used on cumulative curves from sieve analysis of unconsolidated sands.

Seven distinctive petrophysical characteristics were evident from 200 samples of Williston basin carbonate rocks studied. These characteristics may be classified by effective porosity, displacement pressure, and pore distribution. Representative examples from this study show good and intermediate reservoir rock as well as reservoir-trap rock. The concept of low effective porosity can explain high water-cut production from carbonate reservoirs.

INTRODUCTION

With the increasing interest in searching for oil in carbonate reservoirs, it is becoming more necessary to understand completely the stratigraphic entrapment of oil. Understanding stratigraphic entrapment of oil in carbonate rocks involves differentiating the reservoir and trapping properties of rocks such as the two samples in Figure 1. These two photomicrographs are to the same scale and taken under crossed nicols. The rock of Figure 1-A is a clastic limestone with numerous disconnected vugs. Figure 1-B is a tight appearing cryptocrystalline dolomite with few visible pores. However, sample B is reservoir rock from Clear Creek field on the Nesson anticline, capable of flowing 400 barrels of oil and only 20–30 barrels of water per day. This field is a typical undersaturated reservoir under fluid expansion control (Craft and Hawkins, 1959, p. 107–109). Sample A of Figure 1 is the cap rock from the same field. Thus, we see a need to understand more about two rocks such as these; not just that they

[1] Manuscript received, March 14, 1963. Paper presented on April 24, 1963, at the Rocky Mountain Section meeting of the American Association of Petroleum Geologists in Casper, Wyoming.

[2] Geophysicist, Potential Methods Section, California Oil Company, Western Division. The writer thanks The California Oil Company for permission to publish this paper. He is indebted to various members of The Standard Oil Company of California for their contributions to some of the basic research.

are different, but all about their interstices. What makes one a reservoir rock, whereas the other is not? This study has been left to the reservoir engineer as his tool for producing oil from known reservoirs (Amyx et al., 1960, p. 133–174, and Pirson, 1958, p. 97–133). The petrology learned from such a study (Archie, 1952, p. 285–289) would greatly benefit the exploration geologist in his search for new oil in carbonate provinces.

PORE GEOMETRY STUDY

Most studies of pore geometry have been restricted to sandstone-reservoir rock. These results have been applied to the Mission Canyon age carbonate-reservoir rocks of the Williston basin. The schematic enlargement of Figure 2 shows the internal pores and pore throats of a reservoir rock. The large, hachured areas of the illustration are rock fragments. The areas of fine hachuring are isolated patches of secondary mineralization, or recrystallized cement binding the grains together. The sum of the areas between the rock fragments, including the intercrystalline pore space of the cryptocrystalline binder, is porosity in this example. The ratio of this area between the grains to the total area of the illustration is the per cent porosity. This ratio is unduly large in this schematic diagram because of the emphasis on pores and pore throats. It is this total porosity that is measured by core analysis (Pirson, 1958, p. 42–44).

Under subsurface reservoir conditions, this

329

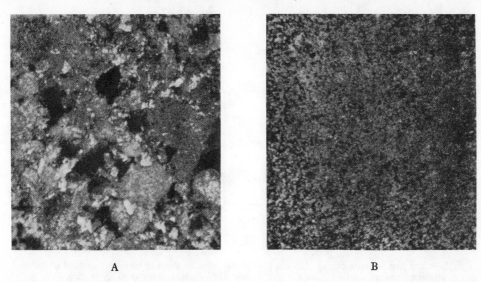

A   B

Fig. 1-A.—Photomicrograph of clastic limestone, cap rock in Clear Creek field, ✕15, crossed nicols. Skelly's Larson well No. 1, depth 9,216 feet. Location: NW. ¼, SE. ¼, sec. 34, T. 152 N., R. 96 W., McKenzie County, North Dakota.

B.—Photomicrograph of cryptocrystalline dolomite, reservoir rock in Clear Creek field, ✕15, crossed nicols. Skelly's Larson well No. 1, depth 9,233 feet.

porosity would be occupied by fluid of two phases—interstitial water (as defined by Levorsen, 1954, p. 298), and oil, shown by the shaded areas in Figure 2. Since this is a water-wet reservoir, there is a thin film of water around all the rock grains. Although the oil is the non-wetting phase, there may be a few patches where oil will adhere to the rock surfaces (Mattax and Kyte, 1961, p. 119) and will remain in pendular suspension even when fluid is produced from this rock. There are also insular globules of oil that may be produced only if the pressure drop is sufficient to overcome the Jamin effect (Pirson, 1958, p. 72), forcing the globule through the pore throats.

In the framework of this pore system, there are pores and interconnecting throats. These throats are present between the rock fragments and also

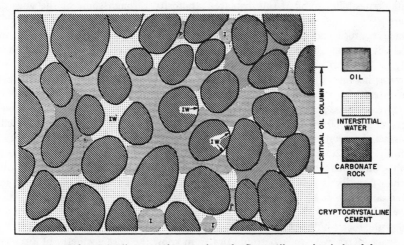

Fig. 2.—Schematic diagram of reservoir rock. Some oil remains isolated from reservoir accumulation in pendular suspension (P) and insular globules (I). Irreducible water (IW) remains within reservoir oil accumulation.

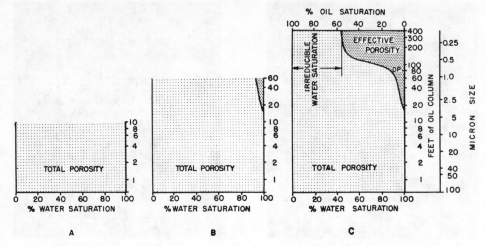

Fig. 3.—Capillary pressure curves showing progressive pore invasion of non-wetting fluid under increasing pressure. Little invasion occurs before displacement pressure (DP) is exceeded.

between the crystals of the cement (Aschenbrenner and Achauer, 1960, p. 236–239). The insular globules of oil can not migrate through these throats because of the high interfacial tension between oil and water under reservoir conditions. If enough globules coalesced by the accretion of smaller globules, the combined effect of the buoyancy of this oil column and dynamics of the reservoir would cause migration of the oil. The critical oil column of Figure 2 is that oil column required to cause oil to displace the interstitial water, or migrate through the smaller pore throats of this example's upper area. The reservoir exhibits a finite permeability to oil at this displacement pressure.

As oil invades the rock's pore space, it forces the wetting fluid out by funicular flow (Mattax and Kyte, 1961, p. 119–122). There will be areas where the water becomes disconnected from the rest of the interstitial water and will remain within the oil reservoir as irreducible water saturation (Amyx et al., 1960, p. 163). This is illustrated by areas of interstitial water within the reservoir oil of Figure 2. This pore space is not available to the oil in this reservoir-rock example. Thus, the total porosity is reduced by this irreducible water saturation to some effective porosity (Amyx et al., 1960, p. 39) that is a much smaller part of the rock's bulk volume. This is an important aspect of reservoir-rock petrophysics.

All reservoir properties depicted by the schematic diagram of Figure 2 can be represented by the series of capillary pressure graphs shown in Figure 3. The area of the graph in part A represents total porosity of the rock sample. This porosity is 100 per cent saturated with interstitial water, although nearby there is an impending continuous column of oil 10 feet high outside this rock. This oil column may be extensive laterally, but its vertical buoyancy is the effective pressure that must overcome the displacement pressure of this rock sample.

At the time of the graph in Figure 3-B additional oil has accumulated to create a 60-foot oil column. Oil has invaded 5–10 per cent of the total porosity through some of the vugs of the rock, but, unless these vugs are connected, there is no appreciable flow of oil into this rock until a critical height of the oil column exceeds the rock's displacement pressure (point DP, Fig. 3-C). At this time, oil imbibes into the effective pore space of the rock. Additional height of the invading oil column does not increase the effectiveness of the rock's porosity because of the isolated patches of irreducible water. The capillary pressure curve rises asymptotically to an irreducible water saturation of 44 per cent of the rock's total porosity. The area to the right of the curve in Figure 3-C is now the effective part of this sample's total porosity.

Muskat (1937, p. 61) points out the necessity to know the pore geometry of a reservoir rock in order to study the movement of fluid through it. Mercury-capillary-pressure measurements are experimental determinations of this pore geometry. The laboratory procedure for capillary pressure measurement by mercury injection is briefly described by Scheidegger (1957, p. 51–52).

The mercury injection method best reproduces reservoir conditions. Displacement methods where water is the wetting phase are affected by the techniques of extracting mud-filtrate and drying core samples. The mercury injection method has been found to be reliable and to have good reproducibility (Burdine et al., 1950, p. 198–199 and 201). Samples of Williston basin carbonate reservoir rock were investigated by this method. As the surface tension of mercury and the applied pressure are known, the size of pore throats invaded can be calculated (Levorsen, 1954, p. 531–532). These sizes are shown on the graph of Figure 3-C in micron measure. The physical relation of laboratory injected mercury to crude oil under reservoir conditions depends on the individual reservoir. An average relation of specific gravity, dissolved gas, and bottom-hole pressure in Mission Canyon formation reservoirs of North Dakota may be considered as $3\frac{2}{3}$ pounds per square inch for each foot of vertical oil column. Feet of oil column is given on the graphs of Figure 3.

The capillary pressure curve is somewhat similar to a cumulative curve from the sieve analysis of sands. The median size, sorting, and other statistical parameters can be calculated and compared with data from other rock samples. This similarity is not completely true since the indurated carbonate rock is examined rather than a disaggregated sample. Not only is the influence of the deposited carbonate fragments measured, but the effects of all diagenesis are evident in the resulting capillary pressure curve.

Pores deep within the indurated rock sample are invaded by the mercury only through the pore throats. Mercury-capillary-pressure curves differ when measured through pressure decline rather than pressure buildup. Mercury is left in the deeply imbedded pores in much the same manner as residual oil in a depleted oil reservoir. The nature of this residual mercury, or hysteresis, resulting from pressure buildup and pressure decline has not been extensively studied. Limitations of the measuring apparatus used could be alleviated through use of newly developed pressure sensing devices similar to the one described by Studier (1962, p. 94–95). These pressure sensors exhibit high volume impedance and instantaneous response to pressure change. Use of an apparatus equipped with such a pressure sensor would be beneficial in both the study of internal pore-space distribution and residual oil in reservoirs.

Carbonate pore geometry in this paper does not include the effects of various fracture systems that may be present in reservoir rock. Naturally occurring fractures, as well as fractures resulting from stimulation techniques used on completing a productive well, would add to the effective pore system discussed here.

PETROPHYSICAL CHARACTERISTICS

Several distinctive characteristics were developed from this study of more than 200 Williston basin carbonate reservoir rocks. Seven photomicrographs and corresponding mercury-capillary-pressure curves are described in this paper to give the most diagnostic features of these rocks. These photomicrographs are all 15-power enlargments and were taken under crossed nicols. The one-millimeter scale is divided into tenths, or 100 microns, to give a visual correlation of the photomicrograph to the capillary curve.

This study was principally concerned with the productivity variations in carbonate reservoir rock. Sampling with this purpose in mind necessarily limited the suite of rocks studied to the zones of high energy deposit. The samples used, therefore, are limestones deposited in moderately to highly agitated waters (Plumley et al., 1962, p. 89–91). Recrystallization and dolomitization of rock deposited in an agitated environment modifies the distinguishing characteristics of this rock.

The most efficient classification of these samples would be one based on the rock's reservoir properties such as Archie's carbonate reservoir rock classification (1952, p. 280–289). The following examples are listed according to the effectiveness of the rock's total porosity, the relative displacement pressure, and the pore distribution.

LOW EFFECTIVE POROSITY

Well sorted pore distribution—low displacement pressure.—Figure 4 is a photomicrograph of a recrystallized pelletoidal limestone in a very fine matrix. The few pores have generally been plugged by clear anhydrite crystals. Dolomitization along a few of the channels has not improved the rock's permeability.

The mercury-capillary-pressure curve shows a well sorted pore distribution and a low displace-

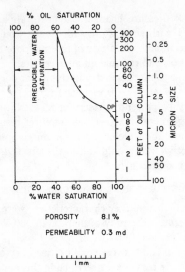

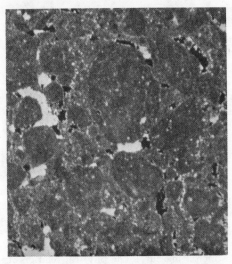

FIG. 4.—Mercury-capillary-pressure curve and corresponding photomicrograph of pelletoidal limestone, ×15, crossed nicols. Cardinal's Brace well No. 1, depth 4,505 feet. Location: NE. ¼, SE. ¼, sec. 33, T. 159 N., R. 81 W., Bottineau County, North Dakota.

ment pressure. The irreducible water saturation is greater than 40 per cent in this sample. The water saturation is considered high if it remains above the quantity of 22 per cent within the applied pressure range in the laboratory (1,015 pounds per square inch). This rock sample would be the compact-crystalline Type I of Archie's carbonate reservoir rock classification.

Poorly sorted pore distribution—high displace-

ment pressure.—Dolomitization may occur to the detriment of a rock's reservoir capacity. The rock example of Figure 5 shows an improvement of permeability over the previous example, but the tightly interlocking rhombs, seen in the photomicrograph, have created a high displacement pressure. Displacement pressure is considered high if the size of the first pore throats that must be invaded is less than 2½ microns in diameter.

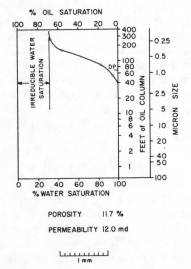

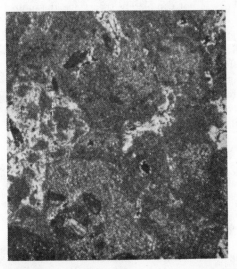

FIG. 5.—Mercury-capillary-pressure curve and corresponding photomicrograph of calcareous dolomite with considerable anhydrite replacement, ×15, crossed nicols. Johnson's Nelson-Durnin well No. 3, depth 4,121 feet. Location: SW. ¼, NW. ¼, sec. 30, T. 161 N., R. 81 W., Bottineau County, North Dakota.

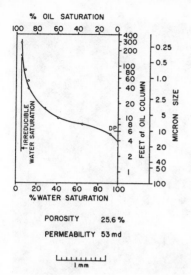

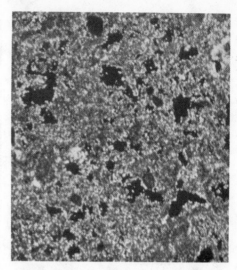

Fig. 6.—Mercury-capillary-pressure curve and corresponding photomicrograph of microcrystalline dolomite, ×15, crossed nicols. California Oil's Hofland No. 1, depth 4,088 feet. Location: SW. ¼, NE. ¼, sec. 24, T. 161 N., R. 82 W., Bottineau County, North Dakota.

High displacement pressure reduces the possibility for this rock to contain oil, the non-wetting phase of a two-phase fluid. Replacement by anhydrite has also reduced the reservoir capacity of this rock.

LOW DISPLACEMENT PRESSURE

Well sorted pore distribution—high effective porosity.—When dolomitization has occurred to the extent it has in Figure 6, the reservoir quality can be optimum. Figure 6 is of a microcrystalline dolomite. This is an interrhombohedral pore space, Type IV, of the classification referred to by Aschenbrenner and Achauer (1960, p. 237), or the saccharoidal, Type III of Archie's classification. In this rock the 25.6 per cent porosity is 95 per cent available to oil saturation. The displacement pressure is low, and the pore distribution is very well sorted. This means the effective porosity is saturated to more than 50 per cent with oil under a small increase in pressure or slightly increased invading oil column. This is a very good reservoir rock.

Poorly sorted pore distribution—low effective porosity.—In Figure 7 the total porosity is only 35 per cent effective, reducing the 15.1 per cent total porosity to about 5 per cent. Murray (1960, p. 72) suggests a rock sample should exhibit 50 per cent effective porosity at a capillary pressure equal to 60 feet of oil column to be considered a commer-

cial reservoir rock. The effective porosity of the sample in Figure 7 is less than this requirement for a reservoir rock. The photomicrograph shows some insight into the high water saturation of this example. The fine, cryptocrystalline material around the more dense pellets holds the interstitial water.

If an oil reservoir contained much of this type of rock, it would be natural to expect a high watercut with the produced oil. This highly watersaturated rock is subjected to a pressure drop at the well-bore annulus as is the oil-saturated rock of Figure 6. Both types of rock occur commonly in the same carbonate reservoir. This is one reason for selectively perforating this type of reservoir.

Poorly sorted pore distribution—high effective porosity.—Figure 8 shows a rock similar to that of Figure 7, but dolomitization has improved the effective porosity. There are all sizes of throats and pores through what was cement material. The cumulative curve is poorly sorted, but the porosity becomes increasingly more effective with pressure. This rock would probably contain commercial oil in a reservoir, although an oil column of 10–12 feet would saturate this rock to only about 5 per cent of the total rock volume.

HIGH DISPLACEMENT PRESSURE

Well sorted pore distribution—low effective porosity.—Figure 9 is an example of the reservoir

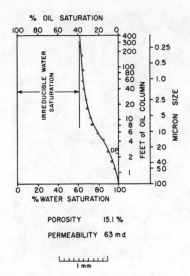

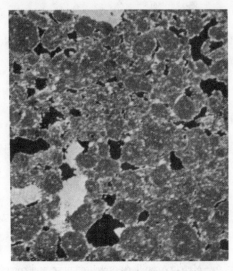

FIG. 7.—Mercury-capillary-pressure curve and corresponding photomicrograph of pelletoidal limestone, ×15, crossed nicols. Johnson's Nelson-Durnin well No. 6, depth 4,123 feet. Location: SW. ¼, SW. ¼, sec. 30, T. 161 N., R. 81 W., Bottineau County, North Dakota.

capacity of a cryptocrystalline dolomite. The porosity of 17.7 per cent is not effective. The low permeability and extremely high displacement pressure are concluding evidence that this would not be reservoir rock.

Well sorted pore distribution—high effective porosity.—In Figure 10, the "pin-point porosity," is more effective although the total porosity is

slightly less than the porosity in the example of Figure 9. The permeability is much improved, but, still, the displacement pressure is so high that under similar reservoir conditions this rock would be essentially a reservoir cap to any of the previous samples of this paper. It is well to point out the porosity of this rock is good, 12.3 per cent and 8.5 millidarcys permeability, but with such a high

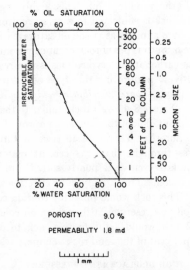

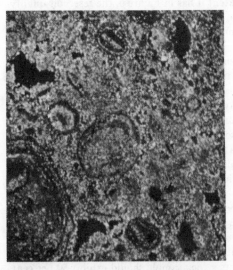

FIG. 8.—Mercury-capillary-pressure curve and corresponding photomicrograph of dolomitic limestone, algal oolites, ×15, crossed nicols. Johnson's Nelson-Durnin No. 1, depth 4,120 feet. Location: NE. ¼, SE. ¼, sec. 25, T. 161 N., R. 82 W., Bottineau County, North Dakota.

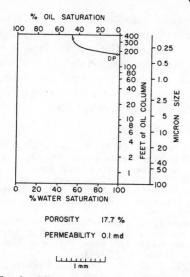

% OIL SATURATION

POROSITY   17.7 %

PERMEABILITY   0.1 md

FIG. 9.—Mercury-capillary-pressure curve and corresponding photomicrograph of cryptocrystalline dolomite, massive algae, ×15, crossed nicols. California Oil's Hofland No. 1, depth 4,086 feet. Location: SW. ¼, NE. ¼, sec. 24, T. 161 N., R. 82 W., Bottineau County, North Dakota.

displacement pressure an oil column of 100 feet would be required to force any appreciable oil into this rock.

CONCLUSIONS

The cap rock-reservoir rock relation is portrayed in the two photomicrographs of Figure 1. In Figure 11, the pore distribution curves of the two rocks in Figure 1 are superimposed to show

the capacity of the reservoir. The reservoir rock has a low displacement pressure equivalent to sustaining a 14-foot column of oil, with a 4-foot transition beneath it. Thirty per cent effective saturation by oil is considered here as the economic limit; the height of the transition zone is dependent on this definition of the economic limit. There is 12 per cent interstitial water in the reservoir, and the water-wet cap rock will sustain up

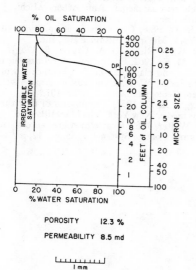

POROSITY   12.3 %

PERMEABILITY   8.5 md

FIG. 10.—Mercury-capillary-pressure curve and corresponding photomicrograph of cryptocrystalline dolomite. ×15, crossed nicols. Johnson's Nelson-Durnin well No. 2, depth 4,100 feet. Location: NE. ¼, NW. ¼, sec. 30, T. 161 N., R. 81 W., Bottineau County, North Dakota.

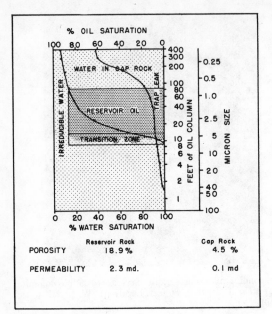

	Reservoir Rock	Cap Rock
POROSITY	18.9 %	4.5 %
PERMEABILITY	2.3 md.	0.1 md

Fig. 11.—Pore geometry of stratigraphic trap. Upper capillary curve represents pore distribution of cap rock shown in Figure 1-A. Lower capillary curve represents pore distribution of reservoir rock shown in Figure 1-B.

to 66 feet of oil in the reservoir. Note there may be 5–10 per cent leakage through the cap if a favorable hydrodynamic gradient were not known to be present. Such a leak is not uncommon in carbonate reservoirs (Hill, 1961, p. 52–56). The extended coarse portion of the cap rock's capillary curve is related to the vugs seen in Figure 1-A.

The seven petrophysical classes suggested in this paper are distinct and can easily be recognized in thin-section and drill-cutting examination. Pore geometry is independent of porosity and permeability measurements, but it is a necessary addition to these data routinely collected. Only a few mercury-capillary-pressure measurements need to be run in a carbonate province to correlate the petrophysics and petrology of the area. The time and expense of extensive laboratory measurements are unwarranted. It is necessary, however, to understand the petrophysics of stratigraphic traps if they are to be explored for with confidence.

REFERENCES

Amyx, J. W., Bass, D. M., Jr., and Whiting, R. L., 1960, Petroleum reservoir engineering; physical properties: New York, McGraw-Hill Book Co., Inc.

Archie, G. E., 1952, Classification of carbonate reservoir rocks and petrophysical considerations: Am. Assoc. Petroleum Geologists Bull., v. 36, no. 2, p. 278–298.

Aschenbrenner, B. C., and Achauer, C. W., 1960, Minimum conditions for migration of oil in water-wet carbonate rocks: Am. Assoc. Petroleum Geologists Bull., v. 44, no. 2, p. 235–243.

Burdine, N. T., Gournay, L. S., and Reichertz, P. P., 1950, Pore size distribution of petroleum reservoir rocks: Trans. Am. Inst. Min. Metall. Engineers, Petroleum Br., v. 189, T.P. 2893, p. 195–204.

Craft, B. C., and Hawkins, M. F., 1959, Applied petroleum reservoir engineering: Englewood Cliffs, N. J., Prentice-Hall, Inc.

Hill, G. A., 1961, Reducing oil-finding costs by use of hydrodynamic evaluations: Economics of petroleum exploration, development and property evaluation: p. 38–69, Dallas, Tex., Internatl. Oil and Gas Educ. Center, SW. Legal Found.

Levorsen, A. I., 1954, Geology of petroleum: San Francisco, Calif., W. H. Freeman and Co.

Mattax, C. C., and Kyte, J. R., 1961, Ever see a water flood?: Oil and Gas Jour., v. 59, no. 42, p. 115–128.

Murray, R. C., 1960, Origin of porosity in carbonate rocks: Jour. Sed. Petrology, v. 30, no. 1, p. 59–84.

Muskat, M., 1937, The flow of homogeneous fluids through porous media: Ann Arbor, Mich., J. W. Edwards, Inc.

Pirson, S. J., 1958, Oil reservoir engineering: 2d ed., New York, McGraw-Hill Book Co., Inc.

Plumley, W. J., Risley, G. A., Graves, R. W., Jr., and Kaley, M. E., 1962, Energy index for limestone interpretation and classification, *in* Classification of carbonate rocks, W. E. Ham, editor: Am. Assoc. Petroleum Geologists Mem. 1, p. 85–107.

Scheidegger, A. E., 1957, The physics of flow through porous media: New York, The MacMillan Co.

Studier, Walter, 1962, Quartz pressure sensors: Instruments and Control Systems, v. 35, no. 12, p. 94–95.

Reprinted from:
BULLETIN OF THE AMERICAN ASSOCIATION OF PETROLEUM GEOLOGISTS
VOL. 50, NO. 3 (MARCH, 1966) PP. 547-559, 14 FIGS., 2 TABLES

CLASSIFICATION OF RESERVOIR ROCKS BY SURFACE TEXTURE[1]

ROBERT B. ROBINSON[2]
Tulsa, Oklahoma

ABSTRACT

Geologists exploring for oil and gas need quantitative field criteria for estimating the reservoir potential of rocks. Such criteria are presented in this paper. They were derived by correlating visual rock characteristics with measured reservoir properties. The criteria are based on approximately 2,000 samples of various lithologic types from several areas.

The rocks were first examined in polished section with the binocular microscope and classified according to surface texture. They then were analyzed for reservoir properties of porosity, permeability, and pore-size distribution. An empirical correlation was found between these rock textures and reservoir properties. A classification was developed in which both sandstone and carbonates were divided into four major surface-textural types. Using the empirical correlation that was found, one can estimate reservoir properties from surface texture alone.

INTRODUCTION

As the search for oil and gas extends into more remote areas and deeper formations, the challenge to the geologist increases. The geologist is meeting this challenge with intensified efforts directed toward better environmental definition and the assessment of its significance in the generation, migration, accumulation, and production of oil and gas.

These efforts are being advanced by updating and re-evaluating many exploration disciplines. One such discipline is the evaluation of the producing potential of reservoir rocks. Many noteworthy papers have been published that deal with processes and problems which influence the petroleum potential of reservoir rocks. Several of the more applicable papers are those by Murry (1960) on the origin of porosity in carbonate rocks, Waldschmidt (1941) on the effect of cementation and compaction on porosity and permeability in sandstone, Waldschmidt et al. (1956) on the classification of porosity fractures in reservoir rocks, Griffiths (1952) on the effect of grain-size distribution on reservoir rocks, and Stout (1964) on the influence of pore geometry

on the producing characteristics of carbonate rocks.

However, the list of papers which evaluate reservoir rocks is shorter. With the notable exceptions of Archie (1952) and Thomas (1962), little has appeared offering quantitative criteria that can be used in the field. In view of the need for additional work in this area, the writer developed an empirical association between surface texture and reservoir-performance properties. About 2,000 samples of sandstone and carbonate rocks from several areas and geological ages were examined. The study included surface as well as subsurface samples. In many instances the empirical associations were supported by production data.

ANALYSIS OF RESERVOIR PROPERTIES AND EXAMINATION OF SURFACE TEXTURE

The production of hydrocarbons involves the flow of water, oil, and gas through porous rocks. The rock properties most indicative of fluid flow are porosity, permeability, and pore-size distribution. Porosity indicates storage capacity available for fluids; permeability indicates the ability to transmit fluids; and pore-size distribution indicates the capability to retain fluids selectively.

ANALYSIS OF RESERVOIR PROPERTIES

Porosity, permeability, and pore-size distribution of each sample were measured. Measurements were made on a cylindrical plug, 1 inch in diameter and 1 inch in length, drilled from the side of the core. In the case of outcrop samples,

[1] This paper is expanded from a talk given before the Society of Economic Paleontologists and Mineralogists at San Francisco, March 28, 1962. Published by permission of Sinclair Oil & Gas Company, Tulsa Research Center. Manuscript received, April 28, 1965.

[2] Sinclair Oil & Gas Company, Tulsa Research Center. The writer expresses his appreciation to J. F. Johnson for his guidance in the initial phase of this study, to J. F. Rogers, who assisted in many of the analyses, and to B. N. Rolfe and A. Chatenever for their review and constructive criticisms of the text.

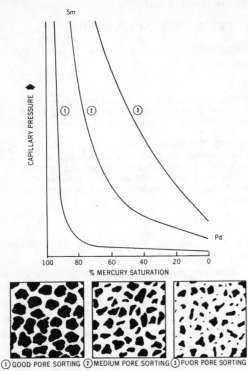

FIG. 1.—Idealized capillary-pressure curves and pore-space diagrams (pores in black) of rocks with (1) good, (2) medium, and (3) poor pore-space sorting.

the plug was drilled parallel with bedding. This procedure, in many cases, orients the sample which is being analyzed in the general direction of reservoir-fluid movement. These analyses also can be made on well cuttings, but some accuracy is sacrificed. The methods of analyses that were used in this study are described briefly.

Porosity.—Bulk volume of the sample was determined by displacement of mercury. Grain volume was determined with gas-expansion apparatus, using Boyle's Law.

Permeability.—Permeability was measured with air at pressures between 1–2 atmospheres.

Pore-size distribution.—Pore size was determined by measuring capillary pressures using the mercury-injection method described by Purcell (1949). Pore radius (r) varies inversely with capillary pressure (Pc). With each increment of pressure applied to the mercury, the volume entering the samples was measured, and a curve was plotted. The capillary-pressure curve represents invasion of successively smaller pores with increasing pressure (Fig. 1).

Capillary-pressure curves measure certain phys-

ical parameters which describe the pore system of a rock. These parameters are entry pressure (Pd) measured in PSIA, minimum unsaturated pore volume (Sm) expressed in per cent, and the geometric description of the curve (C-factor). C-factor is a measure of the pore sorting. A low value indicates good sorting; a high value, poor sorting. The entry pressure (Pd) is indicative of largest pore size, and minimum unsaturated pore volume (Sm) reflects irreducible residual saturation. These three values adequately describe a curve and provide a good basis for pore-system classification. This is similar to, but simpler than, a previously published classification (Thomeer, 1960: see Appendix).

SURFACE-TEXTURE EXAMINATION

The rock surface is examined in polished section with a low-powered binocular microscope. Surface texture is accentuated by using several lamps at very low angle to the rock surface. Photomicrographs of the surface are taken and assembled into comparative suites. It is not imperative that photomicrographs be taken but, by using them, many rock surfaces can be compared simultaneously, making possible a greater degree of definition and speed in classification. The importance of low-angle lighting as an aid in recognizing and classifying surface textures can not be over-emphasized.

Surface-texture characteristics.—Surface texture of both carbonates and sandstone can be described by a relatively few major textural characteristics.

1. *Smoothness* indicates denseness, low porosity, low permeability, and poor reservoir properties.
2. *Granular, open-texture appearance* indicates good grain-sorting, good intergranular porosity, and excellent reservoir properties.
3. *Granular, closed-texture appearance* indicates compacted intergranular porosity and poor reservoir properties.
4. *Granular, clogged-texture appearance* indicates poor grain-sorting, poorly sorted intergranular porosity, and poor reservoir properties.
5. *Visible pore spaces* which are numerous and smaller than about 0.2 mm. indicate moderate porosity and low to moderate permeability.
6. *Vugs* larger than about 0.2 mm., and especially in the range of several millimeters, indicate low porosity and possible high permeability.

Several of these textural characteristics may occur in one rock. An example is a fine-granular, open-textured, saccharoidal dolomite containing a few small vugs. The permeability, which is normally moderate for this type of saccharoidal dolomite, would be greater in this case because of the addition of the vugs.

CLASSIFICATION

Most carbonate reservoirs are characterized by porosity developed through dolomitization and solution processes. Porosity and pore size increase as complete dolomitization is approached, but dolomitization does not begin to produce appreciable porosity until more than 70 per cent of the rock becomes altered (Fairbridge, 1957; Murry, 1960). Texture also is a controlling factor. For example, saccharoidal dolomite has optimum reservoir properties (Fig. 4). Saccharoidal dolomite has mutually interfering texture consisting of euhedral to subhedral crystals which are slightly welded at points of contact. This texture creates well-sorted intercrystalline pore space and a sugary surface texture. As crystal growth increases, this mutually interfering texture is replaced by a more interlocking texture that is characterized by more poorly sorted and less pore space and by denser surface texture (Fig. 5). Rhombs larger than $\frac{1}{2}$ mm. can result from continued crystal growth. When this happens, the dolomite takes on the reservoir properties and surface texture of rocks affected by solution processes.

Porosity created by solution processes can occur in all types of carbonate rock. Porosity development is influenced by the character of the rock and post-depositional events. Limestone containing few large visible vugs can have high permeability if vug alignment is good, but porosity commonly is low. In contrast, limestone containing more numerous but smaller vugs usually has lower permeability and higher porosity.

Porosity in sandstone is intergranular and is greatest before lithification is advanced. Alteration of pore space is by grain compaction or simple pore filling.

The better reservoir sandstones consist of very fine- to fine-size quartz grains, which have undergone slight compaction resulting in some solution and quartz overgrowth at points of grain contact (Griffiths, 1952; Taylor, 1950; Waldschmidt, 1941). Continued compaction decreases pore space by the interlocking of grains of quartz and other minerals as a result of solution at points of contact. This process can continue until the rock becomes completely quartzitic. Pore filling can be caused either by poor grain-size sorting, with increased percentages of silt and clay, or by precipitation of cement from formation solutions. The addition of "fines" (grain-size less than 62μ.) or cement seems to have a greater effect on decrease in permeability than on decrease in porosity. In general, sandstone containing more than about 15 per cent "fines" or cement has low permeability.

By considering the rocks in appropriate categories, a good correlation was found between textural types and reservoir properties. The categories are discussed next.

CARBONATES

Type I. Partly dolomitized limestone.—Rocks with low dolomite content are characterized by a dense smooth surface, vitreous luster, and pinpoint pore spaces. With increased dolomitization, surface texture becomes less dense, luster is reduced, and more and larger pore spaces are evident (Figs. 2, 3). Rocks of low dolomite content have low porosity, low permeability, and poor pore-space sorting (Fig. 2). With increased dolomitization, the capillary-pressure curves in Figures 2 and 3 show decreasing entry pressure (increased pore size) and decreasing C-factor (increased pore-size sorting). Thus, in partly dolomitized limestone containing visible pore spaces, better reservoir properties appear to be associated with higher dolomite content.

A very small part of the total porosity is in the rock framework or "matrix;" visible pore spaces are the greatest contributors. If they are numerous, porosity can be as much as 15 per cent, but usually is half or less of this value. Permeability is greater than about 1–3 md. in only a few samples. Because of this low porosity and permeability, rocks of this type have low producing potential. However, rocks of higher dolomite content (Fig. 3) can become moderately productive.

Type II. Dolomite.—Saccharoidal dolomite is characterized by a sugary surface texture with absence of visible pore spaces (Fig. 4). However, visible pore spaces, which usually are caused by leached fossil casts, can occur. This type is highly dolomitized and has intercrystalline porosity. The capillary-pressure curve in Figure 4 shows low entry pressure, low C-factor, and low minimum unsaturated pore volume—together indicative of large, well-sorted, and extensively interconnected pores.

Dolomite composed of larger rhombs loses the characteristic sugary surface texture of saccharoidal dolomite and has a coarse granular surface

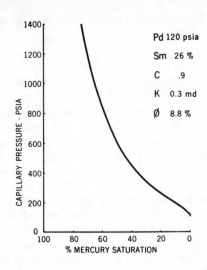

FIG. 2.—Type I. Limestone, partly dolomitized—dense matrix, pin-point pore spaces and vitreous luster. Porosity, permeability, and pore-size sorting are poor. Mississippian, "Midale" carbonates, southeastern Saskatchewan, ×5.

texture (Fig. 5). Larger pore spaces are formed, indicated by lower entry pressure. Permeability is higher, in some samples, but porosity is lower.

Rocks of this reservoir type have excellent producing potential. Porosity ranges from 20 to 35 per cent. Permeability can be as much as 100 md., but usually is less than 50 md. Many of the reservoirs in the Mississippian "Midale" carbonate rocks of southeastern Saskatchewan and in the Permian San Andres Limestone Member of West Texas are composed of this rock type.

Type III. Bioclastic, oölitic, algal, and fine-matrix limestone.—This type of rock is characterized by vuggy void spaces and a dense rock framework. Rocks containing vugs larger than about 0.2 mm. give the misleading impression of having large porosity and permeability. However, vuggy limestone has porosity between 3–8 per

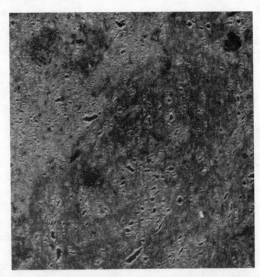

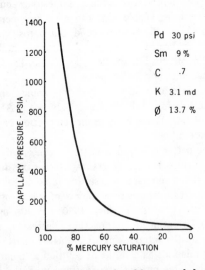

FIG. 3.—Type I. Limestone, partly dolomitized—more and larger pore spaces have reduced luster and density, and increased porosity and permeability (compare with Fig. 2). Permian, San Andres Limestone Member, Garza County, Texas ×5.

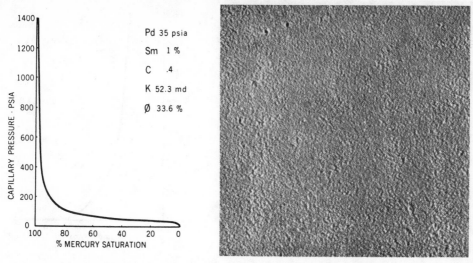

FIG. 4.—Type II. Dolomite, saccharoidal—rough, sugary surface texture; excellent reservoir properties. Mississippian, "Midale" carbonates, southeastern Sasketchewan, ✕5.

cent, whereas permeability depends on vug alignment and can range from less than 1 md. to more than a darcy (Fig. 6). Rocks containing smaller but more numerous vugs usually will have higher porosity, as much as 15 per cent in some samples, and relatively more uniform but lower permeability (Fig. 7). The capillary-pressure curves show high minimum unsaturated pore volume and low entry pressure. This indicates that, though the vugs may be large, they are poorly sorted or aligned. For a discussion on the determination of permeability from pore-space characteristics of carbonate rocks, the reader is referred to a review of Teodorvich's work by Aschenbrenner and Chilingar (1960).

Although porosity is low and unsaturated pore volume high, a large amount of production from limestone reservoirs is from rocks of this type; such rocks can be found in every limestone province. Porosity and resulting production from vuggy limestone are so varied that it is difficult to make meaningful generalizations. However, ex-

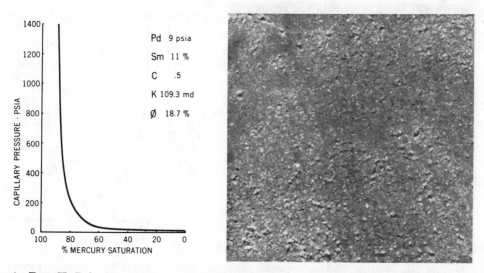

FIG. 5.—Type II. Dolomite—coarse, granular, surface texture. Larger pore spaces have reduced sorting and porosity (compare with Fig. 4). Permian, San Andres Limestone Member, Garza County, Texas, ✕5.

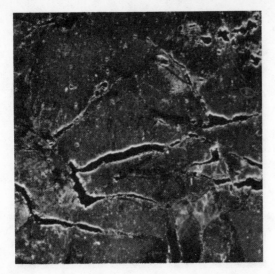

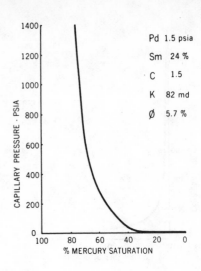

FIG. 6.—Type III. Limestone—dense matrix and vuggy porosity. Pennsylvanian, Oswego Limestone, Dewey County, Oklahoma, ×2.5.

perience has shown that (1) vuggy limestone commonly is a prolific initial producing reservoir, (2) porosity development usually is limited in extent, and (3) total porosity generally is not great unless the producing interval is extremely thick, or unless other factors, such as fracturing, are involved.

Type IV. Dense carbonate.—Rocks of this type have undergone pore filling and mineral replacement. They can be recognized by a smooth, dense surface and an absence of visible pore space (Fig. 8). This type has practically no porosity or permeability, and is more important as a reservoir seal than as a reservoir rock.

Thomas (1962) has described many fine examples of these different carbonate types.

SANDSTONE

Type I. Slightly altered sandstone.—Rocks of this type have a moderately consolidated, very fine- to fine-grained, granular, open-texture surface appearance (Fig. 9). They have good reser-

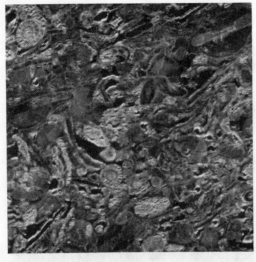

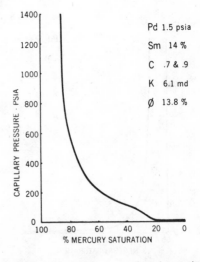

FIG. 7.—Type III. Bioclastic limestone—numerous small vugs. Some of matrix has contributed porosity to rock; this indicated on capillary-pressure curve by change in slope. Pennsylvanian, Kansas City Formation, Russell County, Kansas, ×2.5.

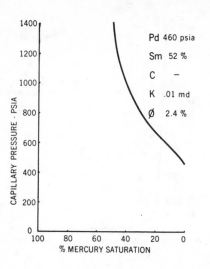

Pd 460 psia

Sm 52 %

C   —

K .01 md

Ø 2.4 %

FIG. 8.—Type IV. Dense carbonate and anhydrite—very low porosity and permeability; important as reservoir seal. Permian, Abo Formation, Eddy County, New Mexico, ×5.

voir properties because of large, well-sorted, and extensively interconnected pore spaces, as well as high porosity and permeability. This is reflected in the capillary-pressure curve (Fig. 9) by low entry pressure, low C-factor, and low unsaturated pore volume.

This type of sandstone makes excellent reservoirs. Porosity generally ranges from 15 to 25 per cent and permeability from 50 to several hundred millidarcys. In the Pennsylvanian Bartlesville sandstone and in the Ordovician "Wilcox"

sandstone, both of Oklahoma, good examples of this rock type can be found.

Type II. Sandstone altered by compaction.—This rock type (Fig. 10) has a granular textural appearance with surface sheen, more closed or dense than that of the slightly altered sandstone in Figure 9. Surface sheen probably is caused by the presence of a small amount of cement and some slight grain solution resulting from compaction. Whereas grain-size and sorting are similar to those in the slightly altered sandstone (Fig. 9),

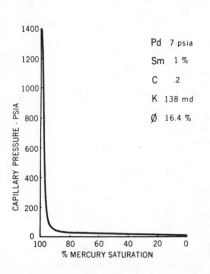

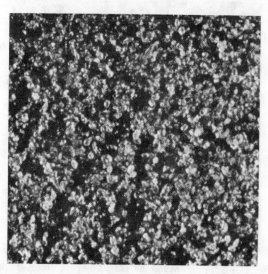

Pd 7 psia

Sm 1 %

C   .2

K 138 md

Ø 16.4 %

FIG. 9.—Type I. Sandstone, slightly altered—very fine- to fine-grained, granular, open surface texture. Excellent reservoir properties. Ordovician, "Wilcox" sandstone, Seminole County, Oklahoma, ×7.

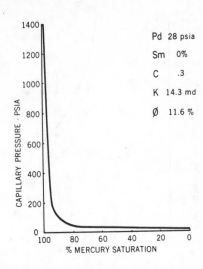

Pd 28 psia

Sm 0%

C .3

K 14.3 md

Ø 11.6 %

FIG. 10.—Type II. Sandstone altered by compaction—granular but closed or denser surface texture (compare with Fig. 9). Compaction has reduced porosity and permeability, but good pore sorting has been retained; good reservoir rock. Pennsylvanian, Tensleep Sandstone, Sweetwater County, Wyoming, ×7.

compaction has reduced the size and sorting of pore spaces and decreased reservoir properties.

The quality of this reservoir type varies inversely with degree of compaction. Porosity averages 10–20 per cent and permeability ranges from 10 md. or less to approximately 50 md. The Pennsylvanian Tensleep Sandstone of Wyoming and the Pennsylvanian Berea Sandstone of Michigan contain beds of this rock type.

Type III. Sandstone altered by pore filling.— Rocks containing appreciable amounts of silt and clay have a friable, granular surface-textural appearance, but more clogged than the open texture in Figure 9. Porosity, permeability, and pore-size sorting are reduced after the addition of "fines" (Fig. 11).[3]

It is difficult to distinguish in polished section

[3] Grain-size less than 62 microns.

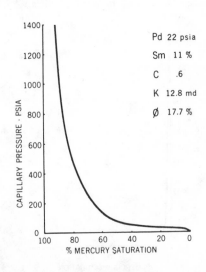

Pd 22 psia

Sm 11 %

C .6

K 12.8 md

Ø 17.7 %

FIG. 11.—Type III. Sandstone altered by pore filling—friable, granular, but clogged surface texture (compare with Fig. 9). Addition of "fines" has reduced pore-size sorting, but rock retains fair reservoir quality. Cretaceous, "J" sandstone, Kimball County, Nebraska, ×7.

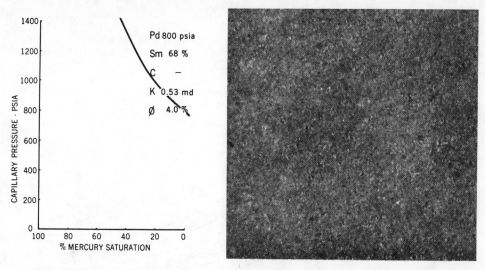

Fig. 12.—Type IV. Sandstone, highly altered—dense, smooth surface texture; important as reservoir seal. Pennsylvanian, Tensleep Sandstone, Natrona County, Wyoming, ×7.

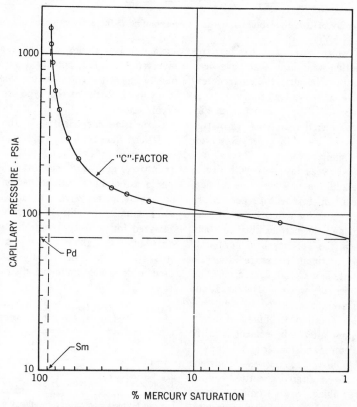

Fig. 13.—Log-log plot of a capillary-pressure curve. Pd at 70 PSIA is extrapolated entry pressure. Unsaturated pore volume is 11 per cent at Sm (100 − 89%). Sorting of pore sizes is descrbied by geometric description "C-factor" of .5. Drawn to one-half scale.

103

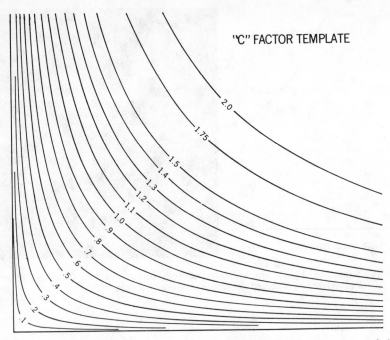

"C" FACTOR TEMPLATE

Fig. 14.—Family of true hyperboles and their corresponding C-factors. Drawn to one-half scale.

between rocks in which pore space has been reduced by cementation and those that have been altered by compaction, because the surface textures of both have a dense appearance. Therefore, the sandstone altered by compaction in Figure 10 could be considered representative of surface texture displayed by both types. Reservoir properties also are similar .

Reservoir quality varies inversely with degree of alteration. The addition to a very fine- to fine-grained sandstone of up to about 15 per cent of "fines" or cement generally reduces the porosity to 10–15 per cent and the permeability to about 10–25 md. Zones in the Tertiary Frio Formation of the Gulf Coast, Permian Delaware Mountain Formation of West Texas, and Cretaceous "D" and "J" sandstones of western Nebraska and eastern Colorado are characterized by sandstone altered through the addition of "fines." A classic example of sandstone altered by cement is in the Ordovician St. Peter Sandstone of Arkansas.

Type IV. Highly altered sandstone.—Sandstone of this type has been altered greatly by grain compaction, pore filling, or a combination of both, rendering the rock so tight and impermeable that it cannot serve as a reservoir. This sandstone type is recognized by a dense, smooth

surface texture where compaction and cement are involved (Fig. 12), and by a granular but completely clogged surface texture where pore filling is involved. Rocks of this type are important reservoir seals.

Correlation coefficients.—In the preceding, associations were found in sandstone between reservoir properties and visual surface expressions of grain-size, grain-size sorting, and compaction. These associations can be demonstrated further by a more quantitative approach. Sixty-two sandstone samples of different reservoir types were analyzed for porosity, permeability, and pore-size distribution (taken from capillary-pressure curves). Common sieve analysis techniques were used to determine grain-size distribution, parame-

TABLE I. CORRELATION COEFFICIENTS* OF RESERVOIR PROPERTIES IN RELATION TO TEXTURE PARAMETERS

	Sorting	Mean Size	Matrix	Coarse Fraction
Porosity	−.84	−.71	−.71	−.34
Log Permeability	−.78	−.72	−.73	−.48
Log (C×Pd)	.91	.82	.82	.47

* 1 or −1 most pronounced correlation; 0 no correlation.
Sorting =grain-size, standard deviation in phi units
Mean size =mean of grain-size in phi units
Matrix =that part of grain-size distribution (<44μ)
Coarse fraction =that one percentile of the distribution curve

TABLE II. GENERALIZED TEXTURE CLASSIFICATION OF RESERVOIR ROCKS

	Type	Visual Characteristics — Major	Visual Characteristics — Minor	Reservoir Properties — Pore-Size Distribution*	Reservoir Properties — Porosity / Permeability	Examples	Remarks
Carbonate	I. Limestone, partly dolomitized	Dense	Few pin-point pore spaces, surface luster	$C=P$, $Pd=H$, $Sm=H$	$\phi=F$, $K=L$	Fig. 2	Poor reservoir quality
		Less dense (than above)	More pin-point pore spaces, reduced luster	$C=M$, $Pd=H\text{-}M$, $Sm=M$	$\phi=M$, $K=F$	Fig. 3	Solution can enlarge and increase pore spaces
	II. Dolomite	Saccharoidal (microgranular)	Sugary, usually brownish in color	$C=G$, $Pd=M$, $Sm=L$	$\phi=E$, $K=G$	Fig. 4	Comprises better carbonate reservoirs; found in association with cal. and anhy. xls.
		Granular	Denser, visible pore spaces	$C=G$, $Pd=L$, $Sm=M\text{-}L$	$\phi=G$, $K=G\text{-}E$	Fig. 5	
	III. Limestones: Bioclastic Oolitic Algal Fine matrix	Few large vugs	Dense rock framework (matrix)	$C=P$, $Pd=VL$, $Sm=H$	$\phi=L$, $K=L\text{-}E$	Fig. 6	Difficult to evaluate permeability from cuttings and small cores
		Many small visible pore spaces	Rock framework breaking up (matrix)	$C=P$, $Pd=VL$, $Sm=M\text{-}H$	$\phi=F$, $K=F\text{-}G$	Fig. 7	Smaller, more numerous pore spaces; usually higher porosity
	IV. Limestone and dolomite, dense	Smooth—dense	No visible pore spaces, assoc. cal. and anhy. xls.	$C=P$, $Pd=H$, $Sm=H$	$\phi=L$, $K=L$	Fig. 8	Usually very dense; important as reservoir seal
Sandstone	I. Slightly altered	Granular	Open surface texture appearance	$C=G$, $Pd=L$, $Sm=L$	$\phi=E$, $K=E$	Fig. 9	Slightly consolidated; clean to handle
	II. Compacted	Granular (but denser than above)	Closed surface texture appearance	$C=G$, $Pd=M$, $Sm=M$	$\phi=F\text{-}G$, $K=G$	Fig. 10	Can become well consolidated and still be of fair reservoir quality
	III. Pores filled	Granular	Clogged surface texture appearance	$C=M$, $Pd=M$, $Sm=M\text{-}H$	$\phi=G$, $K=F\text{-}G$	Fig. 11	Difficult to evaluate permeability; lge. amt. "fines;" spl. dirty to handle
		Granular (but dense)	Closed surface texture appearance	$C=G$, $Pd=M$, $Sm=M$	$\phi=F\text{-}G$, $K=G$		Similar in appearance to Fig. 10
	IV. Highly altered	Dense to dirty	Smooth to gritty surface texture appearance	$C=P$, $Pd=H$, $Sm=H$	$\phi=L$, $K=L$	Fig. 12	Ranges from friable to highly consolidated; imp. as res. seal

* Parameters taken from Pc Curve.

C—Measure of Pore Sorting
.1-.5 Good (G)
.6-1.0 Medium (M)
>1.0 Poor (P)

Pd—Entry Pressure (PSIA)—Indication of Largest Pore Size (microns)
<10 Very Low (VL) >24µ
10-25 Low (L) 24-8µ
25-100 Medium (M) 8-2µ
>100 High (H) <2µ

Sm—Unsaturated Pore Volume in Per Cent
<10 Low (L)
10-20 Medium (M)
>20 High (H)

ϕ—Total Porosity in Per Cent
<5 Low (L)
5-15 Fair (F)
15-25 Good (G)
>25 Excellent (E)

K—Air Permeability in Millidarcys
<1 Low (L)
1-10 Fair (F)
10-100 Good (G)
>100 Excellent (E)

ters of sorting, mean size, matrix, and coarse fraction. Product-moment correlation coefficients were then calculated between these various measurements. The results of these analyses are given in Table I.

This table shows that reservoir properties have (1) the most pronounced correlation with the grain-size parameter of sorting; (2) a prominent, but less marked, correlation with the mean size, which is in almost direct proportion with per cent matrix; and (3) the least pronounced correlation with the coarse fraction. The outstanding correlation, although not surprising, is that between sorting and the product of C-factor and entry pressure. This indicates a nearly 1:1 correlation between grain-size sorting and pore-size sorting.

Although all these data are from the same formation, the results support the concept that there is a correlation between reservoir properties and surface-texture appearance.

A summation of the examinations and analyses of the rock samples used for this study is outlined in Table II. This outline was not designed to be a complete and detailed classification of reservoir rocks, but rather a handy reference describing general reservoir types. Through application, this classification can be modified and refined to meet the user's particular needs.

CONCLUSIONS

By means of simple examinations of easily prepared samples, the geologist can make a fairly reliable estimate of the properties (porosity, permeability, and pore-size distribution) of reservoir rocks. In the absence of core analysis, such information can be of considerable value in estimating net pay zones in outcrop and subsurface, in interpreting logs, and in evaluating drill-stem tests.

As more extensive data and experience are gathered, rock classification by surface texture can become even more reliable. It is hoped that the present work will encourage the growth of this system of analysis.

APPENDIX

Capillary-Pressure Curve Classification

A log-log plot of capillary pressure *versus* fluid saturation of a rock sample will describe a curve which closely approximates an equilateral hyperbole. A general equation for an equilateral hyperbole is:

$$2xy = C^2,$$

where C is equal to one-half of the transverse axis. Although several different hyperboles may possess the same asymptote, the transverse axis will be of different lengths. Therefore, the half transverse axis is a parameter which can be used to describe the shape of the curve. The length of the half axis is herein termed the "C-factor."

The coordinate axes of the plotting paper must be of equal scale. That is, the logarithmic cycle along one axis must be the same length as the cycle along the other axis. Capillary-pressure data are transferred directly to the log-log paper and plotted as values x and y (Fig. 13).

To facilitate determination of C, a family of true hyperboles, along with their corresponding C-factors, has been computed and placed on a template. This template is designed for plotting on K and E 359-112 log-log paper (Fig. 14).

The template is superimposed on a 2 × 3-cycle log-log plot of the capillary-pressure curve, keeping the x and y axes of both the template and plot parallel. The best fit of the template to the capillary-pressure curve determines the C-factor curve. A low C-factor value indicates a sharp-angle curve with a corresponding rock of good sorting or uniform pore-size distribution. A high C-factor value indicates a flat-angle curve with a corresponding rock of poor sorting or a non-uniform pore-size distribution. The curve is plotted on log-log paper only to measure the C-factor. When the curve is graphically presented, it is plotted on cartesian graph paper.

A curve can not be described fully by the C-factor alone, because curves located differently with respect to pressure and saturation axes can have the same C-factor. Therefore, it is necessary to include the extrapolated entry pressure of the non-wetting phase or mercury (Pd) and the minimum unsaturated pore volume (Sm) taken from the capillary-pressure curve to classify the curve completely. The Pd is indicative of the largest pore size of the sample and the Sm reflects irreducible residual saturation of the sample.

REFERENCES

Archie, G. E., 1952, Classification of carbonate reservoir rocks and petrophysical considerations: Am. Assoc. Petroleum Geologists Bull., v. 36, no. 2, p. 278–298.

Aschenbrenner, B. C., and G. V. Chilingar, 1960, Teodorvich's method for determining permeability from pore space characteristics of carbonate rocks: Am. Assoc. Petroleum Geologists Bull., v. 44, no. 8, p. 1421–1424.

Fairbridge, R. W., 1957, The dolomite question, *in* Regional aspects of carbonate deposition: Soc. Econ. Paleontologists and Mineralogists Spec. Publ. 5, p. 125–178.

Griffiths, C. J., 1952, Grain-size distribution and reservoir rock characteristics: Am. Assoc. Petroleum Geologists Bull., v. 36, no. 2, p. 205–227.

Murry, R. C., 1960, Origin of porosity in carbonate rocks: Jour. Sed. Petrology, v. 30, no. 1, p. 59–84.

Purcell, W. R., 1949, Capillary pressures—their measurement using mercury and the calculation of permeability therefrom: Jour. Petroleum Technology, v. 1, no. 2, p. 39–48.

Stout, J. L., 1964, Pore geometry as related to carbonate stratigraphic traps: Am. Assoc. Petroleum Geologists Bull., v. 48, no. 3, p. 329–337.

Taylor, J. M., 1950, Pore-space reduction in sandstones: Am. Assoc. Petroleum Geologists Bull., v. 34, no. 4, p. 701–716.

Thomas, G. E., 1962, Textural and porosity units for mapping purposes, *in* Classification of carbonate rocks: Am. Assoc. Petroleum Geologists Mem. 1, p. 193–224.

Thomeer, J. H. M., 1960, Introduction of a pore geometry factor defined by the capillary pressure curve: Jour. Petroleum Technology, v. 12, no. 3, p. 73–77.

Waldschmidt, W. A., 1941, Cementing materials in sandstones and their probable influence on migration and accumulation of oil and gas: Am. Assoc. Petroleum Geologists Bull., v. 25, no. 10, p. 1839–1879.

—— Fitzgerald, P. E., and C. L. Lunsford, 1956, Classification of porosity and fractures in reservoir rocks: Am. Assoc. Petroleum Geologists Bull., v. 40, no. 5, p. 953–974.

Reprinted from:
BULLETIN OF THE AMERICAN ASSOCIATION OF PETROLEUM GEOLOGISTS
VOL. 52, NO. 9 (SEPTEMBER 1968) PP. 1662-1669, 14 FIGS.

CARBONATE ROCK CHARACTERISTICS AND EFFECT ON OIL ACCUMULATION IN MID-CONTINENT AREA[1]

JOHN F. HARRIS[2]
Tulsa, Oklahoma 74104

ABSTRACT

Detailed sample studies are necessary to evaluate the porosity and permeability characteristics of carbonate reservoirs. Depositional porosity fabrics and the resultant permeability are varied, and may range from highly porous impermeable chalk to less porous but more permeable intergranular porosity in carbonate banks, which may be composed of pellets, oölites, or admixtures of fragmental debris. The presence of fossil cavities, calcispheres, and reefoid deposits may modify the overall fabric. In addition to these depositional characteristics, tectonism can alter the basic porosity-permeability relations by means of fracturing, recrystallization, and/or tectonic dolomitization.

Several of these types of porosity may be present in a single deposit and influence log analysis in either a negative or positive manner. A nonpermeable chalk or calcisphere porosity carrying high water saturation may produce oil if the fracture fabric or associated intergranular permeability is oil bearing. Conversely, nonproducible oil may be trapped in the high-porosity–low-permeability deposits, and the more permeable fracture or intergranular porosity may be water bearing.

These varied porosity fabrics can be recognized by sample and core examination, and a method of qualitative and quantitative logging is suggested. Utilization of well-sample data coordinated with realistic log analysis can lead to successful completion in zones which might be overlooked in a cursory log analysis.

INTRODUCTION

Within the past decade a voluminous literature has been published concerning depositional and epigenetic processes in carbonate sediments, lithofacies studies of ancient deposits, and comparisons with facies fabrics in Holocene carbonate strata. In the search for new methods and technology it is important that geologists not forget the old talents and arts developed by their predecessors. The primary objective of research and field studies by petroleum geologists is the development of new aids for finding petroleum and gas reserves. This exploratory effort culminates with the aptitude of the wellsite geologist, who commonly is the least experienced man in an organization.

In carbonate rocks there may be a complex interrelation among several porosity and permeability types which can be recognized in rotary sample cuttings. Recognition of these factors may lead to successful completion of a well in zones which might be overlooked in a cursory sample-

or mechanical-log examination. A nonpedantic logging technique is suggested which can be used and improved on by the petroleum geologist.

METHODS

In the examination of rotary cuttings it is imperative to remember that the rock fragments reflect to an amazing degree the overall fabric of the original bed. Large cavities, mineralized fractures, or other megascopic textures probably will not be preserved entirely in the cuttings, but their presence must be inferred from the textures and evidence available. The techniques of thin sectioning, staining, etching, and plastic impregnation may be used with valuable results in sample examination and in the study of core specimens.

By these techniques it is possible for an experienced observer to recognize the several types of porosity which may be present in a lithic unit and also to estimate the quantitative importance of each type. Criteria for recognition of these porosity types, photographic examples, and suggested methods of logging follow.

POROSITY TYPES

RECOGNITION AND LOGGING

The porosity and permeability present in carbonate rocks are byproducts of both depositional and structural history. A variety of porosity types may be present in a single rock unit, and the fluid content of each porosity type may be

[1] Manuscript received, January 29, 1968; accepted, March 29, 1968. Modified from a paper given at the 2d Biennial Meeting of the Mid-Continent Section of the Association at Wichita, Kansas, September 27, 1967, under the title, "Some Interesting Aspects of Carbonate Oil Accumulation in Mid-Continent Area."

[2] Independent consulting geologist.

The writer thanks Merrill J. Reynolds for his helpful suggestions and Gary Sample Service for aid in construction of thin sections for illustrations.

similar or different. Recognition of the qualitative and quantitative importance of the porosity types may lead to successful completion in zones which initial analysis might indicate to be nonproductive.

INTERGRANULAR POROSITY

Intergranular porosity is common in carbonate rocks and is generally of depositional origin (Figs. 1, 2). As the name implies, it is porosity between sand-size grains of a carbonate and, as in quartz sand, commonly reflects the degree of sorting and the "cleanness" of the sedimentary deposit. In "dirty" quartz sand the intergranular matrix may be filled with clay particles. In "dirty" carbonate sand the matrix material is usually shale-size carbonate particles. The grain composition of carbonate sand is varied; the sand may range from relatively pure deposits of oölite, pelmicrite, and fossil debris to admixtures of varied carbonate grains.

Estimation of porosity in carbonate sand can be remarkably accurate, depending on the experience of the observer, and is similar in method to the estimation of porosity in quartz-sand deposits. Generally permeability in carbonate sand varies directly with the porosity and in oil zones may be a measure of productive potential. For this reason

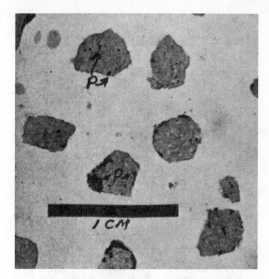

Fig. 2.—Slide made from Ordovician sample chips set in clear plastic. Before thin sectioning, chips were impregnated under pressure with dark plastic (P) to illustrate finely disseminated modified intergranular porosity. Black bar = 1 cm.

it is suggested that recording of these porosity types be done in solid color and that the character of the carbonate-sand deposit be expressed both in the log column by symbol and in the written description on the right of the estimate. Mineralogy (dolomite, calcite, etc.) may be expressed by color differentiation and written description (Fig. 3).

REEFOID POROSITY

Porosity caused by organic growth structure (reefoid) in the preserved geologic column is less common than is suggested by recent literature. All of the porosity types discussed here have been termed "of reef origin" in productive areas. Actually, reefoid porosity is rather distinctive in samples and generally can be distinguished readily by the trained observer. It may comprise all of a single deposit or may be of a "patch" nature in strata whose overall fabric is of an entirely different rock type (i.e., quiet-water deposits, carbonate-sand deposits; Fig. 4).

As with intergranular porosity, the degree of reefoid porosity commonly reflects the productive capacity. Accordingly, it is suggested that estimation of porosity in this type of deposit be plotted in the same way as intergranular porosity types. Reef fabric is identified by symbol in the colum-

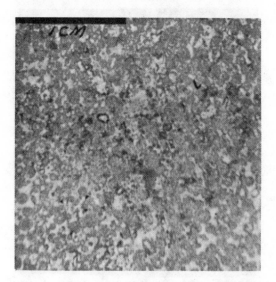

Fig. 1.—Devonian core specimen. Carbonate rock with well-sorted, coarse, sand-size grains and well-developed intergranular porosity. Rounded carbonate grains and pellets are gray to dark gray; intergranular pore spaces are white. Black bar = 1 cm.

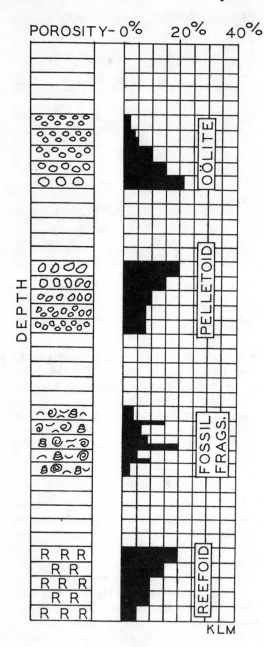

POROSITY- 0%   20%   40%

DEPTH

OÖLITE

PELLETOID

FOSSIL FRAGS.

REEFOID

K L M

FIG. 3.—Porosity log types: intergranular and reef-oid. Suggested method of quantitative logging of intergranular porosity and rock type in carbonate-sand and reefoid porosity.

gas, or water which may be nonproducible or producible only after reservoir stimulation by fracture treatment or acidization. Where thick sections of these types of rocks are oil bearing, the low permeability may be sufficient to permit economic well completion. Recognition of these deposits is necessary for proper economic evaluation of a potential reservoir, and the writer suggests that porosity estimation be logged by means of a hollow-graph symbol as shown on Figure 8.

Quiet-water deposits.—Quiet-water deposits are characterized by silt- to shale-size carbonates deposited in an environment of restricted current action. In many areas they may be of regional facies significance, in a lagoonal or back-barrier environment. These, generally well-sorted, earthy carbonate deposits may have measurable matrix porosity, locally more than 30 percent, but permeability is usually low, in the order of 0.01–0.02 md (Fig. 5).

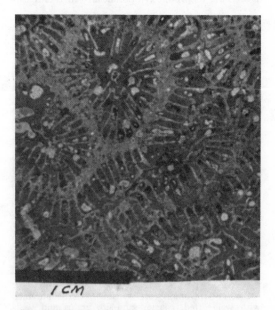

1 CM

FIG. 4.—Plastic-impregnated section of actual reef rock. Plastic is dark gray, original reef rock is light gray. Unfilled pore space and plastic are white. Black bar = 1 cm.

nar part of the log (Fig. 3) and in the written description.

HIGH-POROSITY—LOW-PERMEABILITY DEPOSITS

Many carbonate strata include rock types which have a high porosity but extremely low permeability. These rocks, in which porosity values may exceed 30 percent, may contain oil,

Quiet-water deposits may be associated with patch deposits of reefoid porosity or be interbedded with permeable zones of intergranular sand-size carbonates. In depositional fabric they commonly are similar to chalk deposits which are finely segregated organic debris, generally marine, accumulated under similar quiet-water conditions. The depositional and porosity fabric of the quiet-water-facies rocks is extremely varied and may be modified by borings, areas of plant and animal growth, and in a few places by differential solution of carbonate particles. Generally, however, the permeability is restricted by the fine nature of the sedimentary deposit.

Oölocastic-calcisphere porosity.—High porosity is common in carbonate deposits of oölicastic (oömoldic) or calcisphere-type sediments, but such deposits may have restricted permeability because of the segregated nature of the porosity fabric. Though some may be the result of differential solution, there is good evidence that many of these hollow-spherelike deposits are of depositional origin (calcispheres). Regardless of origin, these deposits produce a measurable log porosity, but may be ineffective as reservoirs unless perme-

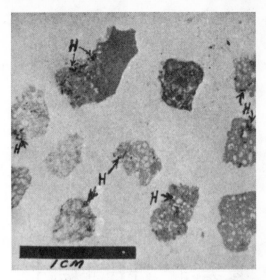

Fig. 6.—Slide made from Pennsylvanian sample chips set in clear plastic. Slide illustrates calcisphere porosity carrying water (clear white spheres) and some intergranular porosity carrying hydrocarbon (dark stain, H). Black bar = 1 cm.

ability has been created naturally (by fracturing, intergranular porosity streaks, *etc.*) or induced by "heavy" completion treatment. Likewise, the fluid content may be relatively nonproducible and influence log analysis in a negative (water) or positive (oil) manner. Depositionally this type

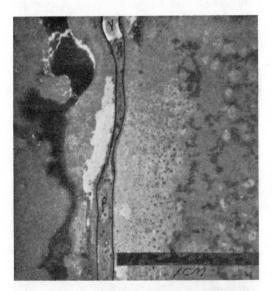

Fig. 5.—Plastic-impregnated, fractured, quiet-water-facies, Mississippian rock; matrix porosity more than 20 percent and matrix permeability 0.01–0.02 md. Note confinement of plastic (P) to vertical fracture trace. V is unfilled void along fracture trace. Dark vertical discoloration on left and disseminated discoloration on right are hydrocarbon staining. Black bar = 1 cm.

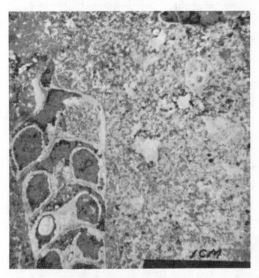

Fig. 7.—Plastic-impregnated fossil-cavity porosity (dark-gray areas, P) in relatively impermeable carbonate matrix. Black bar = 1 cm.

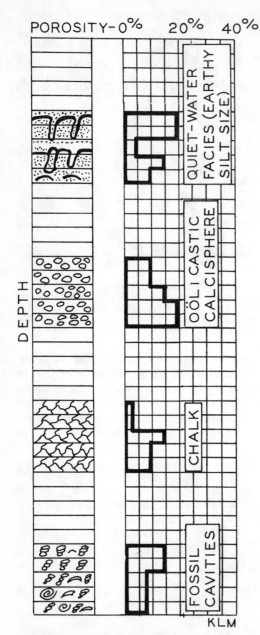

FIG. 8.—Porosity log types: high porosity, low permeability. Suggested method of recognition and quantitative estimation of porosity in high-porosity–low-permeability carbonate rocks.

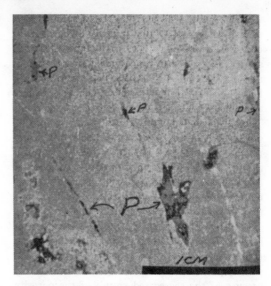

FIG. 9.—Silurian core specimen. Fracture-controlled porosity-permeability fabric in rock of quiet-water deposition. Porosity-permeability channels impregnated with dark plastic (P) prior to thin sectioning. Note lineation and character of porosity development. Black bar = 1 cm.

many types contain hollow fossils or fossil fragments which may represent ineffective porosity, depending on the nature of the enclosing rock. Porosity of this origin may be spectacular in ef-

of carbonate deposit may be an entire bed or a constituent of a more complex sedimentary unit (Fig. 6).

Fossil-cavity porosity.—Carbonate rocks of

FIG. 10.—Ordovician core specimen. Structurally controlled tectonic dolomite. Porosity voids (P) located along fracture and mineralization channels, trends of which are shown by dashed pattern. Channels are very light colored. Black bar = 1 cm.

fect, but commonly the fluid content is relatively nonproducible, depending on the overall permeability fabric of the gross sedimentary unit (Fig. 7).

Logging of the foregoing three general types of porosity in samples is critical for proper mechanical-log interpretation. It is suggested that these porosity types be logged as illustrated in Figure 8.

FRACTURE–TECTONIC–DOLOMITE POROSITY

Tectonic movements, either through local or regional folding, may create or modify porosity-permeability fabrics in carbonate rocks. This may happen as a result of the creation of fractures (Fig. 9) or the development of a structurally controlled or tectonic dolomite (Fig. 10). Such porosity types may comprise the entire porosity fabric of a sedimentary unit or may be only contributory influences. These porosity types can be recognized in samples; however, quantitative evaluation is difficult and is based on such factors as degree of alteration, mineralization, drilling time, and character of drilling (*i.e.*, rough, lost circulation, *etc.*).

The porosity types illustrated in Figures 9 and 10, though seemingly different in overall appearance, actually are of similar origins, being produced by structural folding and fracturing. In both, the porosity is localized on the structure with which it is associated. Obviously, the complete void will not be preserved in many samples and its presence must be inferred from euhedral crystal occurrence, mineralization, and linear fracture traces in cuttings. A suggested method of logging this type of porosity is illustrated in Figure 11.

SOLUTION POROSITY

Solution porosity is common in the geologic column, but personal experience has shown that it generally modifies a preexisting porosity-permeability fabric. Solution enlargement and modification may alter fracture, intergranular, reefoid, quiet-water, or tectonic-dolomite porosity. It is generally possible to determine the original porosity fabric from the rock samples. In the suggested method of logging no provision has been made for separate estimation of solution porosity. In practice it has been the custom to include such modification in the overall analysis of the poros-

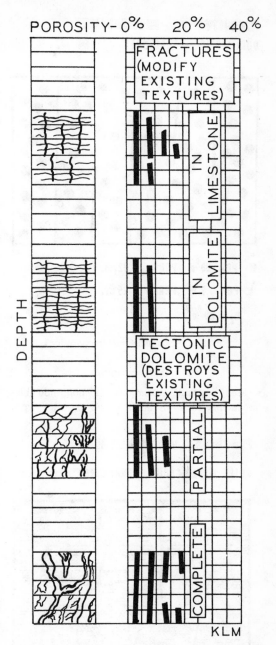

FIG. 11.—Porosity log types: tectonic porosity. Suggested method of recognition and quantitative estimation of porosity in fractured and tectonically dolomitized carbonate rocks.

ity type and to include its recognition in the descriptive part of the log. Undoubtedly there are instances in which a separate identification of porosity caused by solution would be desirable.

POROSITY VS. PERMEABILITY

OÖLICASTIC - - FRACTURES

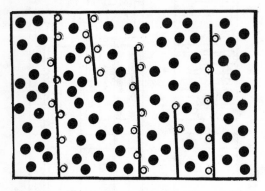

● POR. 20% PERM. .02 md.

◌ POR. 7% PERM. 25 md.

H₂0 80%

FIG. 12.—Oölicastic-fracture porosity.

APPLICATION

Many specific variations of nonproducible-producible reservoir fluids *versus* porosity types

POROSITY VS. PERMEABILITY

QUIET-WATER FACIES ·· FRACTURES

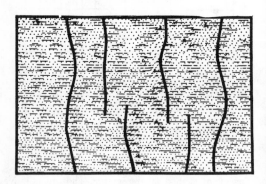

POR. 25% PERM. .01 md.

POR. 4% PERM. 18 md.

H₂0 20%

FIG. 13.—Quiet-water-fracture porosity.

and origins are known among carbonates. Each variation must be analyzed for its own particular relations. Two known occurrences of such variable fabrics are illustrated in Figures 12 and 13.

In Figure 12 the overall fabric of depositional porosity is of oölicastic or calcisphere origin and is water bearing (black dots). Natural fracturing has occurred, and the porosity and well-developed permeability created tectonically are oil bearing (hollow dots). Total porosity of both depositional and tectonic origins is 27 percent, whereas total water saturation is 80 percent. Most of this water is nonproducible because of the low permeability of the oölicastic porosity, and it is possible that a relatively water-free completion could be made from such a reservoir. Conversely, if the oölicastic porosity were oil bearing and the fractures carried water, only water would be produced from an apparently favorable reservoir.

A similar example is illustrated in Figure 6 between water-bearing calcisphere porosity and oil-bearing intergranular porosity where oil was tested from a high-water-saturation reservoir.

In Figure 13 a known relation is illustrated in which a quiet-water calcisiltite with low permeability (dotted pattern) is carrying oil, whereas a natural fracture system with low porosity but high permeability is water bearing (black lines).

FIG. 14.—Ordovician core specimen. Fine-grained, even-bedded, carbonate rock cut by transverse fracture which is filled with fine- to medium-grained quartz sand. Black bar = 1 cm.

Despite the low water saturation of the total rock, probably only water would be produced. Likewise, the converse relation of fractures carrying oil in a water-saturated high-porosity–low-permeability deposit could yield oil in spite of an apparently unfavorable high water saturation. Many examples or modifications of such relations can be cited from diverse oil-producing regions.

In Figure 14, the finely bedded carbonate matrix rock has a porosity and permeability inherent to its depositional type. This rock is cut by a fracture later filled by quartz sand which may also have unique reservoir characteristics. Variable fluid contents and permeability factors would complicate further the reservoir potential of this unusual sedimentary occurrence.

CONCLUSIONS

An experienced wellsite geologist is required for proper interpretation of porosity and permeability fabrics in potential carbonate reservoirs. The complexities mentioned in this brief discussion are perhaps simple in comparison with those found in nature. Proper and detailed logging of the rock types and porosity variations, and estimates of their importance combined with realistic mechanical-log analysis, will aid in the development of new reservoirs.

Reprinted from:
BULLETIN OF THE AMERICAN ASSOCIATION OF PETROLEUM GEOLOGISTS
VOL. 53, NO. 2 (FEBRUARY, 1969) PP. 261-278, 9 FIGS., 4 TABLES

Petrography-Porosity Relations in Carbonate-Quartz System, Gatesburg Formation (Late Cambrian), Pennsylvania[1]

RICHARD E. SMITH[2]
Washington, D.C. 20390

Abstract The Gatesburg Formation of Late Cambrian age in central Pennsylvania consists of cyclic deposits ranging from nearly pure dolomite to nearly pure quartzite containing less than 5 percent clay and 2 percent other minerals. Principal-components and multiple-regression analyses of the petrographic variables of size, shape, sorting, and packing indicate that the degree of packing (quartz-grain to quartz-grain contacts) is the primary property influencing intergranular porosity. The degree of packing accounts for 36 percent of the total variation in porosity explained by linear multiple-regression analysis. Principal-components analysis shows these two variables to be significantly related to each other or associated with common causes. This carbonate-quartz system is interpreted as a beach-lagoon-dune sedimentary system. Development of intergranular porosity, ranging from 2 to 20 percent, is related causally to a quartz-grain-supported framework that isolates and preserves pores where the quartz-carbonate ratio is equal to or greater than 1:1. Of the variables tested, statistically significant correlations were found between (1) packing and amount of quartz, (2) packing and porosity, and (3) amount of quartz and porosity. Almost 50 percent of the total variation in porosity is explained by packing and the amount of quartz; however, the partial correlation coefficient ($r_{13.2}$) between porosity and amount of quartz, with the influence of packing removed, is not significant ($r_{13.2} = 0.173$ at the 5 percent significance level). An unexpected conclusion is that intergranular porosity is not related to grain size in this system.

Permeability values determined for the dolomitic sandstone, dolomitic quartzite, and orthoquartzite are several orders of magnitude higher than those for the sandy dolomite, and range from less than 0.01 to 1,361 md in the carbonate-quartz system.

Results and conclusions of this investigation should be applicable to other carbonate-quartz systems of similar cyclic character.

Introduction

The primary purpose of this investigation was to understand the relations between petrography, porosity, and permeability in a carbonate-quartz system. This necessitates an understanding of the effects of petrographic variables such as composition (the role of the proportions of the two end members, *i.e.*, carbonate and quartz), grain size, shape, sorting, cement, packing of grains and the effects of fractures and joints.

The carbonate-quartz system is used herein to designate the assemblage of rock types that range from nearly pure (quartz-poor) dolomite to nearly pure (carbonate-poor) quartzite. Fig-

ure 1 is a diagrammatic representation of the carbonate-quartz system in terms of the end members, dolomite and quartz, and shows the ranges of the samples studied in the Tyrone

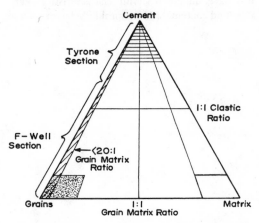

Fig. 1.—Ternary classification of sedimentary rocks using fundamental end members and showing range of samples studied.

and State College, Pennsylvania, areas. Figure 2 is a diagrammatic environmental interpretation of Gatesburg lithologic types in the Tyrone and State College areas as a beach-lagoon-dune sedimentary system. The findings derived from the Tyrone section are minor in comparison to those from the State College (F-well) section. However, in order to show the relation between the end members of the system, in terms of a changing environment

[1] Manuscript received, July 24, 1967; accepted, March 18, 1968. Condensed from Ph.D. dissertation presented to The Pennsylvania State University, 1966.

[2] U.S. Naval Oceanographic Office, Marine Chemistry Branch. J. C. Griffiths and R. R. Parizek of The Pennsylvania State University kindly read and criticized the manuscript. Financial support was received from M. E. Bell, Asst. Dean for Research and Director, Mineral Industries Experiment Station, M. L. Keith, Director, Mineral Conservation Section, L. A. Wright, Head, Dept. of Geology and Geophysics, William Spackman, Coal Research Laboratory, all of the Pennsylvania State University; the Society of Sigma Xi; and Core Laboratories, Inc., Dallas, Texas.

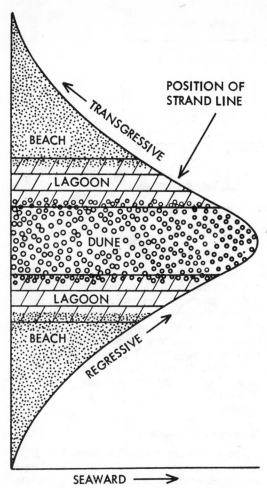

POSITION OF
STRAND LINE

TRANSGRESSIVE

BEACH

LAGOON

DUNE

LAGOON

BEACH

REGRESSIVE

SEAWARD ⟶

Fig. 2.—Hypothetical sedimentary interpretation of Gatesburg rock types in State College and Tyrone areas representing beach-lagoon-dune sedimentary system.

and the development of porosity through a quartz-grain-supported framework, a brief discussion of the Tyrone section is necessary.

Specifically, this investigation is directed toward the determination of (1) the petrographic properties which influence or control intergranular porosity in the carbonate-quartz system, (2) the percentage of intergranular porosity of the compositional ranges shown in Figures 1 and 3, (3) an estimate of the permeability of these rocks, excluding the contributions of fractures and joints, and (4) the effect of vugs on both porosity and permeability.

The cyclic Gatesburg Formation of Late Cambrian age is an excellent example of a carbonate-quartz sedimentary rock system. Gates-

burg rocks underlie a part of the Pennsylvania State University campus in University Park, and there are several excellent exposures near Gatesburg and Tyrone, Pennsylvania, 9 and 22 mi (14.48 and 35.41 km) southwest. A complete range in rock type (rock-type names as defined by Krynine, 1948b), from dolomite through sandy dolomite, dolomitic or, rarely, calcitic sandstone to orthoquartzite, is present in these localities. In the sedimentary units chosen for study, minor amounts of feldspar and heavy minerals are present but the chief non-carbonate mineral is quartz.

Classification of Porosity Studies

The targets of investigations of porosity in sedimentary rocks can be classified as three basic types: (1) primary (original) porosity—depositional fabric and texture such as grain size, shape, orientation, and sorting, (2) secondary porosity (diagenesis)—solution effects, solubility differences caused by variable calcite-dolomite ratios, degree of dolomitization, cementation by circulating waters, recrystallization, and compaction, and (3) tectonic influences on porosity—gross effects of fractures, joints, and compaction.

Most investigations of factors influencing porosity combine two of the three types listed. Intergranular, intercrystalline, and vugular porosity studies concern groups 1 and 2 and fracture porosity studies concern group 3. The writer's study primarily involves the first type.

Importance of Study

Before 1950 there were few clear concepts of the complete process of porosity development in a genetically related sedimentary system. Previous investigations have been focused on either the sandstone end member (including quartzite) or the carbonate end member, but not on a continuous system of sedimentary environments. The Gatesburg Formation affords an opportunity to study porosity development in a genetically related sedimentary system, shown diagrammatically in Figures 1–3. The cyclic pattern of dolomite and quartz which characterizes the Gatesburg Formation in the study area represents a continuously changing and alternating sedimentary environment. In such an integrated sedimentary system, sedimentation, cementation, weathering, and porosity and permeability are closely interrelated. The resulting porosity and permeability basi-

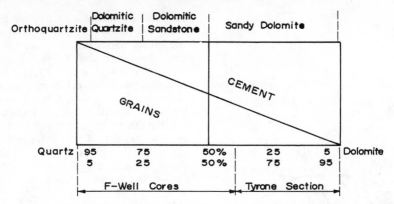

FIG. 3.—End member classification of dolomite-quartz system showing range of samples studied.

cally depend on the initial grain framework. It is desirable, therefore, to study such genetically related units in order to minimize the effect of later differential solution in different rock types. Studying the proportions of cement to grains over a wide range permits the examination of the factors controlling the development of porosity. In such a continuous system evaluation of the intergranular porosity at all levels is possible and the concept of framework as a porosity-builder can be established. One investigation which has applied the system approach to the study of porosity is that of Lucia (1962), who studied the origin of porosity in a limestone-crinoid fragment sysem his crinoid-fragment framework is analogous to the quartz-grain framework in the carbonate-quartz system.

Studies of porosity and permeability are important in effective exploration for and exploitation of oil, gas, and water resources. Gatesburg rocks now are being used in a pilot program for effluent disposal in the State College, Pennsylvania, area and knowledge of their porosity and permeability is essential for the success of monitoring studies in the program. This need is the principal motivation for the writer's study. Related studies of fracture porosity and permeability in Gatesburg rocks (Lattman and Parizek, 1964) are also an integral part of the project. In recent years, the Gatesburg Formation in Pennsylvania also has received increasing attention as a potential reservoir for untapped deep oil and gas reserves because of its sandy character. Where exposed near the surface it serves as a potentially important aquifer for large supplies of ground water of good quality (Smith, 1967).

SAMPLE COLLECTION SITES

The most accessible and best exposure of the dolomitic facies of the Gatesburg Formation is approximately 2.8 mi (4.51 km) southeast of Tyrone, Pennsylvania, along U. S. Highway 322 between Shoenberger and Birmingham, whereas the quartzite facies underlies much of the State College area. Figure 4 shows the location of the Tyrone section and F-well (agronomic cropland and forestry sites) sample collection sites.

GEOLOGIC BACKGROUND

The Gatesburg Formation, named by E. S. Moore from Gatesburg Ridge in the southwestern corner of the Bellefonte quadrangle (Butts, 1918, p. 527), is of Late Cambrian age (Butts et al., 1939 p. 12) and occupies the stratigraphic interval between the underlying early Late Cambrian Warrior Formation and overlying Early Ordovician Stonehenge Limestone (Fig. 5).

The Gatesburg Formation is exposed rather poorly in the State College area, but exposures are excellent along the Little Juniata River near Tyrone and along Logan Branch, 1 mi (1.6 km) northeast of Bellefonte, Pennsylvania. Estimates of the thickness of the Gatesburg Formation range from 1,600 ft (487.68 m) near Tyrone (Pelto, 1942, p. 2) to 2,000 ft (609.60 m) in central Pennsylvania (Wilson, 1952, p. 282).

The cyclic character of the Gatesburg Formation has been described in detail by Pelto (1942, p. 4–15), who noted that a typical cycle may include from top to bottom (1)

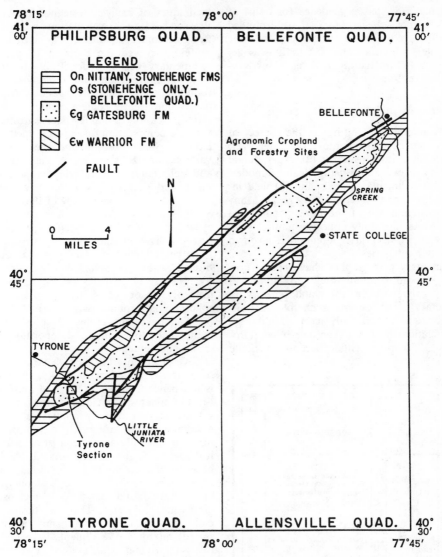

Fig. 4.—Areal distribution of Gatesburg and adjacent formations in central Pennsylvania.

dark, thin-bedded aphanitic silty dolomite, (2) medium- to coarse-grained orthoquartzite, (3) thin-bedded, crystalline and shaly dolomite, (4) massive black medium-crystalline dolomite, and (5) dolomite cryptozoon stromatolite.

Pelto's typical cycle which may include the above sequence certainly is not characteristic of the younger Gatesburg beds in the State College area, where dolomite alternates with quartzite, and all gradations between are present. Further, the Tyrone section is chiefly dolomite and silty or sandy dolomite.

Further description of the Gatesburg Forma-

tion is given by Wilson (1952), Caruccio (1963), and Landon (1963).

PREVIOUS WORK AND RELATED STUDIES
Gatesburg Formation

Krynine (1948a, p. 33) stated that two types of porosity may be present in the Gatesburg orthoquartzite: (1) a primary (original) porosity resulting from incomplete cementation by carbonate, silica, or both during deposition, and (2) a secondary porosity developed by leaching of carbonate cement during uplift and weathering. He cited as evidence for uplift of Gatesburg rocks the presence of well-rounded tourmaline grains in the Bellefonte Sandstone of Middle Ordovician age; the uplift was accompanied by weathering and leaching (Krynine, 1946, p. 9).

Porosity and Permeability Studies

The voluminous literature on the subject of porosity can be divided into three categories: (1) theoretical investigations, (2) experimental laboratory investigations using idealized models or natural sedimentary rocks, and (3) field investigations of natural sedimentary rocks. Many studies combine two of the three possible approaches. As this study concerns natural sedimentary rocks, only brief attention is given to the first two categories.

Sedimentary petrographers have been working for years to determine the interrelations between petrographic variables and porosity in sedimentary rocks. Several such interrelations or associations are generally accepted, although the correlations have not been determined (Rosenfeld, 1950, p. 4) either because adequate

techniques of analysis were not known at the time or because the calculations were too laborious without the aid of digital computers. Rosenfeld surveyed the problem of porosity in sedimentary rocks in detail; his bibliography contains more than 300 references. Marked rounding and sphericity, good sorting, and nearly pure quartz content commonly are associated; lack of rounding, poor sorting, and a variable composition also are grouped. The relation between porosity and the petrographic variables of size, size sorting, shape (roundness and sphericity), mineralogic composition, cement, and packing is commonly complex because of the interdependency of these variables. Similarly, the problem of measuring the properties is complex. A review of several papers on petrography and intergranular porosity shows that the following properties of sediments are thought to be the factors which control porosity: (1) size of particles or grains, (2) uniformity of size or size sorting of the grains, (3) sphericity and roundness (shape) of the grains, (4) packing of the grains, (5) presence of cement, and (6) mineral composition of the grains and cement.

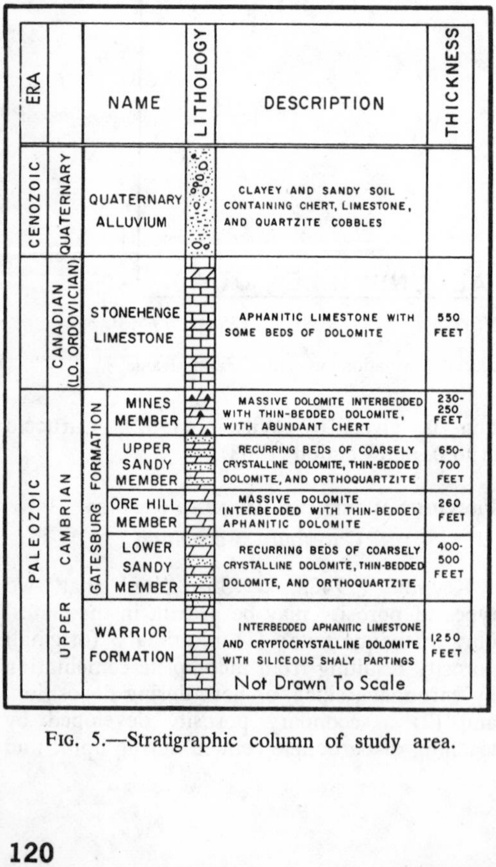

Several authors (Table I) have shown, both theoretically and experimentally, that porosity is independent of particle size in uniform mixtures of spheres. Conclusions drawn from these studies are not directly applicable to natural sediments, which are rarely of uniform grain size and generally do not consist of truly spherical grains. Some investigators (Table I) have observed that assemblages of fine particles have higher porosity than coarser assemblages, and others have found that porosity increases with increasing grain size. There is, however, general agreement that uniformly sized (well sorted) mixtures of sediments have higher porosity than heterogeneous (poorly sorted) mixtures (Table I). The effect on porosity of the arrangement of grains (packing) in natural sedimentary rocks is less clearly understood, but is recognized as an important variable (Table I). The correlation between the amount of cement and porosity in sandstone is much more definite than the correlation of any of the other petrographic variables (Table I). An increase in the amount of cement, other variables being constant, in every case results in a decrease in porosity. In most of the examples cited the influence of other petrographic variables was not controlled, and in studies in which it was controlled the results generally are not applicable to natural sedimenary rocks.

ERA		NAME	LITHOLOGY	DESCRIPTION	THICKNESS
CENOZOIC	QUATERNARY	QUATERNARY ALLUVIUM		CLAYEY AND SANDY SOIL CONTAINING CHERT, LIMESTONE, AND QUARTZITE COBBLES	
PALEOZOIC	CANADIAN (LO. ORDOVICIAN)	STONEHENGE LIMESTONE		APHANITIC LIMESTONE WITH SOME BEDS OF DOLOMITE	550 FEET
	UPPER CAMBRIAN — GATESBURG FORMATION	MINES MEMBER		MASSIVE DOLOMITE INTERBEDDED WITH THIN-BEDDED DOLOMITE, WITH ABUNDANT CHERT	230-250 FEET
		UPPER SANDY MEMBER		RECURRING BEDS OF COARSELY CRYSTALLINE DOLOMITE, THIN-BEDDED DOLOMITE, AND ORTHOQUARTZITE	650-700 FEET
		ORE HILL MEMBER		MASSIVE DOLOMITE INTERBEDDED WITH THIN-BEDDED APHANITIC DOLOMITE	260 FEET
		LOWER SANDY MEMBER		RECURRING BEDS OF COARSELY CRYSTALLINE DOLOMITE, THIN-BEDDED DOLOMITE, AND ORTHOQUARTZITE	400-500 FEET
		WARRIOR FORMATION		INTERBEDDED APHANITIC LIMESTONE AND CRYPTOCRYSTALLINE DOLOMITE WITH SILICEOUS SHALY PARTINGS	1,250 FEET

Not Drawn To Scale

FIG. 5.—Stratigraphic column of study area.

Table I. References to Variables Influencing Porosity

VARIABLES		REFERENCES
	GRAIN SIZE	(1) Scheidegger (1957, p. 18), Slichter (1899, p. 310), Graton and Fraser (1935, p. 805). (2) Ellis and Lee (1919, p. 121-123), Trask (1931, p. 173), Cloud (1941, p. 1039-1040). (3) Pye (1944, p. 106).
	SIZE SORTING	(1) Fraser (1935, p. 918), Pye (1944, p. 106), Tolman (1937, p. 98 and 111), Fettke (1927, p. 222).
	PACKING	(1) Graton and Fraser (1935, p. 805). (2) Rosenfeld (1950, p. 69).
	CEMENT	(1) Bybee (1938, p. 915-918), Fettke (1934, p. 198-204), Folk (1949, p. 37), Howard (1928, p. 1155), Imbt (1950, p. 618), Murray (1930, p. 453), Ondrick (1965, p. 161), Pachman (1961, p. 83), Parsons (1922, p. 63). (2) Griffiths (1960, p. 54).

Quantitative Approach to Sedimentary Rock Analyses

Before 1950, relatively few detailed analyses of sedimentary rocks were evaluated statistically; most were simply descriptive and qualitative. The most recent quantitative approach to the problem of relating petrographic variables to porosity in sandstone was pioneered by Griffiths (1958, 1960, 1961, 1966), who considered all variables simultaneously in a statistical approach. Several Master's theses and Ph.D. dissertations completed under his direction also use a statistical approach and are drawn upon by the writer. The conclusion that can be drawn from these studies is that the mass property, porosity, is dependent on several petrographic variables, but generally one or two have a major influence on or control of porosity in any particular instance.

In the description of a sedimentary rock, properties of fundamental importance must be defined, and procedures described for exact specification of those properties (Griffiths, 1961, p. 488). The petrographic variables must be measured quantitatively and expressed as meaningful numerical values (Griffiths, 1958, p. 15) susceptible to examination by statistical correlation. An understanding of the interrelations of the properties, generally measured by several techniques, is essential before the processes are interpreted.

The process of reducing the definition of a rock specimen to an operational basis has been described by Griffiths (1961, p. 488), who represented the description of a rock specimen (or any other dependent property) symbolically as:

$$P = f\,(m, s, sh, o, p),$$

where

P = the unique index,
f = function of,
m = composition of grains,
s = size of grains,
sh = shape of grains,
o = orientation of grains, and
p = packing of grains.

Griffiths (1961, p. 489) considered these five properties to be the fundamental properties which lead to a unique definition of an aggregate of elements at any level.

One may designate P (the unique index) as porosity, the dependent property, and m, s, sh, o, and p as the independent properties to which numerical values are attached. The magnitude of the contribution of each variable to the variation in p (porosity) then can be estimated. In an analysis of this type, the equation becomes a multiple-regression equation (Griffiths, 1961, p. 496) which provides an understanding of the most important petrographic properties controlling or influencing porosity.

Emery and Griffiths (1953, p. 70) have pointed out that the property of grain packing is important in determining the porosity of many sedimentary rocks. In traverses of unit length across a thin section, packing is a function of composition, size, shape, and orientation of the grains; Emery and Griffiths suggested that the length of the traverse be divided by the mean grain size of the grains whose contacts are being counted in order to remove, "at least partially," the effects of the other variables. According to those authors, differences in reservoir porosity and permeability can be correlated with different arrangements of the sand grains in sandstone.

COLLECTION DATA
Sampling Procedure

Samples of sandy dolomite, ranging from 4 to 40 percent quartz, were taken from exposures of the Gatesburg Formation southeast of Tyrone. The dolomitic sandstone and quartzite samples were obtained from diamond cores taken in the State College (F-well samples) area (see Smith, 1966, Fig. 5, for specific location of core borings and detailed geologic logs, Pl. 7) in conjunction with The Pennsylvania State University Waste Water Research Facility (Fig. 4). These wells (150–300 ft or 45.72–91.44 m deep) penetrate the Mines and Upper Sandy Members of the Gatesburg Formation which are not exposed in the Tyrone section. No sample was taken adjacent to a fracture or joint, in order to avoid the effects of ground-water solution which may have occurred in the adjacent rocks. In all, 65 samples, 9 from Tyrone and 56 from State College, were analyzed.

Measurement of Variables

Thin-section analyses.—Each thin section was divided arbitrarily into 4 equal columns and 20 rows. Five traverses (rows) and two quarters (columns) along each traverse were randomly selected and the size of the first four grains found along the preselected traverse and quarter, and appearing beneath the cross-hairs, was measured. In this manner, the grain size of a total of 40 quartz grains and, in the Tyrone samples, 40 dolomite grains per thin section was measured. The operational definition of grain size proposed by Griffiths and Rosenfeld (1950, p. 205) is used, *i.e.*, the apparent long (a) axis of a grain as observed in thin section. The short (b) axis is determined first because considerable variation is introduced by the difference in choice of the a axis, and the contribution of the a axis to the total variation is better controlled by this procedure (Griffiths, 1967, p. 121). Although the procedure was applied originally to a projected image of a grain, it also was followed with the use of a micro-

scope and a graduated square-mesh grid. The orientation of the thin section and the grains affects the size of a grain as measured, but if the grains are randomly oriented, the mean of several measurements will yield a satisfactory, although biased, estimate of grain size (Smith, 1966, p. 40).

Packing was measured in thin sections of F-well samples in a similar manner. The slide was divided into two columns (halves) instead of four. The contacts of the first four quartz grains found under the cross-hairs along the preselected traverse and column were recorded. Traverses and columns were selected randomly from a table of random numbers (Arkin and Colton, 1962, p. 142-145). A total of 20 quartz grains per thin section was observed for contacts. The packing index or degree of packing is defined as the percentage of quartz grains to quartz-grain contacts or boundaries observed in thin section; packing, then, is an estimate of the proximity of the quartz grains (Emery and Griffiths, 1953, p. 67). If the subsequent point along any given traverse intercepted the second grain involved in a grain-to-grain contact, the next grain (or absence of a contact) was counted (Smith, 1966, p. 41). This procedure of measuring the packing index has been described by Emery (1954, p. 19–20) and Emery and Griffiths (1953, p. 70).

Sorting.—Size sorting is defined as the standard deviation ($\hat{\sigma}$), a measure of dispersion about the mean grain size.

Insoluble-residue analyses.—Weight percent insoluble residue (I. R.) was determined by crushing specimens and dissolving the carbonate part in HCl (Smith, 1966, p. 36).

Grain shape.—As suggested by Griffiths and Rosenfeld (1950, p. 206), the axial ratio (b/a) is a reflection of apparent shape and may be taken as an approximation of the sphericity of the grains or as an estimate of grain shape.

For a spherical grain, b/a equals one. A grain may appear to be spherical and yet be tube-shaped if it is oriented perpendicular to the plane of the thin section. Any section of randomly oriented grains, however, will show, on the average, the same dimensions of axes and axial ratios (Griffiths and Rosenfeld, 1950, p. 206).

Porosity analyses.—Bulk density was measured on a mercury balance, grain volume was measured with a Beckman Air Pycnometer (Model 930), and absolute porosity (Smith, 1966, p. 29–33, 55) was calculated according to the formula:

$$AP = \frac{GD - BD}{GD}(100) = \text{percent porosity},$$

where AP = absolute porosity in percent, GD = grain density in gm/cm³, and BD = bulk density in gm/cm³.

PETROGRAPHY

The suite of Gatesburg rocks studied consists primarily of quartz and dolomite. Feldspar is quantitatively unimportant. Calcite was observed to be present as the carbonate mineral in only one sample; the dolomite is principally recrystallized dolomite mud. Heavy minerals are scarce; according to Pelto (1942, p. 38), they make up less that 1 percent of the rock and generally less than 0.5 percent. The quartz is primarily detrital but overgrowths are not uncommon and chert was observed to be present as cementing material in a few samples of the quartzite and quartzitic sandstone.

DESCRIPTIVE DATA AND INTERPRETATIONS OF F-WELL SAMPLES

The F-well samples represent the range from 40 percent quartz (sandy dolomite) to 100 percent quartz (orthoquartzite) shown in Figure

2. Seven samples contain chert or mixtures of chert and dolomite as the cementing material. The quartz is primarily of fine to medium sand size (Pettijohn, 1957, p. 18); grains range from 0.11 to 0.378 mm and average 0.258 mm. Microcrystalline chert and secondary quartz overgrowths constitute the remaining quartz fraction.

Porosity *Versus* Insoluble Residue

A plot of porosity *versus* insoluble residue (I.R.) shows a definite positive relation between the two properties (Fig. 6). Sandy dolomite from the Tyrone section also is plotted on Figure 6. The increase in porosity with an increase of I. R. (quartz) is very abrupt beyond 50 percent I. R. Porosity ranges from less than 1 to nearly 20 percent for the entire carbonate-quartz system (Smith, 1967).

A few scattered points (Fig. 6) represent relatively higher porosity values than are expected on the basis of their I. R. content and show the trend established by the points. Some of the factors which might contribute to these deviations from the general trend are (1) errors in measurements, (2) minute fracture openings in the samples analyzed, (3) diagenetic processes such as compaction and cemen-

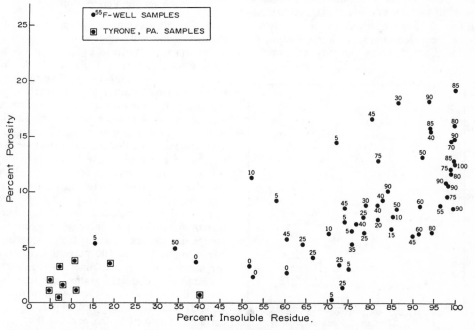

FIG. 6.—Scatter diagram showing relation between percent insoluble residue and percent porosity for F-well and Tyrone samples. Superscript numbers represent percent packing.

tation, (4) vugs, and (5) unexplained error.

Detailed examination of thin sections of F-well cores shows the porosity to be present primarily as (1) intercrystalline or intergranular pores, (2) minute voids in the microcrystalline chert, and (3) vugs ranging from 0.25 to 2 mm. It is inadvisable to consider all the voids observed in a thin section as voids actually present in the rock as a whole, because individual grains and cement may be plucked out during the preparation of the thin section. Where several similar voids are observed, it is reasonable to assume that they are representative of the voids in the rock and therefore contribute to the porosity of the sample.

In addition to the fact that the dolomite grain size is a measured variable in the Tyrone section but not in the F-well section, the relative flatness of the curve below 30 or 40 percent I. R. (Fig. 6) is considered to be sufficient justification for separating these samples into two groups, the Tyrone section samples and the F-well samples, in the principal-components analysis. The apparent lack of samples containing 15–40 percent quartz is not uncommon in similar carbonate-quartz sedimentary rocks (Winchell, 1924, p. 885) and is not a sampling error but the result of a high degree of sedimentary differentiation which would be expected along a stable coastline with a beach-lagoon-dune system as shown diagrammatically in Figure 3. Their absence not only adds support to the paleogeographic interpretation but also indicates that the porosity relationships

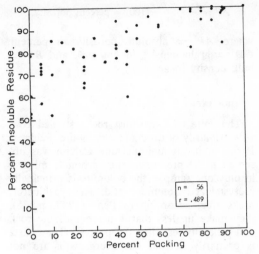

FIG. 8.—Scatter diagram showing relation between percent packing and percent insoluble residue in F-well samples.

may well apply to all of the Gatesburg Formation.

Porosity, size, shape, sorting of the quartz grains, packing, and I. R. were determined for 56 F-well samples covering the ranges of I. R. and porosity observed.

Packing *Versus* Porosity

A plot of packing against porosity (Fig. 7) shows a statistically significant and positive relation. As was shown in Figure 6, porosity increases with increasing I. R. and there should be a statistically significant positive relation between the two "independent" properties, packing and I. R. as shown by Figure 8. The packing values are shown for each sample in Figure 6. It is important to notice that between 80 and 100 percent I. R., the degree of packing is varied over a range of nearly 50 percent. No significant relations with porosity were observed for the other independent variables of grain size, shape, and sorting.

It may be concluded for the carbonate-quartz system that an increase in porosity accompanies an increase in I. R. (quartz) between about 50 and 100 percent I. R. Part of the increase may be explained by the degree of packing of the quartz grains; the interdependency in the system is considered in the components analysis. Intergranular porosity, which certainly is related to the packing (Fig. 7), was observed under the microscope in most of the samples that contained 75–100 percent I. R.

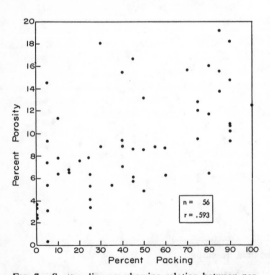

FIG. 7.—Scatter diagram showing relation between percent packing and percent porosity in F-well samples.

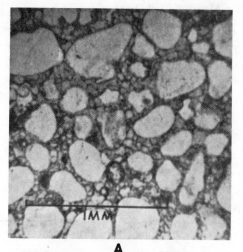

A

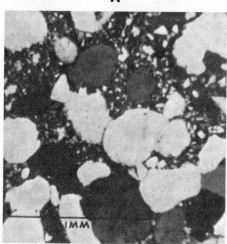

B

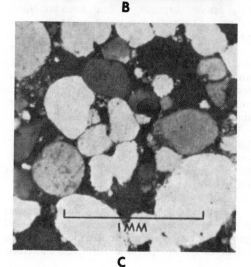

C

Photomicrographs showing three degrees of packing, ranging from 5 to 90 percent, are shown in Figure 9. Cement may never have been deposited in these voids, or the material may have been leached out subsequently by circulating groundwater. The presence of iron oxide stains and clay coatings on quartz grains surrounding vugs in a few samples suggests that solution occurred after the consolidation of the sediment. Samples containing secondary quartz overgrowths are commonly in contact with each other; the result is an effective increase in the degree of packing and, in many instances, isolation of areas with or without carbonate cement. Pressure solution along quartz-grain contacts, presumably as a result of increased effective stress, probably has resulted in deposition of the silica in nearby voids.

Principal Components Analysis

Before components analysis, a "Q-type factor analysis" was run to determine the homogeneity of the F-well samples (Imbrie and Purdy, 1962). No discrete sample groups are apparent; the F-well samples represent a continuous distribution ranging from a high packing index and high porosity to low packing and porosity and thus a homogeneous group (Smith, 1966, p. 166).

In component analysis (Thurstone, 1947) an attempt is made to find components which will allow reduction of the dimensions of variation and elimination of variables containing the same information. Alternately, it will disclose the least number of linearly independent vectors that "form the basis for the entire space" (Griffiths, 1963, p. 650). The objective of this analysis was to determine the relations between the measured properties (petrographic variables) that originally were considered to be independent and to provide further evidence of the linear relations already shown. One seeks to determine the least number of petrographic variables that supply an adequate amount of information and to find the petro-

FIG. 9.—Photomicrographs of thin sections showing range of packing and porosity. **A,** Packing 5 percent, porosity 9.28 percent detrital quartz in dolomite cement, plain light. **B,** Packing 40 percent, porosity 14 percent, detrital quartz in chert cement, crossed nicols. **C,** Packing 90 percent, porosity 10.17 percent, detrital quartz in dolomite cement, crossed nicols.

Table II. Zero Order Correlation Matrix: F-Well Data

	Y_1	X_2	X_3	X_4	X_5	X_6	X_7	X_8	X_9
Y_1	1.00000	.48859*	.00152	-.00347	-.31847*	-.35388*	.01519	-.10948	.59343*
X_2		1.00000	.08249	.05151	-.09145	-.11896	.23109	.00289	.64275*
X_3			1.00000	.98986*	.01193	.08215	.22852	.27015*	.04953
X_4				1.00000	.00469	.12005	.08980	.31004*	.02035
X_5					1.00000	.68146*	.05353	.10262	-.26760*
X_6						1.00000	-.22677	.21011	-.28856*
X_7							1.00000	-.11093	.19858
X_8								1.00000	-.13062
X_9									1.00000

*FOR N = 56, $R_{ij} \geq$ .264, SIGNIFICANT AT .05 LEVEL.

graphic variables that are strongly interrelated. The data matrix $(A_{i,j})_{56,9}$, $i = 56$, $j = 9$ (Griffiths, 1966, p. 655; Smith, 1966, p. 80) was transformed to its transpose $(A^1_{i,j})$ 9×56 by means of a "correl" program (Library Program 8A, L. J. Drew)[3]. The resultant correlation matrix (Smith, 1966, p. 124) summarizes the relations among pairs of variables, but its interpretation is still complex because it contains interdependencies and redundancy as well as experimental error. The main function of the operation is to standardize the data to reduce all means to zero and variances to unity (Griffiths, 1963, p. 651; 1966, p. 661).

The correlation matrix was fed into the "Principal Components Analysis" program (Library Program 6.0.091) and the characteristic equation for the matrix $(r_{i,j})_{56,56}$ in terms of its roots or eigenvalues was obtained (Smith, 1966, p. 126). The principal components analysis attempts to determine the minimum number of linearly independent vectors which may represent the original correlation matrix (Griffiths, 1966, p. 661). Nine petrographic variables were measured: porosity (percent), insoluble residue (percent), $\bar{X}_a$ quartz (phi units), $\bar{X}_b$ quartz (phi units), $_a$ quartz (phi units), $\hat{\sigma}\hat{\sigma}_b$ quartz (phi units), $\bar{X}_{b/a}$ quartz, $\hat{\sigma}_{b/a}$, and packing (percent).

Correlation matrix $(r_{i,j})$.—Based on 56 samples, the correlation coefficients (Table II) are significant at the 5 percent level if equal to or greater than 0.264 (Arkin and Colton,

[3] Referenced computer programs stored in College of Earth & Mineral Sciences computer library, Pennsylvania State University.

1962). There are several significant correlations in this matrix. The long (a) axis and short (b) axis of the quartz grains are highly correlative ($r = 0.990$); such a relation also was found for the Tyrone section data (Smith, 1966, p. 83) and, according to Griffiths (1963, p. 653) and others, is a feature that appears to be characteristic of all such matrices determined. This association is induced partly by the manner in which the axes are ordered ($b<a$ in mm or $b>a$ in phi units); the correlation provides an internal check of these data. The correlation observed between the standard deviations (a measure of sorting) for the a and b axes of the quartz grains is significant ($r = 0.681$). Significant correlations also exist between porosity, I. R., and packing; these relations are not surprising as it has been established (Figs. 7, 8) that the two independent properties, packing and I. R., are associated with porosity.

Further attempts to interpret the correlation matrix would be difficult because of the many and complex interdependencies among the measured variables. Such interdependencies among properties appear to be the rule rather than the exception (Griffiths, 1963, p. 647).

Component matrices and interpretations.— Subjection of the F-well data to components analysis yields a rotated-component matrix containing modified correlation coefficients (Table III) where the components are in columns and the measured properties along rows. The eigenvalues or characteristic roots indicate that six components cumulatively account for nearly 94 percent of the total variation in the system. The relations among the nine variables, therefore,

Table III. Rotated-Component Matrix: F-Well Data

COMPONENT VARIABLE	$\times 10^3$	1	2	3	4	5	6	COMMUNALITY
POROSITY	X_1	421	005	−213	−045	−053	868	991
INSOLUBLE RESIDUE	X_2	926	022	066	124	060	094	941
QUARTZ GRAIN SIZE (a)	X_3	037	986	024	129	096	−003	1.000
QUARTZ GRAIN SIZE (b)	X_4	018	991	030	−006	126	−001	999
SORTING (a)	X_5	−133	−035	932	161	032	−028	957
SORTING (b)	X_6	−049	096	867	−262	091	−211	941
SHAPE (b/a)	X_7	141	110	−035	969	−065	030	988
STANDARD DEVIATION (b/a)	X_8	−030	188	088	−065	973	026	998
PACKING	X_9	818	031	−192	075	−113	289	899
VARIANCE ACCOUNTED FOR		1.746	2.014	1.713	1.077	1.005	.8927	
VARIANCE ACCOUNTED FOR %		19.40	22.38	19.03	11.97	11.17	9.92	
CUMULATIVE % ACCOUNTED FOR		19.40	41.78	60.81	72.78	83.95	93.87	

can be represented in terms of six components, *i.e.*, the rank or dimension of the matrix is closer to six than nine. Generally, extraction of additional components is halted when approximately 90 percent of the total variation has been accounted for (Griffiths, 1966, p. 661); the remaining 10 percent is considered to be random variation or noise. The rotated-component matrix also is represented in a simplified manner in Table IV, where the significant (based on the original correlation matrix where $r = 0.264$, significant at $P_{.05}$) component loadings have been arranged in a new matrix.

In Table IV, component one which accounts for nearly 20 percent of the variation has its heaviest loading on I. R., followed in order by packing and porosity. Because the dependent variable, porosity, is loaded on the same component as the independent variables, I. R. and

Table IV. Rotated-Diagonal Matrix: F-Well Data

COMPONENT VARIABLE	$\times 10^3$	1	2	3	4	5	6
INSOLUBLE RESIDUE	X_2	926					289
PACKING	X_9	818					
QUARTZ GRAIN SIZE (b)	X_4		991				
QUARTZ GRAIN SIZE (a)	X_3		986				
SORTING (a)	X_5			932			
SORTING (b)	X_6			867			
SHAPE (b/a)	X_7				969		
STANDARD DEVIATION (b/a)	X_8					973	
POROSITY	X_1	421					868

packing, it can be concluded that the variation in porosity is associated closely with the variation in the two independent variables. Hence porosity is associated largely with the amount of I. R. and the degree of packing, or all three have common sources of variation.

Component six, where porosity has its highest loading, also includes a significant loading for I. R. (considerably lower than that of component one), which further extends the premise that I. R. and porosity are associated and also reflects the subtle relation between I. R. and packing. The building of a quartz-grain framework necessitates a minimum (50 percent) amount of quartz grains, but at this point packing becomes the principal variable. Component six, however, is independent of, and orthogonal to, component one, so that component six may reflect the fact that "flat space" (orthogonality) is inadequate to represent the relations, *i.e.*, the relations are curved. The relation between porosity and I. R. is important when I. R. > 50 percent, but unimportant when I. R. < 50 percent.

In summary, the dependent property, porosity, is associated closely with the independent properties, I. R. and packing. The other independent properties, quartz grain size, sorting, shape, and standard deviation of shape, are unrelated to each other, and also are unrelated to porosity, packing, and I. R. The factors controlling the variability in porosity, packing, and I. R. therefore are unlike those controlling size, shape, and sorting, or the latter properties respond differently to the same sedimentary processes. Because porosity and I. R. are loaded on component six, which accounts for the least amount of variation in the system, as well as component one, which accounts for nearly 20 percent, component six is considered to be a subsidiary loading of porosity.

The results of the principal components analysis support the bivariate correlations established before, *i.e.*, porosity varies primarily as a function of the amount of I. R. and the degree of packing in the samples. There is no evidence to suggest that porosity is influenced appreciably by grain size in these sedimentary rocks, although grain size, commonly has been shown to be one of the most important variables influencing porosity in other studies of this nature. Shape and sorting of the quartz grains in these samples also are unrelated to porosity.

Partial Correlation

Because of the close association of the three variables of porosity, packing, and I. R. and the relatively high correlation between any two of the variables, further analysis was made of the partial-correlation coefficients.

The sample partial-correlation coefficient estimates the correlation between Y and X_i after the influence of other independent variables has been removed (Crow *et al.*, 1960, p. 176). For a three-variable regression, the partial-correlation coefficients are calculated according to the formula:

$$r_{ij.k} = \frac{r_{ij} - r_{ik} \cdot r_{jk}}{(1 - r^2_{ik})(1 - r^2_{jk})}$$

where

i (1) = porosity,
j (2) = packing,
k (3) = insoluble residue, and
$r_{ij.k}$ = partial-correlation coefficient.

In this instance (Table II), the simple correlation coefficients (r) are:

$r_{12} = 0.593$,
$r_{13} = 0.489$,
$r_{23} = 0.642$,

and calculated partial-correlation coefficients (r) are:

$r_{12.3} = 0.418$ (variation I. R. removed),
$r_{13.2} = 0.173$ (variation in packing removed), and
$r_{23.1} = 0.502$ (variation in porosity removed).

There is a moderate correlation between the variables porosity and I. R. ($r_{13} = 0.489$)

which accounts for nearly 24 percent ($r^2 = 0.24$) of the total variation with the effect of packing included. The partial-correlation coefficient between these variables with the influence of packing removed is not significant ($r_{13.2} = 0.173$ where 0.264 is significant at $P_{0.05}$); the variation in I. R. accounts for only 3 percent ($r^2_{13.2} = 0.03$) and is not significant.

The correlation between the variables of porosity and packing, including the effect of I. R., is 0.593. After removal of the influence of I. R., $r = 0.418$, indicating that the variation in I. R. accounts for a very small part of the total variation in the system. The only way the variation in I. R. contributes to the correlation of packing and porosity is through its correlation with packing ($r_{23} = 0.642$). The variation in porosity, therefore, is associated primarily with the variation in packing. This indicates that the trend observed between porosity and I. R. (Fig. 6) is due primarily to the correlation between I. R. and packing.

Multiple Linear Regression

The observed values of the independent variables, packing and I. R., and the dependent variable, porosity, were submitted to a linear stepwise multiple-regression analysis in order to develop an empirical equation relating the independent variables to the dependent variable. The regression yields an equation of the general form:

$$Y = C + b_1X_1 + b_2X_2 + \ldots + b_kX_k$$

where

Y = dependent variable,
C = a constant,
$b_1, b_2, \ldots, b_k$ = coefficients, and
$X_1, X_2, \ldots, X_k$ = independent variables.

The regression of porosity on packing and I. R. yields the equation:

$$Y = 0.549 + 0.555X_1 + 0.076X_2$$

where

Y = porosity (percent),
X_1 = packing (percent), and
X_2 = insoluble residue (percent).

The amount of variability accounted for in the dependent variable, porosity, can be represented as the multiple coefficient of determination (R^2) in percent (Griffiths, 1963, p. 662). In this instance, "R^2" equals 40.26 percent, *i.e.*, about 40 percent of the variation in porosity is explained by the degree of packing and percent

I. R. if the relation is assumed to be linear. The first variable to come out of the analysis is packing, which accounts for 35.79 percent (R^2 = 0.3579) of the variation in porosity. The second variable, I. R., adds 4.47 percent to "R^2." The addition of a third independent variable, the mean size of the a axis of the quartz grains, which has not been shown to be associated closely with porosity in F-well samples, increases the amount of variation accounted for (R^2) by only 0.18 percent—a negligible amount in comparison to the contributions by packing and I. R., and not statistically significant. The regression analysis indicates that the degree of packing accounts for most of the variation in porosity.

Interpretation of F-Well Data

Porosity values of F-well samples (Fig. 6) show no apparent correlation with I. R. content below a value of 50 percent; a significant positive correlation with higher I. R. values is evident. It seems, therefore, that the quartz grains do not form a supporting framework unless they are present in excess of 50 percent. With the exception of one sample, the degree of packing is zero or near zero between zero and about 55 percent I. R. The Tyrone section samples also have zero percent packing as there are no quartz-quartz grain contacts. The sample with 50 percent packing is a heterogeneous mixture with layers of quartz grains surrounded by irregular patches of nearly quartz-free dolomite. The packing measures in this sample were found to be confined primarily to a quartz-grain layer, and this resulted in an estimate of the packing in the quartz-grain layer instead of an estimate of packing for the whole sample.

About six samples with between 50 and 90 percent insoluble residue yield higher values of porosity than are expected on the basis of the trend established by most of the samples (Fig. 6). Possible explanations have been advanced but, aside from error, which could have been introduced in several places, these higher-than-expected values suggest the presence of vugs which most likely were caused by solution. Thin sections of four of the samples show vugs, most of which appear unrelated to quartz-grain packing and/or the amount of I. R. The vugs range from 0.21 to about 2.0 mm; most do not exceed 0.8 mm (Smith, 1967). Most of the cement of another anomalous sample consists of chert and very fine-grained (<0.06 mm) quartz

with disseminated carbonate particles. Probably the major contribution to the porosity in this sample is from the many small intercrystalline voids in the chert and intergranular voids in the very fine-grained quartz. Another anomalous sample contains vugs up to 2 mm long and consists of silicified oölites chiefly cemented with a micromosaic of very fine-grained chert. Just as close packing of quartz grains serves to isolate voids, some of the oölites have void space between them. As only quartz-grain contacts were measured to estimate the degree of packing, the packing index for this sample is very low (5 percent).

Framework Concept

Of first importance to porosity is the character of the supporting framework of the original sediment. In the carbonate-quartz system, the original porosity of the sediment is reduced as compaction continues until the framework of the grains begins to support the overburden and thus preserve the remaining pores. In the case of a pure limestone or dolomite which is not composed of shells of organisms, pellets, oölites, or intraclasts, compaction reduces the pore space considerably more than it does in a carbonate rock containing those elements or quartz grains which will resist compaction and thereby be causative factors in preserving pore space. Continued addition of clasts or grains to the nonclastic carbonate phase eventually will result in a sufficient number of clast or quartz-grain contacts to form a supporting framework. The fragment or grain framework significantly reduces or prevents compaction and generally preserves larger pores in the sediment. In a sediment consisting of poorly sorted quartz grains, the smaller grains tend to fill the spaces between the larger grains to such an extent that practically all the larger pores are occupied. The porosity would be less than that of a sediment in which all the quartz grains participate in the framework, but there may also be a significant volume of intergranular pore space between the smaller quartz grains.

The probability of having quartz-to-quartz grain contacts and a concomitant quartz-grain-supported framework increases with an increase in quartz content. Carbonate may or may not enter the pores thus preserved; therefore, some of the pores become isolated (surrounded by quartz grains) at least temporarily (Fig. 9). Later solution by ground water may remove these carbonate cements from the framework and increase the porosity. Therefore, in this carbonate-quartz system, porosity depends on (1) the percent of original void space which is a direct function of packing (in this case), (2) the amount of space filled with cements, and (3) the amount of cement subsequently removed.

Lucia (1962, p. 853) found that visible porosity in crinoidal sedimentary rocks is confined to rocks in which the crinoid fossil fragments form a supporting framework which is exactly analogous to the quartz-grain framework in the carbonate-quartz system. Lucia also noted a decrease in porosity as the carbonate rock increased above 20 percent. Similarly, in the carbonate-quartz system, porosity is reduced as the amount of carbonate increases. Lucia suggested that, with increasing carbonate in the crinoidal sediment, the support of the overburden is transferred from the crinoid fragments to the carbonate rock. The writer suggests that the support of the overburden is transferred partly from the quartz grains to the carbonate grains at a carbonate percentage greater than 20–30. Beyond 50 percent carbonate content, the rock is considerably less porous and permeable and less susceptible to leaching.

Lucia (1962, p. 861, 864) also noted a relation between porosity and the volume of crinoid fragments in a dolomitized crinoid limestone from the Andrews South Devonian field, Andrews County, Texas. His diagram shows a rather abrupt decrease in porosity between 60 and 45 percent crinoid fragments, at which point the slope of the curve begins to flatten. On the basis of several assumptions and calculations, Lucia stated that the minimum final porosity is developed in a rock which originally contained 50 percent crinoid fragments, and in which both crinoid-fragment and dolomite-crystal frameworks would be formed at the same time. An increase in the volume of crinoid fragments above 50 percent in the original sediment results in a higher porosity because a crinoid-supported framework develops before a dolomite-crystal framework forms.

On the basis of the writer's data, there is a similar relation in the carbonate-quartz system. Lucia (1962, p. 865) concluded that the leaching process was less effective where carbonate rock supports the load than where the crinoid fragments support it, and that the sedimentary rocks containing the most crinoid fragments have the highest porosity. This is in agreement with the writer's findings for the carbonate-

quartz system and would support the idea that the dolomitization occurred before compaction.

DESCRIPTIVE DATA AND INTERPRETATION OF TYRONE SECTION

The Tyrone section samples have no rock fragments and are predominantly dolomite (grains and recrystallized mud) with varied amounts (5–40 percent) of silt- and sand-size quartz. In the 10 beds originally sampled, the porosity was found to range from zero to about 5 percent. Few voids are seen in thin section under the microscope and they generally are not apparent in photomicrographs. In addition to the variables measured in the F-well samples, the size and shape of the dolomite grains were measured in the Tyrone section samples. A slight (not statistically significant) relation was found between porosity and the size of the dolomite grains, and also between porosity and the sorting ($\hat{\sigma}$) of the quartz grains (Smith, 1966, p. 95). Inasmuch as significant bivariate correlations were not observed, the results and interpretations of the principal-components analysis are discussed only briefly. Porosity was found to be associated with the average dolomite grain size on one component and with quartz sorting where it has its highest numerical loading on another component.

Generally, an increase in porosity is related to a decrease in the size of dolomite grains and to an increase in the sorting of quartz grains.

VUGULAR POROSITY AND PERMEABILITY STUDIES

Permeability was determined for several samples (Smith, 1966, p. 144; 1967, p. 21) and the resulting values were compared with those obtained by Core Laboratories, Inc., for the same samples. Core Laboratories, Inc., also determined the porosity of a few samples which had been measured by the writer.

Generally, the porosity and permeability values obtained by the two sources are in close agreement (Smith, 1966, p. 150; 1967, p. 21). Vugular dolomite samples are not much more porous than their nonvugular equivalents, and the petrographic properties that influence initial or primary porosity and permeability also influence weathering and thus the sites of secondary porosity and permeability (Smith, 1966, p. 156). According to Lattman and Parizek (1964, p. 87), diamond-core test holes that penetrated the Mines Dolomite Member and

the upper sandy member of the Gatesburg Formation showed that solution zones, open and
debris filled, generally concentrate along sandy
dolomite beds and dolomitic sandstone. A detailed study of these cavities might show their
distribution to be limited to beds containing a
considerable amount of sand.

Conclusions

From the analyses of the data obtained from
a group of rocks comprising the carbonate-
quartz system, represented by the Late Cambrian Gatesburg Formation, the following conclusions can be drawn.

1. The intergranular porosity and permeability of sandy dolomite are low (porosity does
not exceed 5.5 percent and permeability is essentially zero). In comparison, the dolomitic
sandstone, dolomitic quartzite, and orthoquartzite have a maximum of 19 percent porosity, and permeability values are several orders
of magnitude higher (the range is from 0.01 to
1,361 md) than those of the sandy dolomite.

2. The nine samples selected from the Tyrone section to cover the range of porosity
values observed in the sandy dolomite indicate
that porosity is most strongly associated with,
or influenced by, the size of the dolomite
grains and the sorting of the quartz grains, although no statistically significant correlations
were observed. Although the size of dolomite
grains influences the porosity, it also may be
said that the factors influencing porosity also
influence the size of the dolomite grains in the
sandy dolomite.

3. With the exception of the vuggy porosity
specifically mentioned, the porosity measured is
intergranular and predominantly primary in the
sandy dolomite, dolomitic sandstone and
quartzite, and the orthoquartzite of the Gatesburg Formation.

4. The comparatively abrupt increase of porosity in the carbonate-quartz system beyond
about 50 percent quartz (I. R.), and the relatively higher porosity values observed for the
dolomitic sandstone, dolomitic quartzite, and
orthoquartzite, compared with the values for
sandy dolomite, are attributed to the shift from
a dolomite-grain-supported framework with
primary submicroscopic pores to a quartz-
grain-supported framework with larger pores.
The quartz-grain-supported framework affords
increasingly more support where the degree of
packing is higher.

5. The degree of packing and the amount of

I. R. are the two petrographic properties most
strongly associated with porosity in the carbonate-quartz system beyond about 50 percent
quartz. The porosity increase beyond 50–60
percent quartz is primarily a function of the
degree of packing, partly a function of the
amount of quartz present, and hence of the
presence or absence of cement, which may be
of primary or secondary origin. An increase in
either the degree of packing or the amount of
quartz results in an increase in porosity. The
degree of packing, however, accounts for a
greater part of the variability in porosity (36
percent) than does the amount of quartz (I.
R.) as shown by multiple-regression and partial-correlation analyses. Packing is, therefore,
the best single predictor of porosity above 50
percent I. R. in the carbonate-quartz system, at
least in the Gatesburg Formation.

6. Vugs ranging from pinhead size to 1 in.
along the long axes (a few are larger), as observed in well-core samples, are confined almost exclusively to the dolomite and sandy dolomite of the Gatesburg Formation. These vugs
which persist throughout any one vugular sample increase only slightly (< 2 percent) the
total porosity of the rock. It is concluded that
most of the vugs are not now interconnected,
but were formed by an earlier solution process.
Such a premise implies that the passageways
between vugs have been sealed by mineral matter precipitated from solution, by the I. R. derived from the space now occupied by vugs, by
a recrystallization process, or by combinations
of the three processes.

7. The samples containing chert and/or microcrystalline quartz exclusively, or chert and
carbonate, as the cementing material consistently yield relatively high porosity values. In
addition to the influence of the degree of packing of the quartz grains, submicroscopic pores
in the chert and microcrystalline quartz contribute to the total porosity.

8. If flow along fractures, joints, and bedding planes is disregarded, the relatively higher
permeability and porosity values observed for
the quartzite and dolomitic sandstone of the
Gatesburg Formation indicate that the major
flow path for fluids is along the dolomitic sandstone and quartzite members and to a minor
extent along the sandy dolomite members. It is
suggested that solution and removal of the carbonate fraction of a sandy dolomite or a carbonate sandstone by the movement of fluids results in a reduction in volume of the bed and
the creation of cavities.

9. The porosity values determined by the writer are characteristic of the Gatesburg Formation for lithologic types similar to those sampled in this study and represent the best present estimates of porosity to depths as great as 300 ft.

SELECTED REFERENCES

Arkin, H., and R. Colton, 1962, Tables for statisticians: College Outline Series, New York, Barnes & Noble, Inc., 152 p.

Butts, C., 1918, Geologic section of Blair and Huntingdon Counties central Pennsylvania: Am. Jour. Science, 4th ser., v. 46, p. 523–537.

———— F. M. Swartz, and B. Willard, 1939, Geology and mineral resources of the Tyrone quadrangle, in Atlas of Pennsylvania, no. 96: Pennsylvania Geol. Survey, 4th ser., 118 p.

Bybee, H. P., 1938, Possible nature of limestone reservoirs in the Permian basin: Am. Assoc. Petroleum Geologists Bull., v. 22, p. 915–918.

Caruccio, F. T., 1963, The hydro-geology of the sewage disposal experiment area: Unpub. M.S. thesis, Dept. Geology and Geophysics, Pennsylvania State Univ., 132 p.

Cloud, W. F., 1941, Effects of sand grain size distribution upon porosity and permeability: Oil Weekly, v. 103, October, p. 25–32.

Crow, E. L., F. A. Davis, and M. W. Maxfield, 1960, Statistics manual: New York, Dover Pubs., 288 p.

Ellis, A. J., and C. H. Lee, 1919, Geology and ground waters of western part of San Diego County, California: U. S. Geological Survey Water-Supply Paper 446, 313 p.

Emery, J. R., 1954, The application of a discriminant function to a problem in petroleum petrology: Unpub. M.S. thesis, Dept. Geochemistry and Mineralogy, Pennsylvania State Univ., 120 p.

———— and J. C. Griffiths, 1953, Reconnaissance investigation into relationships between behavior and petrographic properties of some Mississippian sediments: Pennsylvania State University Mineral Industries Expt. Sta. Bull. 62, p. 67–73.

Fettke, C. R., 1927, Core studies of the Second Sand of the Venango group from Oil City, Pennsylvania, in Petroleum Development and Technology in 1926: Am. Inst. Min. Metall. Engineers, p. 219–230.

———— 1934, Physical characteristics of Bradford Sand, Bradford field, Pennsylvania, and relation to production of oil: Am. Assoc. Petroleum Geologists Bull., v. 18, p. 191–211.

Folk, R. L., 1949, Petrography and reservoir potentialities of the Nittany Dolomite: Producers Monthly, v. 13, p. 35–38.

Fraser, H. J., 1935, Experimental study of porosity and permeability of clastic sediments: Jour. Geology, v. 43, p. 910–1010.

Graton, L. C., and H. J. Fraser, 1935, Systematic packing of spheres with particular relation to porosity and permeability: Jour. Geology, v. 43, p. 785–909.

Griffiths, J. C., 1958, Petrography and porosity of the Cow Run Sand, St. Marys, West Virginia: Jour. Sed. Petrology, v. 28, no. 1, p. 15–30.

———— 1960, Relationships between reservoir petrography and reservoir behavior of some Appalachian oil sands: Tulsa Geol. Soc. Digest, v. 28, p. 43–58.

———— 1961, Measurement of the properties of sediments: Jour. Geology, v. 69, no. 5, p. 487–497.

———— 1963, Statistical approach to the study of potential oil reservoir sandstones, in Computers in the mineral industries: 3d Ann. Stanford-Arizona Computer Conf. Proc., June, pt. 2, v. 9, no. 2, p. 637–668.

———— 1966, A genetic model for the interpretative petrology of detrital sediments: Jour. Geology, v. 74, no. 5, p. 655–672.

———— 1967, Scientific method in the analysis of sediments: New York, McGraw-Hill, 508 p.

———— and M. A. Rosenfeld, 1950, Progress in measurement of grain orientation in Bradford Sand: Pennsylvania State Univ. Mineral Industries Expt. Sta. Bull. 56, p. 202–236.

Howard, W. V., 1928, A classification of limestone reservoirs: Am. Assoc. Petroleum Geologists Bull., v. 12, p. 1153–1161.

Imbrie, J., and E. G. Purdy, 1962, Classification of modern Bahamian carbonate sediments, in Classification of carbonate rocks: Am. Assoc. Petroleum Geologists Mem. 1, p. 253–272.

Imbt, W. C., 1950, Carbonate porosity and permeability, in Applied sedimentation: New York, p. 616–632, John Wiley & Sons, 707 p.

Krynine, P. D., 1946, From the Cambrian to the Silurian near State College and Tyrone: Pennsylvania State Geologists 12th Ann. Fld. Conf. Guidebook (mimeographed), 29 p.

———— 1948a, Petrologic aspects of prospecting for deep oil horizons in Pennsylvania: Producers Monthly, v. 12, no. 3, p. 28–33.

———— 1948b, The megascopic study and field classification of sedimentary rocks: Jour. Geology, v. 56, p. 130–165.

Landon, R. A., 1963, The geology of the Gatesburg Formation in the Bellefonte quadrangle and its general relationship to the occurrence and movement of ground water: Unpub. M.S. thesis, Dept. Geology and Geophysics, Pennsylvania State Univ., 88 p.

Lattman, L. H., and R. R. Parizek, 1964, Relationship between fracture traces and the occurrence of ground water in carbonate rocks: Jour. Hydrology, v. 2, p. 73–91.

Lucia, F. J., 1962, Diagenesis of a crinoidal sediment: Jour. Sed. Petrology, v. 32, no. 4, p. 848–865.

Murray, A. N., 1930, Limestone oil reservoirs of the northeastern United States and of Ontario, Canada: Econ. Geology, v. 25, p. 452–469.

Ondrick, C. W., 1965, Statistical comparison of the Keener and Big Injun Sands, Pleasants County, West Virginia: Unpub. M.S. thesis, Dept. Geochemistry and Mineralogy, Pennsylvania State Univ., 185 p.

Pachman, J. M., 1961, Interrelations among petrographic, textural, and oil reservoir properties in the Chipmunk Sandstone: Unpub. Ph.D. thesis, Dept. Geochemistry and Mineralogy, Pennsylvania State Univ., 95 p.

Parsons, L. M., 1922, Dolomitization in the Carboniferous limestone of the Midlands: Geol. Mag., v. 59, p. 51–63.

Pelto, C. R., 1942, Petrology of the Gatesburg Formation of central Pennsylvania: Unpub. M.S. thesis, Dept. Geochemistry and Mineralogy, Pennsylvania State Univ., 60 p.

Pettijohn, F. J., 1957, Sedimentary rocks, 2d ed.: New York, Harper and Brothers, 718 p.

Pye, W. D., 1944, Petrology of Bethel Sandstone of

south-central Illinois: Am. Assoc. Petroleum Geologists Bull., v. 28, p. 63–122.

Rosenfeld, M. A., 1950, Porosity, a survey of the problem, pt. 1; Some statistical techniques applied to porosity data, pt. 2: Unpub. M.S. thesis, Dept. Geochemistry and Mineralogy, Pennsylvania State Univ., 149 p.

Scheidegger, A. E., 1957, The physics of flow through porous media: New York, Macmillan, 236 p.

Slichter, G. S., 1899, Theoretical investigation of the motion of ground waters: U. S. Geological Survey 19th Ann. Rept., pt. 2, p. 295–384.

Smith, R. E., 1966, Petrographic properties influencing porosity and permeability in the carbonate-quartz system as represented by the Gatesburg Formation: Unpub. Ph.D. thesis, Dept. Geology and Geophysics, Pennsylvania State Univ., 196 p.

——— 1967, Petrographic properties influencing the reservoir potential of the Gatesburg Formation based on studies near State College and Tyrone, Pennsylvania: Producers Monthly, June, p. 18–23.

Thurstone, L. L., 1947, Multiple factor analysis: Chicago, Illinois, Univ. Chicago Press, 535 p.

Tolman, C. F., 1937, Ground water: New York, McGraw-Hill, 593 p.

Trask, P. D., 1931, Compaction of sediments: Am. Assoc. Petroleum Geologists Bull., v. 15, p. 271–276.

Wilson, J. L., 1952, Upper Cambrian stratigraphy in the central Appalachians: Geol. Soc. America Bull., v. 63, no. 3, p. 275–322.

Winchell, A. N., 1924, Petrographic studies of limestone alterations at Bingham: American Inst. Min. Metall. Engineers Trans., v. 70, p. 884–903.

Reprinted from:
BULLETIN OF THE AMERICAN ASSOCIATION OF PETROLEUM GEOLOGISTS
VOL. 53, NO. 3 (MARCH, 1969) PP. 503-512, 3 FIGS.

Evaporite-Solution Brecciation and Devonian Carbonate Reservoir Porosity in Western Canada[1]

F. W. BEALES[2] and A. E. OLDERSHAW[2]

Toronto, Ontario

Abstract The presence of "primary porosity" in ancient reef or bank sequences is generally assumed. Evaporite solution porosity in exposed Devonian reef-bank complexes of western Canada, however, is important. Detailed investigations are likely to show that such solution porosity is more general in the laterally equivalent subsurface petroleum reservoirs than the literature suggests. Much of the so-called primary porosity in reef reservoirs may be evaporite solution porosity.

INTRODUCTION

Reservoir porosity is normally the product of a complex series of genetic and diagenetic events. Reconstruction of these events is commonly of purely academic interest but may be of economic significance where the events are clearly decipherable and can be related to exploration. Several years of work, mainly on surface exposures of Devonian reef/bank complexes in western Canada prompt the suggestion that breccia-moldic and breccia-interstitial evaporite solution porosity are of greater importance than has been recognized. The evidence commonly is indistinct because of modification of the original fabrics by later diagenetic changes.

Present-day reefs and recently emergent reefs have very high porosity. In many examples, interskeletal, intraskeletal and intergranular voids may exceed 50 percent of the total rock, by volume. In ancient reef limestone, *evidence* for the persistence of much of this primary porosity is commonly absent; even the intraskeletal voids generally are totally occluded by carbonate cement. Evaporitic conditions may accompany the evolution of reef-bank environments and the resulting evaporites both preserve and enhance the porosity potential of the carbonate rocks. Indications of an evaporitic association commonly are present long after most of the evaporites have been removed by solution.

[1] Manuscript received, January 8, 1968; accepted, September 5, 1968.

[2] Department of Geology, University of Toronto. Financial assistance from the National Research Council of Canada is gratefully acknowledged.

Environmental Association of Evaporites with Reef-Bank Carbonate Complexes

Reefs and limestone banks have an ecologically controlled tendency to grow to sea level. In many reefs this is caused by the growth of the framework organisms at rates which greatly exceed reasonable rates of tectonic subsidence. For example, coral reef growth in southern Florida has been estimated to be of the order of 1.5–3.0 ft/100 years (Hoffmeister and Multer, 1964); some estimates indicate that the growth rates of individual reef-building corals may even be faster (Goreau, 1961; Vaughan, 1915). On banks, potential production of calcium carbonate also greatly exceeds the likely rate of subsidence, despite the large amounts of material that presumably are washed off during storms. There is doubt as to the relative roles of organic and inorganic precipitation in limestone bank building, but it generally is agreed that there is no lack of material to maintain the bank near sea level. In this situation, minor fluctuations in sea level and the buildup of supratidal shoals by storm waves commonly must have caused the formation of restricted lagoons and the development of ephemeral evaporitic conditions.

Studies of Holocene marine-margin environments have done much to elucidate possible genetic models for the formation of ancient evaporites. In particular, the sabkhas of the Persian Gulf, described by Illing *et al.* (1965) and Kinsman (1966), appear to resemble the environments in which some of the Upper Devonian sedimentary rocks of Alberta were formed (Stanton, 1966). Gray (1967) drew attention to comparable environments in the Pennsylvanian Cache field reservoir in southwestern Colorado. Kerr and Thompson (1963), however, compared the nodular and bedded anhydrite in Permian shelf sedimentary rocks of Texas with similar features in the modern deposits of Laguna Madre. In each example, similar thin evaporite beds, nodular layers, and rosettes and bladed crystals in the modern sediments can be matched, or are pseudomorphed, in the ancient rocks. The high proportion of impurities in many ancient evaporites is consistent with such an environment and accounts for the source of the large volume of fine-grained material present in some ancient breccias.

It seems probable that the development of short-lived, interreefal and intrareefal/intraflat evaporites, within an environment of migrating, extremely shallow, supratidal or shoal-restricted lagoons and saline flats, provides a satisfactory genetic model for the origin of widespread bedded breccia. Thus, barrier-island bars, oölite shoals, emergent skeletal shoals, eolianites, extensive prograding supratidal flats and, in places, major "back-reef" evaporite basins can be fitted to different scales of a similar model. The sabkha model is mentioned here because it is particularly useful in a review of ancient brecciated sequences, particularly the Devonian examples discussed below. Specifically, the migration of facies belts in relation to a migrating sabkha surface implies that widespread, bedded evaporitic sequences can develop, and that they will have a much greater areal continuity than the local environment possessed at the time of its formation.

The crystallinity of the evaporites is usually the coarsest element of the local sediment texture, and solution of the evaporites commonly results in the most important porosity. Until solution takes place, the evaporites inhibit pressure solution effects that are normally detrimental to carbonate rock porosity following burial. Thus, evaporites in a carbonate rock sequence commonly enhance its reservoir potential. For this reason familiarity with the indicators that may be useful in the recognition of evaporite solution breccias and associated sedimentary features is desirable.

CRITERIA FOR THE RECOGNITION OF EVAPORITE SOLUTION BRECCIAS

The following criteria are not individually diagnostic of solution breccias, but taken collectively they can support a definitive conclusion.

Development of box-work texture.—Breccia-moldic porosity (Fig. 1A, B) is common in some dolostones and clearly originates by solution processes. In outcrop, breccia-moldic porosity normally is associated with complete solution of the breccia fragments, and the matrix rock is a sucrosic dolomite; the resultant voids may or may not be lined with white sparry dolomite. The mold-generating clasts could have been limestone, but anhydrite or gypsum is favored because of the ubiquitous dolomite association and because of their early lithification. The presence of a dolomite matrix is also consistent with the high salinity environment required for the precipitation of gypsum or anhydrite.

The breccia molds generally range in size from a few millimeters to a few centimeters, consonant with derivation from an original thin-bedded sequence. In some beds, the disordered and complex nature of the porosity suggests that repeated solution and precipitation occurred. Such repetition could occur very readily in mixed carbonate/evaporite sequences developed in a near-marine, supratidal environment, particularly if intermittent precipitation and solution of the more soluble halite were involved in the process.

Figure 2 (A, B) illustrates an unusual example of anhydrite hydration expansion and consequent brecciation, that affected an anhydrite surface left exposed for about 20 years at Dingwall, Nova Scotia, after gypsum had been

>>>→

FIG. 1.—**A.** Bedding-plane section of 4-in. core of fine-grained saccharoidal dolomite from Crossfield Member of Upper Devonian Wabamum Formation of central Alberta. Relic molds of rectangular anhydrite crystals mark surface. Insoluble residue contained small anhydrite crystals. **B.** Two-in. core of Middle Devonian Presqu'ile Dolostone from Pine Point. Numerous crystal molds probably after gypsum, with bituminous staining, in coarse-grained saccharoidal dolomite. **C.** Bedding plane section of 2-in. core of Middle Devonian Presqu'ile Dolostone from Pine Point. Angular breccia-moldic porosity probably after anhydrite clasts, in coarsely crystalline dolomite matrix. **D.** Breccia-moldic porosity probably after anhydrite in hand specimen of Presqu'ile Dolostone from Pine Point. **E.** Dolostone breccia clasts with interstitial porosity infilled with galena and sphalerite, from ore zone in Presqu'ile Dolostone at Pine Point. **F.** Minor erosion surface in 4-in. core from Middle Devonian Swan Hills "reef" member from Swan Hills in northwestern Alberta. Massive stromatoporoid, lying on its side, was truncated, weathered to varied depth (brought out by bituminous impregnation), and overlain by additional stromatoporoidal rubble.

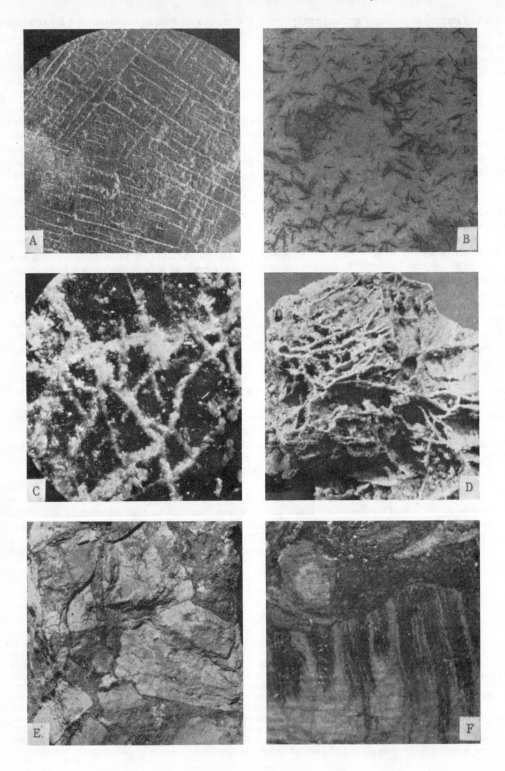

scalped from the surface during mining operations. Anhydrite or gypsum clasts such as those illustrated, if interbedded with, or later enveloped by, carbonate sand and mud, might on solution give rise to breccia-moldic porosity of the type shown in Figures 1–3.

Development of breccia-interstitial porosity texture.—Characteristic textures may develop where breccia fragments form a grain-supported fabric, with the clasts sufficiently lithified to retain their angular shape (Figs. 1E, 2C). Breccia of this type, which consists predominantly of dolostone clasts with interstitial porosity, contrasts with the dolostone with breccia-moldic porosity in that the clasts are much more varied in size and may be polygenetic. All the lithoclasts, however, usually can be identified within the superjacent stratigraphic sequence. Blebs and lenses of finely fragmented or residual shaly material may occlude parts of the porosity. Such breccias, even where interstratified with unbrecciated rocks, are not in themselves diagnostic of evaporitic conditions. If the clasts are largely monogenetic and predominantly dolomitic, or if they are polygenetic and appear to be derived from thin- to medium-bedded strata that match the superjacent nonbrecciated sequence, the probability of an evaporite-solution origin increases. Breccias with a more heterogeneous composition and grain size are more likely to be the products of cavern collapse associated with extensive carbonate rock solution.

Artificial solution breccias have been produced in the laboratory and many of their features are similar to those observed in known or suspected breccias from western Canada. Specifically, the breccia fragments released by solution were angular; they were relatively uniform, though some breccias showed vertical size grading. The volume of fine-grained material released was generally considerable and the experiment consisted essentially of dolomite, reddish-brown lutite, detrital quartz silt, anhydrite laths, and gypsum crystal bundles. Floored cavities and geopetal structures were developed within interstitial cavities in all of the artificial breccias. Although it is possible that in ancient rocks some fines were produced during postdepositional flowage of salt, the persistence of crude bedding in many cores suggests that such crushing was not great. Fines should probably be ascribed, at least in such cores, to the trapping of original fine sediment and possibly to disaggregation resulting from intrasediment crystal formation.

Uniform base and irregular top.—Regional layers of solution breccia are likely to be areally diachronous, having been formed by local accumulation and solution of soluble constituents. Because of irregularities of local slump and breccia packing, the surface of a breccia layer may be markedly irregular in comparison with its base. Where multiple brecciated layers are present, this relation may be less obvious because of disruption and draping of the less brecciated layers. In such cases, good exposure of the strata may show arching and support in one area relative to another, and the collapsed nature of the whole is readily demonstrable. Stanton (1966) has suggested that local adjustments to solution will include evaporite flowage that generally cushions the collapse process.

Anhydrite replacement pseudomorphs.—Small to microscopic rectangular reentrants

----

←◀◀◀

Fig. 2.—**A.** Floor of gypsum quarry at Dingwall, Nova Scotia, abandoned 20 years ago; pressure blister on anhydrite surface at pit floor marked by numerous pressure ridges and blisters. Pressure-generated cracks permit percolation of rain water; interior surfaces of blisters were moist although pit floor was dry at time of observation. (Scale: 18-in. hammer.) **B.** Detail of collapse and brecciation of another expansion blister at Dingwall. Broken surfaces of pale blue-gray anhydrite showed extensive alteration to milky gypsum. Surface brecciation and spalling develop as hydration proceeds. (Scale 18-in. hammer.) **C.** Breccia-interstitial porosity in pale, saccharoidal dolostone. Upper Fairholme Formation, Whiteman's Pass, Alberta. Specimen illustrates commonest form of breccia layer in Fairholme dolostone. These breccias commonly are resealed and difficult to detect unless suitably weathered surfaces are available. Part of even-bedded layer between unbrecciated layers of closely similar dolostones. Clasts are irregular, angular, and unsorted; no channeling or current-bedding apparent. Where breccia is recemented, cement is dolomite, whereas tectonic breccias in area are commonly calcite-veined and cemented. True scale. **D.** Breccia-moldic porosity in pale, finely crystalline, saccharoidal dolostone. Upper Fairholme Formation, Whiteman's Pass. Talus boulder cracked open along bedding plane. Breccia molds are bedded, platy, angular, and "unsorted." Such moldic porosity is less common than interstitial porosity in Fairholme Formation but, in contrast, is the common variety in Presqu'ile Dolostone. (See Fig. 3 A-C.) True scale.

(Murray, 1960), tabular or rosette crystal molds, and calcite pseudomorphs after anhydrite may be common in strata closely associated with a suspected breccia sequence (Fig. 1). In small-diameter diamond-drill cores these molds and calcite casts may be more conspicuous than a breccia solution fabric because large angular voids or honeycomb rocks promote grinding and loss of core during drilling.

Laterally equivalent evaporites in subsurface. —Evaporites rarely persist in surface outcrops, but both gypsum and anhydrite commonly are observed as vug and vein fillings in cores recovered from deep drilling. Even in well-leached surface material, insoluble residues from brecciated dolostones may contain abundant small gypsum crystal bundles.

Association with very shallow water sequences.—Desiccation cracks, oölites, stromatolites, reef rocks, overlying redbeds, *etc.* may be considered as evidence for the existence of shallow-water or supratidal conditions and, as such, would logically be associated with evaporite solution breccias.

Demonstrable sag in superjacent strata.— Evaporite solution collapse, either early in association with pronounced sediment-thickness changes, or late in association with draping of strata over leached areas, has been documented in numerous reports (*e.g.,* de Mille *et al.,* 1964).

Penecontemporaneous dolomitization.— Evaporite solution collapse breccias commonly consist of dolomitic clasts with dolomite cement. Limestone clasts are present locally. In solution breccias, the matrix is normally saccharoidal dolomite, whereas sparry calcite is common in tectonic breccias. The complexity of some breccias, or of breccia-moldic porosity, is suggestive of multiple episodes. The complexity fits an environmental model of shallow supratidal to lagoonal conditions in which repeated desiccation and intra- and suprasediment precipitation of evaporites could alternate with solution upon subsequent flooding. Removal of calcium ions by sulfate precipitation during concentration of the brines would promote dolomitization (Deffeyes *et al.,* 1965; Kinsman, 1966), and the persistence of limestone in such an environment would be unlikely.

It is rarely possible, in any single example, to recognize all of the criteria for evaporite solution brecciation. An aid to field identification, however, can be developed from a consideration of the composite environmental and diagenetic model. If all available details of lithology and stratigraphy are considered it is commonly difficult to formulate an alternative genesis that satisfactorily fits the data.

The criteria listed were found to be particularly useful during an attempt to determine the relative importance of evaporite solution in the development of porosity in well-exposed surface equivalents of petroleum reservoir rocks in western Alberta and the Northwest Territories of Canada.

SOLUTION BRECCIAS OF THE FAIRHOLME FORMATION OF WESTERN ALBERTA

The Upper Devonian Fairholme Formation is a major segment of the strata exposed in a series of overthrust sheets that form the steeply dipping to gently undulating sequence in the Rocky Mountains of western Alberta. The Fairholme strata have been interpreted as local reef-controlled platform deposits and interspersed basin sediments, commonly referred to as the "reef" and "offreef" sequences.

The organic framework of the Fairholme reefs consists largely of a rubble of "cabbage" and platy stromatoporoids, associated with abundant *Stachyodes* in the frontal zone and giving place to *Amphipora* biostromes, with scattered to very sparse bulbous stromatoporoids, in the backreef areas. The entire reef-controlled complex normally is altered to a saccharoidal dolomite fabric, in which most of the original detail is obliterated. The coarser skeletal debris generally can be distinguished as lighter colored relic shapes in a dark, brownish-gray, bituminous matrix.

Some layers of vuggy solution porosity can be recognized where skeletal debris escaped dolomitization and subsequently was dissolved. Such layers are common in the darker, lower Fairholme strata, but in the upper, lighter brown to pale-buff sequence, the origin of the bedded vuggy porosity is less obvious.

The Devonian stromatoporoid reefs and associated platform carbonate sediments almost certainly built up near sea level and were prone to dolomitization. Recent literature concerning the process of penecontemporaneous dolomitization has stressed the importance of hypersaline environments in which evaporite precipitation is prevalent, however, relatively little reference can be found to evaporites and their relic trace, solution breccias, in the literature concerning the ancient analogues of these modern sediments. Reexamination of numerous Fairholme areas has led the writers to the conclusion that the evidence, though not obvious, is present (Fig. 2 C, D). Generally pale, vaguely brecciated, and subsequently resealed layers are common in the upper Fairholme rocks and much of the vuggy porosity is associated with such layers. The breccia clasts are normally monogenetic and rather uniform, ranging from grit size to small pebble size. Because of their uniform lithology, recrystallization and resealing, the individual clasts are generally difficult to recognize; it is necessary to check along the strike to find suitably weathered surfaces or better preserved lenses. Almost invariably the most diagnostic samples come from talus material, much of which can be related confidently to source strata. Insoluble residues of such strata commonly contain microsheafs of gypsum crystals; subsurface cores of very similar lithology, from the same stratigraphic zone contain associated anhydrite (e.g., Stanton, 1966).

Erosion surfaces, characterized by truncated skeletal debris and scour channels, are common within the Fairholme strata. Many bedding planes are stylolitic and might be considered to be entirely the result of interstratal solution but for the fact that truncation of recognizable material is more common at the top of a stylolite-bounded layer than at the base. Rarely, the presence of a weathered layer is suggested by surface alteration of skeletal material (Fig. 1 F). These features and the lenticular and patchy nature of the brecciation, apparent as many porous layers are traced along the strike, are consistent with a very shallow lagoonal to supratidal environment of deposition.

In conclusion, apparent evaporite-solution breccias are common in the upper Fairholme section in the mountains, and the unit is very similar to the most prolific producing zone in the adjacent oil fields on the east.

SOLUTION BRECCIAS OF THE PRESQU'ILE DOLOSTONE OF THE PINE POINT AREA

North of the Alberta-Northwest Territories boundary, on the south shore of Great Slave Lake, new exposures have been excavated in opening a group of large lead-zinc ore bodies by Pine Point Mines Ltd. The ore host rock comprises the Presqu'ile and Pine Point Dolostones of Middle Devonian age (Beales and Jackson, 1966; Jackson and Beales, 1967; Norris, 1965). These strata, which are well exposed, are laterally equivalent to very similar petroleum reservoir rocks in the Rainbow-Zama Lake areas on the west. The dolostones are well bedded, medium to coarsely crystal-

line, and contain abundant traces of extensively replaced skeletal debris. Closely spaced drilling by Pine Point Mines Ltd. has shown that the area was probably the site of an axis of reduced subsidence in Middle Devonian time. Along this axis a reef-controlled carbonate shoal developed and at times built up into a supratidal barrier. The following discussion pertains almost entirely to the Presqu'ile Dolostone part of the carbonate complex, because that unit is well exposed in the walls of the present pits at Pine Point.

The well-bedded nature of the Presqu'ile unit is emphasized by the presence of layers with coarse, vuggy porosity which contain good examples of breccia-moldic fabrics; minor vuggy porosity is of undoubted skeletal origin and probably resulted from the leaching of spaghetti-like *Amphipora* colonies. Perhaps because of the reef association and the fact that the unit can be traced into prolific producing reefs on the west, the porosity generally has been regarded as being derived mainly from the selective solution of skeletal material. At Pine Point, this is definitely not the case. The details of the original solution breccias commonly have been masked by subsequent precipitation of white sparry dolomite, but many good examples remain (Fig. 3).

The most common type of breccia appears to have been derived from the solution of anhydrite or gypsum clasts that originally formed a grain-supported fabric with interstitial carbonate mud, now medium to coarsely crystalline saccharoidal dolomite. Bedded dolostones with conspicuous breccia-moldic porosity are well exposed in the pit faces. Where split parallel with the bedding, the dolostones show an unmistakable pattern of leached clasts (Fig. 3).

Five characteristics support a solution origin for the breccias: (1) the bedded repetition of angular breccia-moldic porosity, (2) the complex dolomitization of the box-work texture and intervening strata, (3) the presence of brecciated breccia fragments (suggestive of repeated precipitation and solution), (4) the local sag and collapse of some layers, and (5) the restricted variety and paucity of faunal content.

The solution porosity at Pine Point is probably of Devonian[3] age and much of it appears to

[3] Several episodes of emergence and evaporite solution have been reported from the equivalent Middle Devonian sequence on the west (McCamis and Griffith, 1967).

FIG. 3.—Middle Devonian Presqu'ile Formation, Pine Point, Northwest Territories. **A.** Bedded and disordered breccia-moldic porosity, after anhydrite, in pale, coarse, saccharoidal dolomite, cavities partly infilled with white sparry dolomite. Wall of ramp to 042 pit. **B.** Detail of **A** showing typical somewhat slumped boxwork texture. **C.** Detail of hand specimen from outcrop shown in **A.** Bedding-surface section showing molds after angular anhydrite or gypsum clasts.

be related to episodes of karst development. Discussion of the precise origin of the porosity and its time of formation, however, is beyond the scope of this paper. As with the Fairholme breccias, compaction-generated basinal waters may have been instrumental in porosity development, because bitumen, dead oil, and complex ore and carbonate gangue deposits commonly occlude the original breccia-moldic porosity.

Another type of breccia found at Pine Point comprises a series of cross-cutting megabreccias with polygenetic clasts. These breccias may be related to a later episode of carbonate solution involving the development of extensive karst topography. They are poorly graded and are characterized by clasts with an association of lithologies related to the overlying sequence. They are grain-supported with open interstitial porosity, or with a matrix of fine-grained rubble. The bedding orientation of the clasts is generally random, but wherever broken-up bedded units can be recognized, their mutual relations suggest subsidence and draping as the most recent event. There is a coincidence of ore bodies with such breccias in the three pits now open at the mine.

DISCUSSION AND CONCLUSIONS

It is possible to argue that the Fairholme and Pine Point strata are surface exposures and that the solution porosity is therefore a surface feature unrelated to reservoir porosity. The removal of evaporites is certainly more complete at the surface, but there are numerous possibilities for, and indications of, emergence of subsurface reservoir rocks in the past. There is no reason to regard the basic data as only present surface phenomena. Surface exposures were chosen primarily because they provide a much greater area for study, and an advantage where indications are subtle and elusive. Traces of re-sealed breccia are common in slabbed Leduc (Fairholme equivalent) reservoir cores, and the mountain exposures certainly support the possibility that some of the breccias are the result of evaporite solution. Presumably the development of breccia-moldic porosity reflects brecciation earlier than breccia-interstitial porosity which clearly follows lithification of associated dolostone layers.

Most solution breccias originate by the solution of sediment-incorporated chloride, sulfate, and carbonate. It is considered likely that (1) salt flowage and solution were the causes of many monogenetic, well-graded breccias in which breccia-interstitial porosity predomi-

nates, (2) anhydrite-gypsum hydration and solution caused the well-developed breccia-moldic porosity in many highly porous dolostones, and (3) carbonate solution was the cause of many cross-cutting, rather than stratified, monogenetic to polygenetic breccias (predominantly dolostone varieties).

Where evaporite-solution breccias are polygenetic, the lithic types involved generally are associated with thin-bedded strata in the superjacent nonbrecciated sequence. Several generations of solution and precipitation are clearly indicated in individual examples. Some solution effects were penecontemporaneous with original sedimentation, and others were very much later.

The postulated depositional environment of an emergent rimmed atoll or platform reef is consistent with seasonal or cyclic climatic episodes. Present environments that are probably comparable have ephemeral evaporite accumulations. Petroleum exploration may benefit from a study of reef-bank associations in paleo-latitude reconstructions of the ancient, humid tropical reef belts with skeletal and carbonate solution porosity; and reconstructions of the paleo-north and paleo-south dry belts of subtropical reefs with evaporite solution porosity. If interstitial pore fluids can escape and if evaporite support is destroyed, pressure solution will normally eliminate porosity. The double role of evaporites in providing both a seal against fluid escape and a lithostatic support against pressure solution welding makes the paleoclimatic dry belt a promising exploration target. Of potential interest to petroleum geologists is the association of Mississippi Valley type lead-zinc mineralization with solution-breccia porosity (Jackson and Beales, 1967).

Recognition of the very common occurrence of breccia-moldic and breccia-interstitial porosity in ancient reef-bank carbonate rock complexes suggests that the possible presence of ephemeral supratidal and lagoonal salinas should be considered in environmental reconstruction. Evaporite solution is commonly difficult to recognize and has not received the attention it warrants. Detailed studies of the paleoclimatology of large regions may be aided by the recognition of two belts of salinas corresponding to the north and south tropical dry belts, and the enhanced reservoir porosity that may be related to them.

SELECTED REFERENCES

Beales, F. W., and S. A. Jackson, 1966, Precipitation of lead-zinc in carbonate reservoirs as illustrated by

Pine Point ore field, Canada: London Inst. Min. Metal. Trans., v. 75, p. B278–285; Discussion, 1967, v. 76, p. B130–B136, B175–B177.

Cloud, P. E., 1962, Environment of calcium carbonate deposition west of Andros Island, Bahamas: U.S. Geol. Survey Prof. Paper 350, p. 1–138.

Deffeyes, K. S., F. J. Lucia, and P. K. Weyl, 1965, Dolomitization of Recent and Plio-Pleistocene sediments by marine evaporite waters on Bonaire, Netherlands Antilles: Soc. Econ. Paleontologists and Mineralogists Spec. Pub. No. 13, p. 71–88.

Goreau, T. F., 1961, Problems of growth and calcium deposition in reef corals: Endeavour, v. 20, p. 32–39.

Gray, R. S., 1967, Cache field—a Pennsylvanian algal reservoir in southwestern Colorado: Am. Assoc. Petroleum Geologists Bull., v. 51, p. 1959–1976.

Hoffmeister, J. E., and H. G. Multer, 1964, Growth rate estimates of a Pleistocene coral reef of Florida: Geol. Soc. America Bull., v. 75, p. 353–358.

Illing, L. V., A. J. Wells, and J. C. M. Taylor, 1965, Penecontemporary dolomite in the Persian Gulf: Soc. Econ. Paleontologists and Mineralogists Spec. Pub. No. 13, p. 89–111.

Jackson, S. A., and F. W. Beales, 1967, An aspect of sedimentary basin evolution, the concentration of Mississippi Valley type ores during the late stages of diagenesis: Bull. Canadian Petroleum Geology, v. 15, no. 4, p. 383–433.

Kerr, S. D., Jr., and A. Thomson, 1963, Origin of nodular and bedded anhydrite in Permian shelf sediments, Texas and New Mexico: Am. Assoc. Petroleum Geologists Bull., v. 47, p. 1726–1732.

Kinsman, D. J. J., 1966a, Recent carbonate environments, Part 3, Carbonate seminar: Permian Basin Section, Soc. Econ. Paleontologists and Mineralogists, 11th Ann. Mtg., Midland, Texas, p. 1–34.

—— 1966b, Gypsum and anhydrite of recent age, Trucial Coast, Persian Gulf: Second Symposium on Salt, Northern Ohio Geol. Soc., Cleveland, v. 1, p. 302–326.

McCamis, J. G., and L. S. Griffith, 1967, Middle Devonian facies relationships, Zama area, Alberta: Bull. Canadian Petroleum Geology, v. 15, no. 4, p. 434–467.

Middleton, G. V., 1961, Evaporite solution breccias from the Mississippian of southwest Montana: Jour. Sed. Petrology, v. 31, p. 189–195.

Mille, G. de, J. R. Shouldice, and H. W. Nelson, 1964, Collapse structures related to evaporites of the Prairie Formation, Saskatchewan: Geol. Soc. America Bull., v. 75, p. 706–716.

Murray, R. C., 1960, Origin of porosity in carbonate rocks: Jour. Sed. Petrology, v. 30, p. 59–84.

—— 1964, Origin and diagenesis of gypsum and anhydrites: Jour. Sed. Petrology, v. 34, p. 512–523.

Norris, A. W., 1965, Stratigraphy of Middle Devonian and older Paleozoic rocks of the Great Slave Lake region, N.W.T.: Geol. Survey Canada Mem. 322, p. 1–180.

Shinn, E. A., R. N. Ginsburg, and R. M. Lloyd, 1965, Recent supratidal dolomite from Andros Island, Bahamas: Soc. Econ. Paleontologists and Mineralogists Spec. Pub. No. 13, p. 112–124.

Stanton, R. J., Jr., 1966, The solution brecciation process: Geol. Soc. America Bull., v. 77, p. 843–848.

Vaughan, T. W., 1915, Growth of Floridian and Bahaman shoal-water corals: Carnegie Inst. Washington Year Book 14, p. 220–232.

Reprinted from:
BULLETIN OF THE AMERICAN ASSOCIATION OF PETROLEUM GEOLOGISTS
VOL. 53, NO. 2 (FEBRUARY, 1969) PP. 251-260, 6 FIGS., 4 TABLES

Heat Conductivity of Some Carbonate Rocks and Clayey Sandstones[1]

H. ZIERFUSS[2]

Rijswijk, The Netherlands

Abstract Present knowledge on the heat conductivity of porous carbonate materials is reviewed briefly and the promising empirical formula of Sugawara and Yoshizawa is chosen to serve as a yardstick in the discussion of results. The results pertain to heat conductivity values and the more regular petrophysical characteristics of about 1,000 Iranian samples of Tertiary and Jurassic ages. The conclusions are that: (1) Heat conductivity decreases as porosity increases, (2) dolomite is a better heat conductor than limestone of the same porosity, (3) anhydrite, if comprising more than 50 percent of the rock, causes extremely high heat conductivity values, and (4) no useful value of the empirical exponent of the formula of Sugawara and Yoshizawa can be given for all carbonates.

The heat conductivity values of several clayey sandstones from Indonesia and Venezuela compared with those of clean sandstones showed that (1) the heat conductivity of a clayey sandstone is appreciably lower than that of a clean sandstone of the same porosity, (2) correlations between heat conductivity and clay content are poor, and (3) the heat conductivity values of clayey sandstones can be related reasonably to the sum of porosity and clay content.

INTRODUCTION

There are several reasons for interest in the heat conductivity of rock. It is desirable to know whether measurement of heat conductivity can be used for *in situ* formation evaluation, and if it can aid the oil industry in discriminating among different types of rock or in determining the shaliness of sandstone. In addition, the heat conductivity of a porous rock sample must be related to that of its constituents, porosity, degree of cementation, geometry, size of pores, *etc.*

Zierfuss and van der Vliet (1956) reported heat-conductivity measurements made on sands and sandstones. The present paper reports on similar work on carbonate rocks and shaly sandstones. A formal treatment of the problem was given by Eucken (1932), who used the similarity of the flows of heat and electricity. Maxwell (1873) and Burger (1919) gave the formulas for the electrical conductivity of a

[1] Manuscript received, November 11, 1966; revised, October 19, 1967; accepted, April 5, 1968.

[2] Koninklijke/Shell, Exploratie en Produktie Laboratorium.

Published with permission of Shell.

medium containing spherical or ellipsoid particles. Their hypotheses were refined by Smoluchowski (1910), Gehrcke (1900), and Lasareff (1912), who incorporated resistance to energy transfer at the boundary of the particles. Grain-to-grain contacts were disregarded purposely in the hypotheses in order to avoid mathematical complications. Nevertheless, such contacts are present in nature, and they do promote heat conduction. This was shown by Prins *et al.* (1950) and by Schumann and Voss (1934), who evacuated grain packs and found that the heat conductivity approached finite values as gas pressure was reduced. Because a theoretical investigation of the importance of grain contacts is cumbersome, experimental information must be obtained. A brief review of certain experimental studies shows the present state of knowledge, in particular that regarding the influence of temperature, pressure, convection, radiation, and porosity.

Eucken (1911) found that the thermal resistance (reciprocal conductivity) of crystals of silica and calcium carbonate increases proportionally with temperature. Consequently, heat conductivity decreases hyperbolically with temperature. These results were confirmed by Birch and Clark (1940a,b) and Ratcliffe (1960). Ratcliffe observed a conductivity decrease of about 0.6 percent per degree centigrade for water-saturated oceanic sediments.

Increase in pressure, however, promotes heat conduction. Bridgman (1924) measured a conductivity increase of 0.5–3 percent per 1,000 atm for various materials. Clark (1941) found an increase of 2–6 percent per 1,000 atm for sandstones.

Convection of pore fluids and radiation hardly affect heat conductivity, provided that the grains are smaller than 2 mm (de Vries, 1952).

Porosity is important in heat transmission as illustrated by some literature data in Table I. Heat conductivity invariably decreases as porosity increases. Hence, matrix materials conduct heat better than any of the saturating fluids used. Moreover, consolidated rocks

Table I. Relations of Porosity and Heat Conductivity in Various Lithologic Types

Material	Porosity Range (% BV)[1]	Heat Conductivity (millical/cm sec °C)			Author
		Saturant			
		Water	Oil	Gas	
Oceanic sediment	40–70	2.5–1.5	—	—	Ratcliffe (1960)
Quartz sand	19–59	12.3–5.17	—	15.7–0.416	Woodside and Messmer (1961a)
Quartz sandstone	3–59	17.7–4.86	17.0–2.1	15.5–1.26	Woodside and Messmer (1961b)
Various sandstones	4.4–36.8	10.5–3.8	10.5–2.9	10.5–1.63	Zierfuss and van der Vliet (1956)
Various limestones	4.9–36.9	9.1–3.8	8.2–2.9	6.2–2.2	Zierfuss and van der Vliet (1956)

[1] BV = bulk volume.

yield greater conductivity values than grain packs, undoubtedly because of better grain-to-grain contacts in the former.

Most investigators have attempted to represent their results by empirical formulas in which porosity and pore structure are incorporated. Kunii and Smith (1960) and Sugawara and Yoshizawa (1962) derived useful equations by considering rocks to be consolidated and cemented grain packs. The writer's results are discussed in the light of the formulas of Sugawara and Yoshizawa.

SCOPE OF PRESENT INVESTIGATION

About 1,000 samples from Iran, Indonesia, and Venezuela were used for the investigation.

The Iranian rock types include limestone, dolomite, and anhydrite of Oligocene-Miocene and Jurassic ages. Heat conductivity was plotted as a function of sample depth to determine the feasibility of petrophysical differentiation. Correlations between the heat conductivity and porosity data characterizing Oligocene-Miocene samples were compared with similar correla-

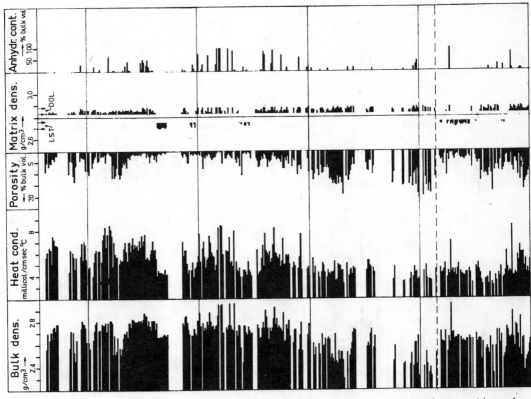

FIG. 1.—Well data from cored interval

tions made for Jurassic samples in order to obtain information on the influence of environmental conditions.

The Indonesian and Venezuelan samples are from Tertiary clayey sandstone. The effect of clay on heat conductivity was studied. Several clean sandstones from The Netherlands were used as "base" samples, having "zero clay content," to facilitate the interpretation of the data from clayey samples.

EXPERIMENTAL METHODS

The heat-conductivity measurements were carried out by means of apparatus that has been described elsewhere (Zierfuss, 1963). The sample is placed on top of a hot copper bar. After about 30 seconds the temperature at the interface reaches a steady value which is a measure of the sample's heat conductivity. The area of contact between copper bar and sample, and hence the region tested, is small (8 mm in diameter). The heat conductivity of a sample therefore was taken as the arithmetic

mean of 5–10 tests made at different places on its surface.

The well-consolidated limestone and dolomite samples were saturated with water before their heat conductivity was measured. This was impossible to do with friable clayey sandstone, which therefore was tested immediately after the samples had been taken out of well-sealed sample boxes. Additional petrophysical analyses were made later.

CARBONATE ROCK SAMPLES

Depth plots of data from Gach Saran Oligocene-Miocene samples.—Samples were taken from 1,100 ft of cored section in a Gach Saran (Iran) well. In addition to the heat-conductivity measurements, other petrophysical analyses, such as the determination of porosity, permeability, and matrix density, were performed. Visual inspection under $10\times$ magnification permitted an estimation of anhydrite content and determination of the Archie (1952) classification. A review of pertinent data is given in Fig-

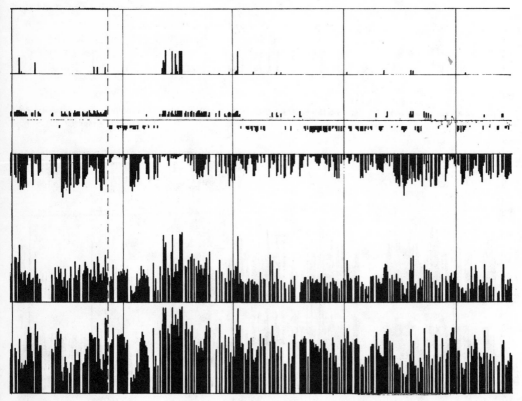

of Asmari Limestone, Gach Saran, Iran.

Heat conductivity
millical/cm sec °C

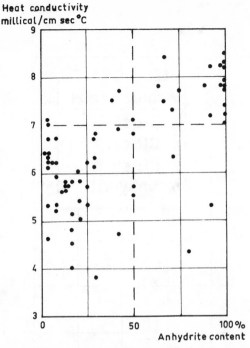

FIG. 2.—Heat conductivity of anhydrite containing carbonates, porosity values less than 5 percent BV.

ure 1. In the matrix-density column two separate ranges are indicated. The writer considers the range of matrix density from 2.70 to 2.75 g/cm³ to indicate limestone and that from 2.83 to 2.88 g/cm³ to indicate dolomite.

Five conclusions are drawn from Figure 1.

1. Distinct heat conductivity peaks occur where anhydrite makes up more than 50 percent of the sample volume. This phenomenon is illustrated in more detail by Figure 2, where the heat conductivity values of anhydrite-containing rocks are plotted against anhydrite content. A cluster of good conductors is shown for an anhydrite content exceeding 50 percent, whereas most samples containing less than 50 percent anhydrite have conductivity values lower than 7 millical/cm see °C.

2. Heat-conductivity and bulk-density diagrams appear to be similar.

3. A comparison of porosity data with the heat-conductivity diagram suggests that there is some reciprocal correlation between conductivity and porosity.

4. Heat-conductivity values generally are higher for dolomite than for limestone.

5. Low-porosity limestone may be as conductive as high-porosity dolomite because of the opposite effects of matrix density and porosity (see dotted depth lines on Fig. 1).

The writer believes that the Gach Saran results strongly suggest that porosity is a dominant factor in heat transmission. Porosity plots therefore are used in the following sections.

Porosity plots of carbonate samples.—A diagram of the heat-conductivity values of all Gach Saran carbonate and anhydrite samples plotted against porosity is shown in Figure 3. The samples are differentiated according to Archie's classification. The plot confirms that heat conductivity generally decreases with increasing porosity and that anhydrites are the best heat conductors. It shows also that the chalky class II carbonate rocks are the poorest conductors. However, no clear-cut relation between heat conductivity and classification can be observed.

A plot of the heat-conductivity values of dolomite and limestone is presented in Figure 4, which demonstrates further that there is a reciprocal relation between heat conductivity and porosity, and that dolomite is a better conductor than limestone. The best fitting curves, based on the formulas of Sugawara and Yoshizawa (1961, 1962), show that the ratio of the heat conductivity values of dolomite and limestone is roughly constant because it ranges only from 1.35 for zero porosity to 1.28 for 20 percent porosity. This result suggests that dolomite and limestone might be differentiated on the basis of their heat conductivity values.

Clearly, the conclusions based on a cursory inspection of the Gach Saran results shown in Figure 1, are well substantiated.

Comparison between Oligocene-Miocene and Jurassic carbonates.—The Jurassic of Iran is appreciably different from the Oligocene-Miocene Asmari in both age and tectonic history. A heat-conductivity/porosity plot of cores taken from wells of the Dukhan field (Qatar) is given in Figure 5; the trends were calculated on the basis of Sugawara and Yoshizawa's equations. A comparison of this diagram with the Gach Saran data (Fig. 4) shows that (1) the heat conductivity values are much higher for Dukhan than for Gach Saran samples, (2) Dukhan trends are steeper than those of Gach Saran rocks, and (3) the ratio of the heat conductivity values of dolomite and limestone of equal porosity is of the same order for Dukhan (*ca.* 1.5) and Gach Saran (*ca.* 1.3) rocks.

Although the conclusions drawn from the Gach Saran results are applicable to the Dukhan

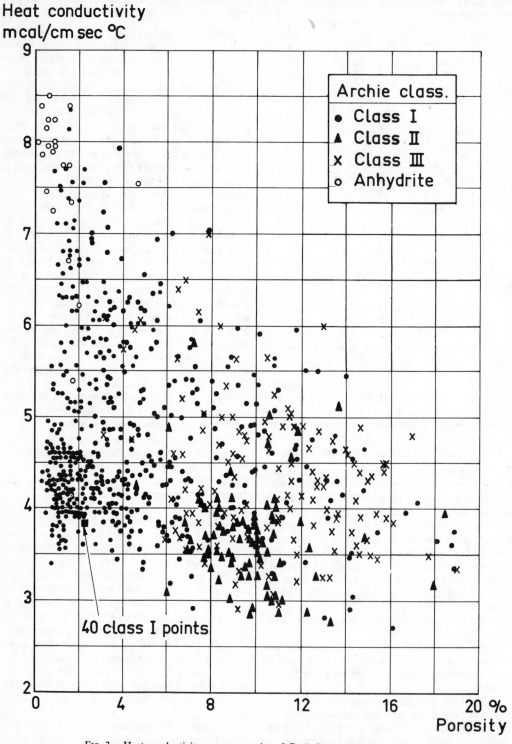

FIG. 3.—Heat conductivity *versus* porosity of Gach Saran carbonate rocks

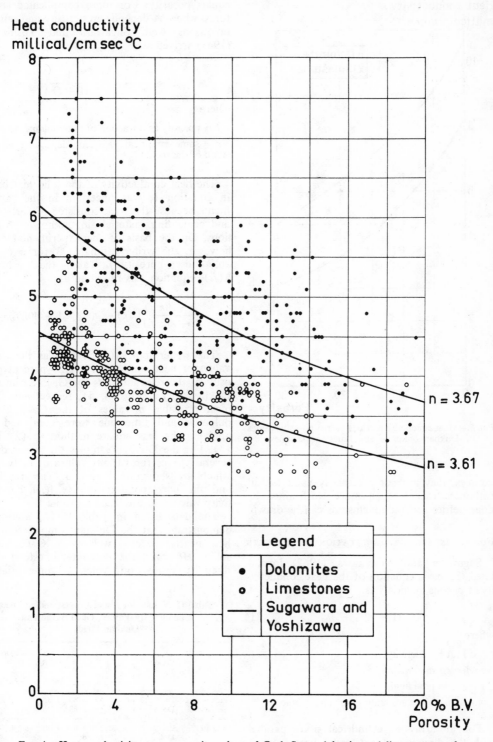

FIG. 4.—Heat conductivity *versus* porosity values of Gach Saran dolomite and limestone samples.

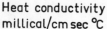

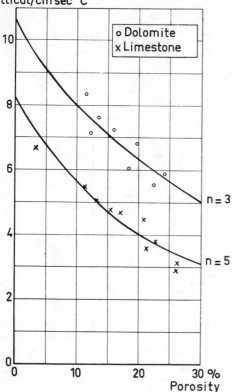

FIG. 5.—Heat conductivity values *versus* porosity values of Dukhan dolomite and limestone samples.

samples, they are not necessarily valid for all carbonate rocks. Much more work must be done before general conclusions can be drawn.

FORMULAS FOR REPRESENTATION OF RESULTS

Sugawara and Yoshizawa (1962) formulated the basic equation of the heat conductivity of porous materials as

$$\lambda = (1 - A)\lambda_s + A\lambda_p \qquad (1)$$

where:

λ is heat conductivity,

s refers to solid matrix,

p refers to pore fluid,

A is some factor accounting for pore geometry.

For an array of cylindrical pores parallel with the direction of a (steady) heat flow, A

equals porosity. For more complicated structures, where A depends on porosity and cementation as well, Sugawara and Yoshizawa (1961) arrived at

$$A = \frac{2^n}{2^n - 1}\left\{1 - \frac{1}{(1 + f)^n}\right\} \qquad (2)$$

where

f = porosity as a fraction of bulk volume, and

n = some empirical exponent depending on the abric of the rock.

The heat conductivity of the solid matrix, λ_s in equation 1, was uncertain in the experiments because the rock consisted of carbonate and cementing materials in unknown proportions. On the basis of the experimental data, however, the writer estimated λ for a favorably chosen porosity, f_o. Taking the λ value as $\lambda(f_o)$, equation 1 is rewritten as

$$\lambda(f) = \frac{1 - A(n, f)}{1 - A(n, f_o)}\{\lambda(f_o) - A(n, f)\lambda_p\} + A(n, f_o)\lambda_p. \qquad (3)$$

The writer took $\lambda(f_o)$ values as the mean values of heat conductivity at 20 percent porosity of the relevant plots for Gach Saran and Dukhan rocks (Figs. 4, 5), respectively. The most probable n values of the Gach Saran dolomite and limestone were computed by applying the least-square method to (2) and (3). For the Dukhan samples the writer drew several curves for various values of n, two of which are shown in Figure 5. The n values and the corresponding matrix heat conductivity values, λ_s, are listed in Table II.

The data listed in Table II (λ_s and λ_{20}) demonstrate that the Dukhan samples conduct heat nearly twice as well as do Gach Saran solids. However, the dolomite/limestone conductivity ratios, on which a differentiation

Table II. Values for n and Corresponding Heat Conductivity Values, Gach Saran and Dukhan Fields

Field	Rock Type	n	λ_s	λ_{20}	Conductivity Ratio Dol./Ls.	
					Solids	20% Por. Rock
Gach Saran	Ls.	3.61	4.55	2.85	1.35	1.29
	Dol.	3.67	6.15	3.68		
Dukhan	Ls.	5	8.2	4.0	1.30	1.58
	Dol.	3	10.7	6.3		

method might be based, are of the same order.

Although the empirical curves represent the measured data fairly well, no fixed value of n can be recommended for carbonates, as was possible for sandstones ($n = 2$, Sugawara and Yoshizawa, 1962). Consequently, several samples of a formation must be tested before useful values of n and $\lambda(f_o)$ can be substituted in equations (2) and (3).

CLAYEY SANDSTONES

Heat conductivity values of clayey sandstones could be measured only for fresh samples. The presence of pore fluids of different chemical compositions (oil, gas, water) is certainly a complication; but the matrix conducts heat so much better than any pore fluid (*see* Table III), that the effect of pore fluids on the gross conductivity is small for rocks of moderate porosity.[3]

After the heat-conductivity measurements had been made, the fresh samples were subjected to visual inspection and petrophysical and chemical analyses to determine porosity, sand, silt, and clay content, and quantitative composition of the pore fluids.

The measured heat conductivity values are plotted against porosity values in Figure 6a; it is seen that the heat conductivity values of clayey sandstone are less than those of clean sandstone. The reduction in heat conductivity caused by the presence of clay was calculated for several samples in the 15–20 percent porosity range; a clean-sandstone conductivity of 6.5 millical/cm sec °C (based on the dots of Fig. 6a) was assumed. The data obtained are arranged according to increasing clay content in Table IV, in which no clear trends in heat-conductivity reduction can be observed. Negative results also were obtained when relations were sought between heat-conductivity reduction and oil and/or water content of the pores.

[3] The reverse is true for large porosity; *e.g.*, Bullard *et al.* (1956).

Table III. Heat Conductivity Values of Rock Components

Material	Heat Conductivity (approx.) (millical/cm sec °C)	Source
Gas	0.1	McAdams (1951)
Oil	0.3	Hodgman *et al.* (1962)
Water	1.4	Hodgman *et al.* (1962)
Clay	2.4	Ingersoll *et al.* (1948)
Quartzite	6.8–18.9	Clark (1966)

Table IV. Heat-Conductivity Reduction of Clayey Sands

Clay (% BV[1])	Heat Conductivity (millical/cm sec °C)	Porosity (% BV)	Heat Conductivity Reduction (millical/cm sec °C)
nil	6.5	15–20	nil
4	4.05	15.0	2.45
6.5	4.35	20	2.15
8	4.9	17.5	1.6
10	5.2	15	1.3
10	4.6	18	1.9
10	3.8	19	2.7
11	4.35	16	2.15
11	3.95	18	2.55
18.5	4.35	17.5	2.15
24	5.1	20	1.4
25	4.85	18.5	1.65
26.5	4.15	17.5	2.35
40	2.5	20	4.5
45	2.55	15	3.95
56.5	2.5	18.5	4.0

[1] BV = bulk volume of sample.

Another attempt to account for clay content was more successful. Because clay is a poor heat conductor in comparison with quartzitic material (see Table III), the writer considered it as part of the pore fluid. According to this reasoning actual porosity is virtually increased by volumetric clay percentage. Plotting of the heat conductivity values of Figure 6a against porosity plus clay content yields Figure 6b. The average curve, drawn by hand, might be useful for estimating heat conductivity on the basis of clay content and porosity data. It seems of particular interest for beds in which shaliness increases or decreases.

CONCLUSIONS

The heat conductivity values of carbonate rocks depend on rock fabric and porosity. Rocks containing more than 50 percent anhydrite are the best conductors. The heat conductivity values of porous dolomite and limestone are lower, and decrease further in younger rocks and in rocks of higher porosity. The heat conductivity of carbonate rocks is described fairly well by the formulas of Sugawara and Yoshizawa (1962), provided that proper values of the critical constants are introduced.

The heat conductivity of clayey sandstone can be expressed best in terms of porosity-plus-clay content (as a percentage of bulk volume).

REFERENCES CITED

Archie, G. E., 1952, Classification of carbonate reservoir rocks and petrophysical considerations: Am.

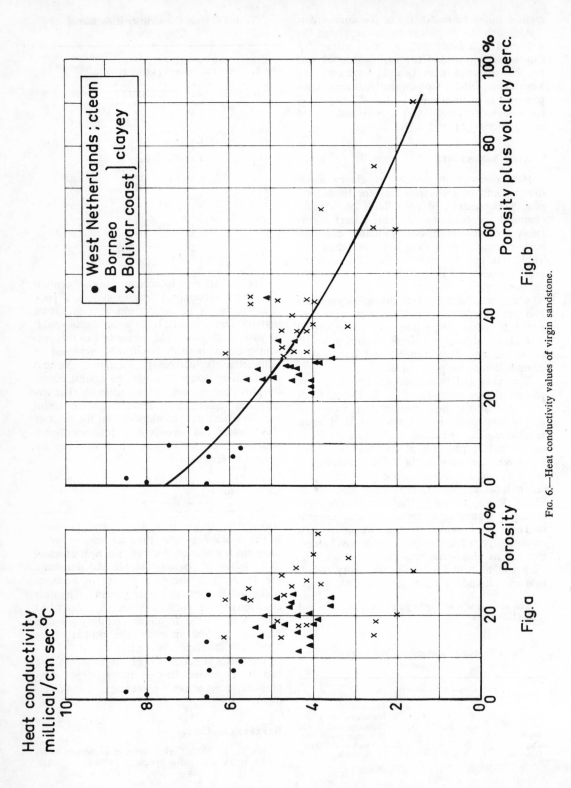

Fig. 6.—Heat conductivity values of virgin sandstone.

Assoc. Petroleum Geologists Bull., v. 36, no. 2, p. 278–298.

Birch, A. F., and H. Clark, 1940a, The thermal conductivity of rocks and its dependence upon temperature and composition, pt. 1: Am. Jour. Sci., v. 238, p. 529–558.

———— and ———— 1940b, The thermal conductivity of rocks and its dependence upon temperature and composition, pt. 2: Am. Jour. Sci., v. 238, p. 613–635.

Bridgman, P. W., 1924, The thermal conductivity and compressibility of several rocks under high pressures: Am. Jour. Sci., v. 7, 5th ser., p. 81–102.

Bullard, E. C., A. E. Maxwell, and R. Revelle, 1956, Heat flow through the deep sea floor, in H. E. Landsberg, ed., Advances in geophysics, v. 3: New York, Academic Press, p. 153–181.

Burger, H. C., 1919, Das Leitvermögen verdünnter Mischkristallfreier Legierungen: Physikalische Zeitschrift, v. 20, no. 4, p. 73–75.

Clark, H., 1941, The effects of simple compression and wetting on the thermal conductivity of rocks: Am. Geophys. Union Trans., v. 22, p. 543–544.

Clark, S. P., Jr., ed., 1966, Handbook of physical constants: Geol. Soc. America Mem. 97, 587 p.

Eucken, A., 1911, Über die Temperaturabhängigkeit der Wärmeleitfähigkeit fester Nichtmetallen: Ann. Physik, v. 34, no. 2, p. 185–221.

———— 1932, Die Wärmeleitfähigkeit keramischer feuerfester Stoffe, ihre Berechnung aus der Wärmeleitfähigkeit der Bestandteile: V.D.I. Forschungsheft, v. 353, 16 p.

Gehrcke, E., 1900, Über die Wärmeleitung verdünnter Gase, mit einer Einleitung von E. Warburg: Ann. Physik, v. 2, no. 4, p. 102–114.

Hodgman, Ch. D., et al., 1962, Handbook of chemistry and physics: 44th ed., Cleveland, Chemical Rubber Pub. Co., 3604 p.

Ingersoll, L. R., O. J. Zobel, and A. C. Ingersoll, 1948, Heat conduction; with engineering and geological applications: New York, McGraw-Hill, 278 p.

Kunii, D., and J. M. Smith, 1960, Heat transfer characteristics of porous rocks: Am. Inst. Chem. Engineers Jour., v. 6, no. 1, p. 71–78.

Lasareff, P., 1912, Über den Temperatursprung an der Grenze zwischen Metall und Gas: Ann. Physik, v. 37, no. 4, p. 233–246.

Maxwell, C., 1873, Treatise on electricity and magnetism, I: London, Macmillan.

McAdams, W. H., 1951, Heat transmission, revised ed.: New York, McGraw-Hill, 459 p.

Prins, J. A., J. Schenk, and A. J. G. L. Schram, 1950, Heat conduction by powder in various gaseous atmospheres at low pressure: Physica, v. 16, no. 4, p. 379–380.

Ratcliffe, E. W., 1960, The thermal conductivities of ocean sediments: Jour. Geophys. Research, v. 65, no. 5, p. 1535–1541.

Schumann, T. E. W., and V. Voss, 1934, Heat flow through granulated material: Fuel, v. 13, no. 8, p. 249–256.

Smoluchowski, M., 1910, The thermal conductivity of powdered substances: Acad. Sci. Cracovie (Poland) Bull. Internat., sér. A, p. 129–153.

Sugawara, A., and Y. Yoshizawa, 1961, An investigation on the thermal conductivity of porous materials and its application to porous rock: Australian Jour. Physics, v. 14, no. 4, p. 469–480.

———— and ———— 1962, An experimental investigation on the thermal conductivity of consolidated porous materials: Jour. Applied Physics, v. 33, no. 10, p. 3135–3138.

Vries, D. A. de, 1952, Het warmtegeleidingsvermogen van grond: Mededel. Landbouwhogeschool Wageningen, v. 52, no. 1, 73 p.

Woodside, W., and J. H. Messmer, 1961a, Thermal conductivity of porous media, I. Unconsolidated sands: Jour. Applied Physics, v. 32, no. 9, p. 1688–1699.

———— and ———— 1961b, Thermal conductivity of porous media, II. Consolidated rocks: Jour. Applied Physics, v. 32, no. 9, p. 1699–1706.

Zierfuss, H., 1963, An apparatus for the rapid determination of the heat conductivity of poor conductors: Jour. Scientific Instruments, v. 40, p. 69–71.

———— and G. van der Vliet, 1956, Laboratory measurements of heat conductivity of sedimentary rocks: Am. Assoc. Petroleum Geologists Bull., v. 40, no. 10, p. 2475–2488.

Reprinted from:
BULLETIN OF THE AMERICAN ASSOCIATION OF PETROLEUM GEOLOGISTS
VOL. 54, NO. 2 (FEBRUARY, 1970) PP. 207-250, 13 FIGS., 3 TABLES

Geologic Nomenclature and Classification of Porosity in Sedimentary Carbonates[1]

PHILIP W. CHOQUETTE[2] and LLOYD C. PRAY[3]
Littleton, Colorado 80121, and Madison, Wisconsin 53706

TABLE OF CONTENTS

Abstract Pore systems in sedimentary carbonates are generally complex in their geometry and genesis, and commonly differ markedly from those of sandstones. Current nomenclature and classifications appear inadequate for concise description or for interpretation of porosity in sedimentary carbonates. In this article we review current nomenclature, propose several new terms, and present a classification of porosity which stresses interrelations between porosity and other geologic features.

The time and place in which porosity is created or modified are important elements of a genetically oriented classification. Three major geologic events in the history of a sedimentary carbonate form a practical basis for dating origin and modification of porosity, independent of the stage of lithification. These events are (1) creation of the sedimentary framework by clastic accumulation or accretionary precipitation (final deposition), (2) passage of a deposit below the zone of major influence by processes related to and operating from the deposition surface, and (3) passage of the sedimentary rock into the zone of influence by processes operating from an erosion surface (unconformity). The first event, final deposition, permits recognition of predepositional, depositional, and postdepositional stages of porosity evolution. Cessation of final deposition is the most practical basis for distinguishing primary and secondary (postdepositional) porosity. Many of the key postdepositional changes in sedimentary carbonates and their pore systems occur near the surface, either very early in burial history or at a penultimate stage associated with uplift and erosion. Porosity created or modified at these times commonly

can be differentiated. On the basis of the three major events heretofore distinguished, we propose to term the early burial stage "eogenetic," the late stage "telogenetic," and the normally very long intermediate stage "mesogenetic." These new terms are also applicable to process, zones of burial, or porosity formed in these times or zones (e.g., eogenetic cementation, mesogenetic zone, telogenetic porosity).

The proposed classification is designed to aid in geologic description and interpretation of pore systems

[1] Manuscript received, December 31, 1968; revised, July 16, 1969; accepted, July 31, 1969. Published with permission of Marathon Oil Company.

[2] Denver Research Center, Marathon Oil Company.

[3] Department of Geology and Geophysics, University of Wisconsin.

This article was largely formulated and written while both writers were part of a continuing research program on carbonate facies at the Denver Research Center of Marathon Oil Company. We are pleased to acknowledge the very appreciable help received from our colleagues, both within and outside Marathon, in evolving concepts expressed in this article. We extend special thanks to D. H. Craig, D. B. MacKenzie, P. N. McDaniel, and R. D. Russell of Marathon, R. G. C. Bathurst of the University of Liverpool, and P. O. Roehl of Union Oil Company for critical reviews of drafts of the manuscript and to A. S. Campbell of the Oasis Oil Company of Libya, Inc., for stimulating discussions.

and their carbonate host rocks. It is a descriptive and genetic system in which 15 basic porosity types are recognized: seven abundant types (interparticle, intraparticle, intercrystal, moldic, fenestral, fracture, and vug), and eight more specialized types. Modifying terms are used to characterize genesis, size and shape, and abundance of porosity. The genetic modifiers involve (1) process of modification (solution, cementation, and internal sedimentation), (2) direction or stage of modification (enlarged, reduced, or filled), and (3) time of porosity formation (primary, secondary, predepositional, depositional, eogenetic, mesogenetic, and telogenetic). Used with the basic porosity type, these genetic modifiers permit explicit designation of porosity origin and evolution. Pore shapes are classed as irregular or regular, and the latter are subdivided into equant, tubular, and platy shapes. A grade scale for size of regular-shaped pores, utilizing the average diameter of equant or tubular pores and the width of platy pores, has three main classes: micropores ($<$ 1/16 mm), mesopores (1/16–4 mm), and megapores (4–256 mm). Megapores and mesopores are divided further into small and large subclasses. Abundance is noted by percent volume and/or by ratios of porosity types.

Most porosity in sedimentary carbonates can be related specifically to sedimentary or diagenetic components that constitute the texture or fabric (fabric-selective porosity). Some porosity cannot be related to these features. Fabric selectivity commonly distinguishes pore systems of primary and early postdepositional (eogenetic) origin from those of later (telogenetic)[4] origin that normally form after extensive diagenesis has transformed the very porous assemblage of stable and unstable carbonate minerals into a much less porous aggregate of ordered dolomite and/or calcite. Porosity in most carbonate facies, including most carbonate petroleum reservoir rocks, is largely fabric selective.

INTRODUCTION

Most sedimentary carbonate rocks have very little porosity , but the minority that does contain more than a few percent pore space is collectively of immense economic importance. Porous limestone and dolomite facies contain about one half the world's known reserves of oil and gas and are sites of many significant ore deposits. Programs of exploration for oil and gas and mineral deposits based on an understanding of the geometry and genesis of the pore systems in such exploration targets are becoming increasingly practical. Sedimentary carbonates form aquifers in many regions, and a knowledge of the nature of their pore systems

[4] In this article, diagenesis is used to encompass "those natural changes which occur in sediments or sedimentary rocks between the time of initial deposition and the time—if ever—when the changes created by elevated temperature, or pressure, or other conditions can be considered to have crossed the threshold into the realm of metamorphism" (Murray and Pray, 1965). It is independent of the process of lithification and may include weathering (cf., Chilingar et al., 1967; Fairbridge, 1967).

is useful for hydrologic interpretations. Even the utility of carbonate rocks for building stone, concrete aggregate, or other such purposes can be influenced by the nature and amount of their porosity. Hence, economics alone amply justifies a concern with the pore systems of this group of sedimentary rocks.

Carbonate-rock pore systems also can help to elucidate geologic history, for carbonate sediments and rocks and their pore systems are relatively sensitive indicators of physicochemical events. Much of the record of diagenesis is intertwined inextricably with the creation, modification, and obliteration of porosity. Understanding the evolution of porosity from that of an original sediment to that of an ancient carbonate rock can contribute to the unraveling of both depositional and postdepositional events, and can aid in interpreting the history of interaction between sedimentary strata and their contained fluids.

Because of the economic and interpretive value of porosity studies, it is unfortunate that porosity has been neglected in much of the research on sedimentary carbonates published in the past two decades. In many works it is ignored or is described in terms of volume percent, with little other description, illustration, or interpretation. Where aspects of porosity other than pore volume are described, the terminology commonly lacks descriptive clarity or genetic meaning, or both.

Evaluation of the literature relevant to carbonate porosity reveals the need for a more rigorous nomenclature and a more systematic, genetically oriented classification of carbonate pores and pore systems. An integrated system of nomenclature and classification fostering more precise descriptions and a more direct focus on pore genesis would aid interpretation not only of porous carbonates, but also of the many limestones and dolomite facies from which porosity has been essentially eliminated (Pray and Choquette, 1966). Though such systems may have been devised, they either have not been published or have not come to our attention. In any case, they are not generally available.

The purpose of this article is to present a comprehensive system of geologic nomenclature and classification that can be applied to the porosity of sedimentary carbonates. The goal of the system is to facilitate geologic description of porosity, and to assist in improving genetic interpretations of porosity across the broad spectrum of carbonate facies.

This article is in three main parts, each somewhat dependent on the others. Part 1 provides perspectives on the nature of porosity in sedimentary carbonates. It stresses the genetic and geometric complexity of carbonate pore systems, the distinctiveness of most carbonate porosity in comparison to that of porous sandstones, and the importance of ascertaining relations of porosity to fabric elements of carbonate rocks—the concept of fabric selectivity. Part 2 presents the more general aspects of porosity nomenclature. The general terms *porosity, pore, pore system,* and *pore interconnections* are reviewed. Terminology relating to the time of porosity origin and modification is discussed, and new terms and related concepts useful in designating time (and place) of porosity origin are presented. Part 3 presents the classification we propose. The major elements of the system are summarized in Figure 2 and illustrations of its use are given in Figures 3–12. Following the text is a glossary and discussion of most geologic terms that have been applied to the porosity of sedimentary carbonates in the past several decades (Appendix A). Most terms are defined briefly as befits a glossary, but more extended discussions are provided for important and much-used terms such as "vug", for which we believe that clarified definitions and more consistent usage are needed. The glossary is intended to serve both as a general reference and as the main source for definitions and usages of the terms employed in our proposed classification.

Considerations of nomenclature and classification in any scientific field present a reviewer with two end-member alternatives: either adapt preexisting terminology to the present state of knowledge of the field under review, or create a new system with a new nomenclature. Despite some distinct advantages in the second alternative for the description, classification, and interpretation of pore systems in sedimentary carbonates, we do not believe that wholesale changes in the current body of terms are justified by the present "state of the art." For the present, it seems more practical to use current terms as much as possible, sharpening or restricting usage where current concepts suggest that this will improve the precision or clarity of the term.

PART 1. PERSPECTIVES ON
POROSITY IN SEDIMENTARY CARBONATES

Sedimentary carbonates are being recognized increasingly as a complex and distinctive rock family. Their porosity is likewise complex and distinctive. Awareness of the many possible stages in porosity evolution is essential for geologists concerned with studies of carbonate facies, whether porous or not.

Although the origins of porosity are reasonably well understood, many modifications of porosity in carbonates are still inadequately known. For example, it long has been recognized that much pore space in sedimentary carbonates is created after deposition, and attention has been given to the processes of solution and dolomitization believed to have created most of this porosity. But much less attention seems to have been given to the dominant process in porosity evolution, which is the wholesale obliteration of both primary and secondary porosity that has occurred in most ancient carbonates. Newly deposited carbonate sediments commonly have porosity of 40–70 percent; ancient carbonates with more than a few percent porosity are unusual. The volume of pore-filling cement in ancient carbonates commonly may approach or exceed the volume of the initial sediment (Pray and Choquette, 1966). Most porous ancient carbonates are regarded more correctly as representing arrested stages in the normal trend toward obliteration of porosity than as examples of enhanced porosity in formerly less porous facies. Even the creation of molds by solution of aragonite particles, widely regarded as increasing rock porosity, may not involve much net change in pore volume, and the change may be a slight diminution rather than an increase in the pore volume (Harris and Matthews, 1967; Land *et al.*, 1967). The long-claimed increase of porosity that occurs during dolomitization is quantitatively minor compared to the overall porosity decrease which must have occurred in nearly all ancient dolomites. Processes causing this large decrease, however, have been largely neglected. Clearly, the evolution of porosity (both its genesis and modification) in sedimentary carbonates not only is commonly complex, but also records a very important part of the formation of ancient carbonate facies.

The discussion that follows stresses features of porosity in sedimentary carbonates that provide useful perspective for the consideration of nomenclature and the classification presented in Parts 2 and 3.

Complexity of Carbonate Pore Systems

The pores and pore systems of sedimentary carbonates are normally complex both physically and genetically. The pore space of some sedimentary carbonates consists almost entirely of interparticle (intergranular) openings between nonporous sediment grains of relatively uniform size and shape. Porosity of this kind may be relatively simple in geometry. If it formed at the time of deposition and was little modified by later diagenesis, the resulting pore system may closely resemble that of many well-sorted sandstones. It represents a physical and genetic simplicity that is unusual in sedimentary carbonates; much greater complexity is the rule.

It is not surprising that geologists generally have not attempted to describe quantitatively the geometry of pore openings; their sizes, shapes, and the nature of their boundaries commonly show extreme variability. The three-dimensional physical complexity can be visualized readily in some carbonates, but in many it is appreciated best by injecting plastic into the pore system, dissolving the rock with acid after the plastic has hardened, and directly observing the pore system. Illustrations of the results of this technique (Nuss and Whiting, 1947) are provided in articles by Imbt and Ellison (1946) and Etienne (1963).

The size and shape complexity of pores in carbonate rocks is caused by many factors. It relates partly to the wide range in size and shape of sedimentary carbonate particles, which create pores either by their packing or by their solution. It also relates partly to the size and shape variation of pores created within sedimentary particles by skeletal secretion. Extensive size and shape variation relates in part to the filling of former openings by carbonate cement or internal sediment.

The physical complexity of porosity in carbonate rocks is increased greatly by solution processes, which may create pore space that precisely mimics the size and shape of depositional particles or form pores that are independent of both depositional particles and diagenetic crystal textures. Fracture openings also are common in carbonate rocks and can strongly influence solution. Pores range in size from openings 1μ or less in diameter (if a single linear measure is applicable) to openings hundreds of meters across like the "Big Room" at Carlsbad Caverns, New Mexico, termed a "macropore" by Adams and Frenzel (1950, p. 305). Size complexity, in addition to a wide range in possible pore sizes, may involve juxtaposition of large and minute openings in the same rock unit or single sample. Size and shape complexity applies equally well to all openings,

whether pores or pore interconnections.

Pores in sedimentary carbonates are fully as complex genetically as they are geometrically. Carbonate porosity is polygenetic in the sense of both time and modes of origin. Although interparticle porosity created at the time of final sediment deposition or accretion is important in many carbonate rocks, porosity created in sedimentary particles either before their final deposition or after deposition commonly ranks in importance with interparticle porosity of depositional origin.

Processes by which porosity is created and modified are greatly varied. Porosity can form by secretion of skeletal carbonate that creates cells, chambers, or other openings; it can form by sediment packing, sediment shrinkage, sediment distention as by gas evolution, or rock fracturing; and it can form by selective solution of sedimentary particles or indiscriminate solution of the rock, organic boring or burrowing, organic decomposition, or in other ways. Though not all of these genetic types of porosity may be present in the same sediment or rock, several generations of porosity and several types of processes may be involved in the genesis of pores in the same facies or even the same sample. Pore-modification processes also are diverse. The many possible processes of porosity creation and modification, operating through a long depositional and diagenetic history, make genetic as well as physical complexity the norm in sedimentary carbonates.

Comparison of Porosity in Sandstones and Sedimentary Carbonates

Many geologists interpret carbonate rocks and their pore systems by analogy with detrital sandstone, siltstone, and shale. Valid analogies can be drawn, but generally it is more useful to focus on the distinctiveness of carbonate pore systems and on their many differences from pores in detrital analogs. The most common analogy, particularly in analysis of petroleum reservoirs, is made between the pore systems of sandstones and those of carbonate rocks.

To illustrate the danger in reasoning by analogy, consider a comparison between the pore system of a sucrose dolomite composed of silt-size rhombic dolomite crystals and that of a slightly cemented quartz siltstone. The size, shape, and sorting of component crystals or particles may be very similar in the two rocks, and superficial analysis would suggest that their pore geometries and hence their fluid-flow properties might be comparable. But there must be basic differences in these pore systems. Few quartz siltstones are oil productive, and those which do constitute oil reservoirs have grain sizes near the upper end of the silt size range (0.06 mm). However, many petroleum reservoirs produce from dolomites with intercrystal porosity that is no more abundant, and superficially is no coarser, than that of nonproductive siltstone. In fact, several dolomite petroleum reservoirs produce from intercrystal porosity in which the crystals are in the smaller silt sizes, some as small as 0.01 mm or less. The good reservoir qualities of such microcrystalline dolomites might not be anticipated if one relied solely on knowledge of porosity characteristics of their apparent textural analogs, the siltstones.

A general comparison of carbonate rocks and sandstones shows a major difference between them in porosity evolution. Both families of rocks have evolved from sediments that had high initial porosity. Even though newly deposited carbonate sand and silt commonly are more porous than newly deposited detrital sand, ancient carbonate rocks commonly have much less pore space than sandstone, and may have none. Porosity reduction is much more extensive in carbonate facies. The normal postdepositional modification of porosity in sandstone is by cementation and minor compaction. This generally causes only modest reduction in original interparticle pore volume without substantial changes in the kind or position of pores. In most carbonates, much or all original pore space is obliterated during diagenesis, new voids are created, and these in turn may be partly or completely filled.

The more significant differences in porosity between sandstones and sedimentary carbonate rocks are summarized in Table 1. The many differences suggest not only that reasoning by analogy has pitfalls, but also that a nomenclature and classification of porosity adequate for sandstones is not adequate for sedimentary carbonates.

Concept of Fabric Selectivity

The relation between pore space and solid depositional and diagenetic constituents of a sediment or rock, though commonly ignored, is important for geologic interpretation of sedimentary carbonates. The solid constituents include the various types of primary sediment particles and later formed diagenetic elements such as carbonate cement or recrystallization products, dolomite crystals, and gypsum and anhydrite crystals. These primary and secondary solid constituents, including their textural

Table 1. Comparison of Porosity in Sandstone and Carbonate Rocks

Aspect	Sandstone	Carbonate
Amount of primary porosity in sediments	Commonly 25–40%	Commonly 40–70%
Amount of ultimate porosity in rocks	Commonly half or more of initial porosity; 15–30% common	Commonly none or only small fraction of initial porosity; 5–15% common in reservoir facies
Type(s) of primary porosity	Almost exclusively interparticle	Interparticle commonly predominates, but intraparticle and other types are important
Type(s) of ultimate porosity	Almost exclusively primary interparticle	Widely varied because of postdepositional modifications
Sizes of pores	Diameter and throat sizes closely related to sedimentary particle size and sorting	Diameter and throat sizes commonly show little relation to sedimentary particle size or sorting
Shape of pores	Strong dependence on particle shape—a "negative" of particles	Greatly varied, ranges from strongly dependent "positive" or "negative" of particles to form completely independent of shapes of depositional or diagenetic components
Uniformity of size, shape, and distribution	Commonly fairly uniform within homogeneous body	Variable, ranging from fairly uniform to extremely heterogeneous, even within body made up of single rock type
Influence of diagenesis	Minor; usually minor reduction of primary porosity by compaction and cementation	Major; can create, obliterate, or completely modify porosity; cementation and solution important
Influence of fracturing	Generally not of major importance in reservoir properties	Of major importance in reservoir properties if present
Visual evaluation of porosity and permeability	Semiquantitative visual estimates commonly relatively easy	Variable; semiquantitative visual estimates range from easy to virtually impossible; instrument measurements of porosity, permeability and capillary pressure commonly needed
Adequacy of core analysis for reservoir evaluation	Core plugs of 1-in. diameter commonly adequate for "matrix" porosity	Core plugs commonly inadequate; even whole cores (~3-in. diameter) may be inadequate for large pores
Permeability-porosity interrelations	Relatively consistent; commonly dependent on particle size and sorting	Greatly varied; commonly independent of particle size and sorting

and smaller structural features, are here collectively referred to as the "fabric elements." The relation between the pore space and fabric elements of carbonate facies ranges from complete dependence, as for primary interparticle porosity, to complete independence, as for tectonic fractures in nonporous limestone. If a dependent relation can be discerned between porosity and fabric elements, we refer to the porosity as *fabric selective*. If such a relation cannot be established, we classify the porosity as *not fabric selective*. Most primary porosity and a large proportion of secondary porosity in carbonate facies are fabric selective. Fabric selectivity is especially useful in determining the time of origin of pores in relation to other events in the diagenetic evolution.

For better observation, description, and interpretation of carbonate porosity it is important to assess fabric selectivity, which we incorporate into our classification (Fig. 2). Interparticle, intercrystal, moldic, fenestral, shelter, and growth-framework porosity are almost invariably fabric selective. Most intraparticle porosity in carbonates is a primary constructional fabric and hence is fabric selective. But like "interparticle," the term refers to position, and some internal pores may form by nonselective solution, boring, or other processes. Fracture, vug, and channel porosity generally are not fabric selective in terms of their origins or by definition. Other types of porosity—boring, burrow, breccia, and shrinkage—are classed as "fabric selective or not" as there is no consistent relation for these types.

Two factors are involved in establishing fabric selectivity: the configuration of the pore boundary and the position of the pore relative to fabric elements. For most primary porosity, both boundary configuration and position of the pore are determined completely by the fabric elements. Thus, the boundaries of interparticle pores in an unconsolidated sediment are shaped by the depositional particles and the pore position is determined by these primary fabric elements. The same dependence of pore boundary and position occurs with internal pores formed by the growth of a skeletal organism. With secondary porosity, the degree of fabric selectivity ranges from complete dependence of both pore boundaries and position upon the fabric elements to apparent independence. For example, the selective removal of aragonite oöliths or gastropod shells from a calcitic rock, or secondary anhydrite crystals from a dolomite, results in pores the size and shape of the dissolved constituents. These molds are fabric selective in both boundaries and positions. However, the tortuous mazes of many phreatic caverns commonly show no positional relation to the depositional or diagenetic fabric elements of the rock (they commonly reflect joint systems). The commonly smooth walls of such caverns further demonstrate the independence of the pore boundary from small-scale fabric elements. The same indiscriminate relation of position and boundary can characterize smaller scale pores—pores we classify as vugs or channels. Such pore systems are not fabric selective. Fabric selectivity is independent of scale of pore.

Two types of fabric selectivity can be usefully differentiated: depositional and diagenetic. Depositional fabric selectivity shows a dependence on either the primary fabric elements or later features that reflect the primary fabric elements. This type of fabric selectivity would include primary interparticle porosity, fenestral porosity that formed shortly after sedimentation, and molds formed by selective removal of depositional particles. Depositional fabric selectivity also can apply to pores of more complex origin. For example, consider a pore occupying the site of a shell that was dissolved selectively to form a mold, which then was filled completely with sparry calcite cement that resisted subsequent dolomitization of the matrix rock but later was dissolved selectively to form a second-generation mold. The final pore still reflects a positional and configuration control by the original shell, a primary fabric element.

Diagenetic fabric selectivity shows a dependence of pore location and configuration upon postdepositional features. Thus, molds may be examples of diagenetic fabric selectivity if they formed by selective removal of diagenetic gypsum or anhydrite crystals. The intercrystal porosity of dolomites is determined by shape and arrangement of the constituent crystals, which normally were created during diagenesis. Their individual position does not coincide with recognizable primary elements in the sediment; hence, most dolomite porosity is diagenetic fabric selective. Many dolomites show evidence of another aspect of selectivity that should be distinguished from the diagenetic fabric selectivity. It relates to the broader scale influence of heterogeneities in depositional fabric, such as "lime mud" versus grains. The importance of fabric heterogeneities like these has been stressed repeatedly by R. C. Murray (*cf*. 1960, 1964; Murray and Lucia, 1967; Lucia and Murray, 1967) and others.

As expected in natural phenomena, there is a spectrum of fabric selectivity; pores and pore systems may have intermediate fabric-selectivity characteristics, but most carbonate porosity can be classified without ambiguity as fabric selective or not. Intermediate types are far less prevalent than the end members of the spectrum, and most of them are solution-enlarged pore systems. Some are pores which occupy positions related to former fabric elements, but have boundaries that cut indiscriminately across the diverse fabric elements. Others are pores that have fabric-selective boundaries, but are so large that their positional relation to smaller scale fabric elements or to former pores cannot be determined. Some caverns have these characteristics. Some pores show gradations in degree of fabric selectivity along their boundaries. Many pores of gradational or intermediate fabric selectivity result from two or more periods of pore development.

Characterization of secondary porosity as fabric selective or not assists in dating the origin of porosity in relation to the diagenetic evolution of a sediment or rock. Two major diagenetic changes of carbonates from newly deposited sediment to typical ancient rock are the change from a very porous sediment to a rock with little porosity, and the change from a mineral assemblage including unstable forms such as aragonite, high-magnesium calcite, and disordered forms of dolomite into a stable assemblage of low-magnesium calcite and/or ordered dolomite (*e.g.,* Land *et al.,* 1967). In essence, very porous, heterogeneous mixtures of stable and unstable carbonate minerals become nonporous rocks composed of calcite or dolomite.

As a broad generalization, most fabric-selective porosity of secondary origin formed before pervasive cementation (the predominant porosity-reducing process), and/or it formed at a time when unstable mineral components were present to influence porosity development. The selective solution of "lime mud" from between the coarser grains to form secondary interparticle porosity almost surely occurs before cementation. Most, if not almost all, of the many porosity fabrics that can be related to selective removal or other diagenetic modification of aragonitic components in sediments must have occurred before or during the elimination of aragonite. At the other extreme, most secondary porosity that is not fabric selective probably developed after pervasive cementation and mineralogic stabilization. The porosity normally associated with tectonic fracturing and with the late-stage solution that may accompany development of major unconformities is rarely fabric selective. Localization of solution porosity that is not fabric selective seems related chiefly to access of permeating water, and to the indiscriminate solution of calcium carbonate along the walls of major flow passageways. The lack of response to fabric elements suggests that the rock material acted largely as a homogeneous source of calcium and carbonate ions. Differences in size, shape, internal porosity, or minor compositional or structural aspects of the component particles or crystals being dissolved apparently had minor influence at this stage.

Other concepts somewhat related to fabric selectivity are also useful in interpreting porosity of carbonate facies. Adams (1953) stressed the importance of preexisting porosity in the development of secondary porosity by solution processes in the rock underlying an erosion surface. His valuable perspectives lead to a concept that can be termed "facies-selective porosity." A spectacular example is present in the Cretaceous El Abra formation of northeastern Mexico (Bonet, 1952). There, unconformity-related cavern systems have been developed by extensive solution within formerly porous rudistid-rich carbonate buildups, but are absent from the enclosing carbonate facies which presumably had little porosity and permeability at the time the unconformity was created. The El Abra example is only one type of facies-selective porosity. Many petroleum reservoirs are found in only one or a very few specific facies of an entire carbonate complex, the other facies being essentially nonporous or impermeable. Such reservoirs exemplify the "specific-reservoir concept" (Pray and Choquette, 1966). Pore systems in most specific reservoirs are fabric-selective types.

In summary, porosity is rarely fortuitous; usually "there is a reason" (Rittenhouse, 1959). Critical study of pore space in relation to the solid constituents of the rock too commonly is neglected. It can aid in interpreting the geologic history, as well as in exploiting the fluid contents of carbonate facies. The concept of fabric selectivity is useful in interpreting the origin of porosity and in relating its occurrence to specific facies. We believe most petroleum reservoirs consist predominantly of fabric-selective pore systems. As with carbonate rocks in general, "there is no substitute for looking at the rocks themselves" (Ham and Pray, 1962, p. 19), and with pore systems in carbonate rocks the need is not only to see the porosity, but to discern its relation to the enclosing solid rock.

One needs, in the American idiom, "to see both the doughnut and the hole."

PART 2. GENERAL CONSIDERATIONS OF POROSITY NOMENCLATURE

The nomenclature applied to porosity in sedimentary carbonates is not extensive, but a review of current terms and their usages suggests that it is inadequate to permit geologists to describe porosity succinctly or to interpret its evolution. Many terms have become part of the nomenclature haphazardly, as by adaptation from common to technical usage. Moreover, some terms have had more than one definition or usage, and others have been used with neither explicit definition nor clear connotations. An example can be seen in the usage of the venerable term "vug," which is discussed in some detail in the glossary. Some of the terms for porosity fail to convey effectively either descriptive geologic attributes or specific genetic information. The imprecise, varied, and changing usage of nomenclature for sedimentary carbonates has made much of the descriptive and interpretive literature on carbonate porosity less useful than it might have been. Because of these considerations and because recent advances in knowledge of sedimentary carbonates have shed new light on the origins of porosity, a reappraisal of the nomenclature applied to porosity seems both timely and needed.

Our views on porosity nomenclature are given in this section and in the glossary. The glossary provides definitions and discussion of most of the terms that have been applied to porosity in carbonates, including the several proposed herein. In this section two aspects of nomenclature are presented. First, the definitions and a brief discussion of the most general terms—*pore, pore interconnection, porosity,* and *pore system*—are given to avoid possible confusion in succeeding parts of this article. Second, an extensive discussion is provided relating to the nomenclature and concepts pertaining to the time at which porosity is formed or modified. Existing porosity-time nomenclature is reviewed, and several new terms are proposed to recognize important stages of porosity evolution of sedimentary carbonates. The new terms also can be used to denote the zones in which porosity evolution takes place. These terms and the ideas they embody require an integrated discussion beyond that feasible for a glossary.

Definitions of General Porosity Terms

The most general terms—*pore, pore interconnection, porosity,* and *pore system*—are usually employed in a way that leaves little or no doubt about their meanings.

The term "pore" was derived from the Greek word, *poros,* meaning passageway. Although it is used in this general sense, more often it is used restrictively to designate local swellings or enlargements along or within a pore system, as well as apparently discrete individual openings within a sediment or rock. In this usage, such discrete pores are distinguished from the more constricted openings that serve as "pore interconnections" or "pore throats." The distinction is useful and we use pore in this manner. Pores so defined constitute most of the porosity and fluid storage volume of the rock. The interconnections or throats generally contribute a small fraction of the total pore volume, but exert decisive control on the permeability and hence the fluid "deliverability" of the rock. The size, shape, and distribution of pores can be described with relative accuracy by macroscopic and microscopic visual observations. Pore interconnections are more difficult or impossible to assess visually, and capillary pressure measurements commonly are used to assess them quantitatively.

The term "porosity" long has been applied by geologists to all openings in the mineral framework of sediments or rocks. It is used in this broadest and most general sense in this article. "Porosity" also is used commonly to denote the amount of a sediment or rock composed of openings, generally expressed as a percent of bulk volume. Collectively, all the openings of sediments or rocks are usefully referred to as the "pore system." The term "pore system" can also denote each of several types of associated porosity, as in "the reservoir porosity consists of an interparticle pore system supplemented by a very permeable pore system of open fractures."

The classification of porosity presented in Part 3 is concerned primarily with the size, shape, and distribution of pores rather than with pore interconnections, and with pore systems in fractured and other carbonates where a distinction between pores and interconnections is either impractical or impossible. Although pore interconnections are not classified or evaluated directly in this article, for some types of porosity descriptions of the types and sizes of pores allow inferences about the nature and effectiveness of pore interconnections.

Porosity Terms of Time Significance

Introduction and summary.—Pore space can be created, modified, or destroyed at many stages in the history of a sedimentary carbonate. A nomenclature for the important phases of porosity evolution is an essential part of a genetically oriented system of classification. This section is concerned with the terminology pertaining to the time of porosity origin and time of significant porosity modification. Processes involved in creating and modifying pore space and the zones in which they operate are considered in relation to the time terms.

The traditional time terms for porosity in carbonates are "primary" and "secondary." These terms are firmly entrenched in the literature, and, despite some variation in meaning, are useful. Their general time significance is clear and generally is sufficiently explicit. As used by most geologists, "primary porosity" includes all pore space present immediately after final deposition, and "secondary porosity" designates any created after final deposition. This usage is still appropriate.

For detailed consideration of porosity evolution, however, such a simple two-fold time classification is inadequate. One carbonate sedimentary cycle begins with the secretion or precipitation of carbonate particles or growth frameworks and ends with metamorphism or erosion of long-buried carbonate rock. Important changes in porosity can occur between the time when sedimentary particles first form (commonly with intraparticle pore space) and the time when these particles, or aggregates of fragments derived from them, come to rest at their final site of deposition and later burial. Afterward, creation, modification, and/or elimination of porosity can occur at any time or continuously during the postdepositional period. This period is generally long, and the porosity history may be complex.

For a somewhat more detailed time characterization than is possible with "primary" and "secondary," three major time periods can be identified in their relation to the most easily defined and recognizable event in porosity evolution, final deposition. "Final deposition" here means the deposition just preceding final burial of the sediment or rock, in contrast to possible earlier phases of deposition, erosion and reworking, and redeposition. The three major stages of porosity evolution are: (1) *predepositional*, (2) *depositional*, and (3) *postdepositional*. To subdivide further the long and significant postdepositional period, we propose three formal subdivisions related to burial stages. Two of these are stages of shallow burial, when the major porosity-influencing processes operate from or are closely related to the surface—a subaerial or subaqueous interface. The third stage is the commonly long intermediate period of deeper burial. We refer to the time of early burial as *eogenetic,* the time of deeper burial as *mesogenetic,* and the late stage associated with erosion of long-buried carbonates as *telogenetic.* These terms also can be applied to porosity created during the three stages, to processes acting during the stages, or to the respective burial zones. Our usage of the major time-porosity terms is summarized in Figure 1. The major time terms and some aspects pertaining to the nature of porosity related to time, the processes important in porosity evolution, and the sites at which these processes operate are discussed in more detail hereafter.

Primary and secondary porosity.—The general meaning of "primary" and "secondary," simple and long-used terms for designating time of porosity genesis, is clear from the normal connotation of these words. The terms are most commonly and better used to refer to the porosity, as in "secondary porosity," than to a time period, such as "secondary time" (Fig. 1, top). Nomenclature problems with these terms arise from minor differences in their definitions and usages. We consider *primary porosity* to be any which was present in the sediment or rock immediately after final deposition. It includes any pore space present within individual sediment or rock components at the time of final deposition, or any which formed during the process of final deposition. This definition appears to be consistent with most current usage (*e.g.,* Illing *et al.,* 1967, p. 488; Murray, 1960, p. 61). It conflicts, however, with usage by Hohlt (1948, p. 6) and others who regard primary porosity as any which developed either before or during lithification. We believe a definition based on the time of final deposition to be much more useful, precise, and practical than one based on lithification. *Secondary porosity* is considered here to be any porosity created in a sediment or rock after final deposition.

Primary porosity and secondary porosity, as used here, depend only on the time when the pore opening was created; their definitions are independent of both the mode of origin of the pore space and the state of lithification. Any porosity formed before or during deposition is

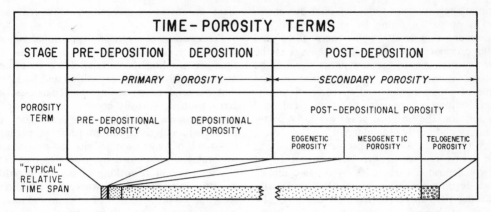

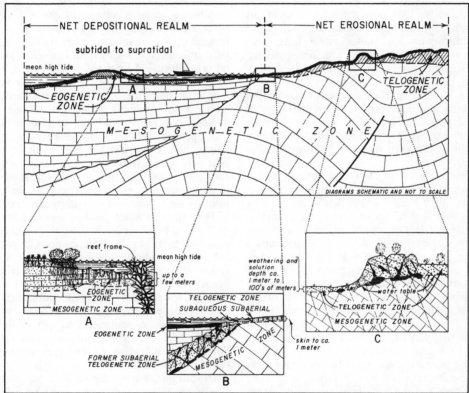

FIG. 1.—Time-porosity terms and zones of creation and modification of porosity in sedimentary carbonates.

Upper diagram: Interrelation of major time-porosity terms. *Primary* porosity either originates at time of deposition (*depositional* porosity) or was present in particles before their final deposition (*predepositional* porosity). *Secondary* or *postdepositional* porosity originates after final deposition and is subdivided into *eogenetic, mesogenetic,* or *telogenetic* porosity depending on stage or burial zone in which it develops (see lower diagram). Bar diagram depicts our concept of "typical" relative durations of stages.

Lower diagram: Schematic representation of major surface and burial zones in which porosity is created or modified. Two major surface realms are those of net deposition and net erosion. Upper cross section and enlarged diagrams **A, B,** and **C** depict three major postdepositional zones. Eogenetic zone extends from surface of newly deposited carbonate to depths where processes genetically related to surface become ineffective. Telogenetic zone extends from erosion surface to depths at which major surface-related erosional processes become ineffective. Below a subaerial erosion surface, practical lower limit of telogenesis is at or near water table. Mesogenetic zone lies below major influences of processes operating at surface. The three terms also apply to time, processes, or features developed in respective zones.

primary regardless of reduction later by cementation or partial filling by internal sediment. However, if primary pores were filled and later processes developed new openings at the sites of these pores, the new porosity would be classed as secondary or postdepositional. The time of origin of the void space is all important. Similarly, if primary pores were enlarged by solution, the resulting space would be partly primary and partly secondary.

A minor classification problem in applying the terms relates to the space occupied in newly deposited carbonates by organic matter that decomposes after burial. We arbitrarily consider pore space created after deposition by decay of buried particles of wood, fibrous roots, and the like to be secondary porosity of a moldic type. However, appreciable pore space in sedimentary carbonates could have been filled at the time of burial with living matter, mucilaginous slimes, or related partly decomposed organic matter, and this space commonly cannot be distinguished from similar pore space which was empty at the time of final deposition. Therefore it is generally practical to classify porosity of these latter kinds, as well as the pore space of body cavities, as primary porosity.

The complexity of carbonate porosity evolution and of differentiation of primary and secondary space becomes apparent if the porosity of individual particles or intraclasts is considered independent of the porosity of the final sedimentary aggregate. By definition all pore space present in a sediment at final deposition is primary porosity. But primary porosity of the sedimentary aggregate may be either primary or secondary in regard to the individual clasts. For example, intraclasts normally contain primary depositional porosity of an interparticle nature that was formed when the source material of the intraclast was deposited. Later, secondary porosity could have been developed in such an intraclast by boring, solution, or some other means, before the final (recycled) deposition of the intraclast. Likewise, porosity "inherited" in clasts derived by erosion of older rocks contributes to the primary porosity of the host sediment, but in relation to the clast itself such inherited porosity may be of primary or secondary origin. Thus, the terms *primary* and *secondary* can by applied usefully to each of the depositional events in which carbonate constituents take part enroute to their final sedimentation, but for these special applications the context in which the terms are used must make

clear the cycle of deposition to which they refer.

Predepositional stage, predepositional porosity.—The *predepositional stage* begins at the time when sedimentary material first is formed and ends with the final deposition and burial of that material or of sedimentary particles derived from it. Porosity created in this stage is *predepositional porosity*. The duration of predepositional time can range from perhaps thousands of years in areas with low sedimentation rates accompanied by processes that permit intermittent reworking of bottom deposits to virtually no time at all where there is direct secretion or precipitation of calcium carbonate into an accreting growth framework.

Although a wide variety of porosity types contribute to predepositional porosity, most are formed by the creation of internal cells, chambers, or other openings within individual skeletal organisms, and by porosity within multiparticle individual grains such as pellets. The volumetric significance of conspicuous cellular openings in skeletal grains can hardly be missed. But nonskeletal grains can also contain much primary predepositional porosity. For example, pellets can contain more than 50 percent pore space. Individual oöliths have appreciable porosity, and in many of the solid-appearing parts of skeletal organisms there is some porosity between or within the crystals.

The extent to which predepositional porosity of both skeletal and nonskeletal particles is modified prior to final deposition is poorly known and needs much research. Illing (1954) called attention to cementation of individual "grains-of-matrix" and composite grains on the Bahama sea floor. More recent work, such as that of Purdy (1963) and of Bathurst (1964, 1966) on Bahama sediments, suggests both the importance and the complexity of porosity genesis and modification in the predepositional stage.

Depositional stage, depositional porosity.—The *depositional stage* is the time period involved in the final deposition, at its site of ultimate burial, of a sediment or an accreting growth framework. Porosity created at this stage is *depositional porosity*. The importance of this stage in porosity formation is out of proportion to its short duration. Depositional porosity may form two thirds or more of the volume of many carbonate muds. In coarser, well-sorted carbonate sediments, depositional porosity commonly forms more than a third of the bulk volume. Most depositional porosity in carbonates is of an interparticle nature; a small amount is created by the growth frameworks of organic or, rarely, inorganic (*e.g.,* travertine) boundstones, but some porosity in boundstones is formed by boring, solution, or other processes at the depositional interface.

Postdepositional stage, postdepositional (secondary) porosity.—The postdepositional stage encompasses all the time after final deposition (Fig. 1). The term "postdepositional" can be used interchangeably with "secondary" in referring to porosity, to processes of porosity origin or evolution, or to the stage in which they occur. The postdepositional time interval is generally long, and there are significant differences in the time-related processes involved in creating and modifying pore space, as well as in the nature of this pore space. Moreover, the geologic zones in which these postdepositional processes operate also differ significantly. There are many ways to subdivide postdepositional time. A practical time subdivision of the postdepositional stage should distinguish among times of major "bursts" in porosity evolution, and should be based on criteria that can be recognized in many ancient carbonate facies. Our approach involves burial stages that commonly can be distinguished by the study of the pore systems of ancient carbonates. The three subdivisions we propose (*eogenetic, mesogenetic,* and *telogenetic*) are based on the importance in porosity evolution of very early and very late postdepositional events. These can be related to surficial processes in contrast to those occurring at greater depths. This approach also is based on the recognition that porosity created or modified early ("eo-") in postdepositional time commonly is very different from porosity created or modified in the late or final ("telo-") stage associated with an erosional surface carved into long-buried rock. The early porosity generally has fabric-selective characteristics and the late does not.

Alternative approaches to porosity evolution relate to the evolution of mineral assemblages or crystal fabrics, or both; to changing conditions of temperature or pressure during a burial cycle; to changes in formation fluids or the origin of formation water involved in diagenesis; and to the evolution of porosity in relation to lithification.

The responses of mineral assemblages and crystal fabrics to changing physicochemical conditions are clearly important and gradually are becoming better understood, as are the changes in fluid composition that occur during diagenesis of carbonates. However, at least at present, these considerations do not serve to establish general subdivisions of the burial cycle that are useful for porosity evolution.

A diagenetic classification (Fairbridge, 1967) proposed for all sediments emphasizes the origin, nature, and direction of movement of formation water. It recognizes that the impact of early and late surface-related processes, and the zones of syndiagenesis, anadiagenesis, and epidiagenesis, are broadly comparable with the zones of eogenesis, mesogenesis, and telogenesis proposed herein. A major difference is that the epidiagenetic zone extends to the recognizable limit of meteoric water, and appears to exclude surficial weathering; the telogenetic zone includes surficial weathering and extends downward through the vadose zone to about the water table. Other contrasts exist. We prefer the system proposed herein for porosity studies of carbonates, but the two approaches are not mutually exclusive.

Lithification is used as a definitive element in several approaches to diagenesis in carbonates (*e.g.,* Chilingar et al., 1967; Hohlt, 1948). But lithification is an impractical criterion. One reason is, "What constitutes lithification?" Is lithification achieved when a granular sediment is cemented just enough to be coherent? Or when a rock is cemented sufficiently to be truly rigid even though rather porous? Or is lithification completed only when all porosity has been obliterated? More fundamental difficulties in using lithification, whatever definition is used, arise from the wide range in time of lithification, even for contemporaneous carbonate deposits of a very small area, and from the problems of determining that time. Some carbonates are essentially "born lithified," such as coral-algal reef frameworks or travertine. Closely associated clastic limestones may be lithified much later. Some carbonates, composed initially of loose aggregates, become lithified while still in the depositional environment, such as carbonate beachrock or supratidal dolomite crusts. Sea-floor cementation of carbonate deposits in subtidal environments is becoming recognized as a significant process as more examples are reported from ancient and Holocene carbonate studies (*e.g.,* Fischer and Garrison, 1967; Friedman, 1965; Ginsburg *et al.,* 1967; Lees, 1964; Lindstrom, 1963; Milliman, 1966; Pray, 1964, 1965; Taft and Harbaugh, 1964). At the other end of the time spectrum some ancient limestones, notably chalks and some oölitic carbonates, are essentially unlithified. Hence, the range in time required for lithification, the complexity of lithification in

ɔnates, and the difficulty of deciding when
ication has been achieved severely limit
the use of lithification as a time reference to
which porosity can be related.

Eogenetic stage, eogenetic porosity.—The
eogenetic stage applies to the time interval between final deposition and burial of the newly deposited sediment or rock below the depth of significant influence by processes that either operate from the surface or depend for their effectiveness on proximity to the surface. *Eogenetic porosity* is that formed in the eogenetic stage. The term can also be used to designate processes occurring during this stage and the zone in which they occur.

The upper limit of the eogenetic zone is the surface (Fig. 1). This is normally a depositional interface, but it may be a surface of temporary nondeposition, or a surface of erosion during a temporary interruption in sedimentation. The upper surface of the eogenetic zone can be subaqueous or subaerial. The lower boundary is gradational with the underlying mesogenetic zone and is less clearly definable, because the effectiveness of some surface-related processes may diminish gradually with depth, and different processes can operate down to different depths. In many carbonate depositional environments, the boundary of the eogenetic zone may be only a few meters below the surface. Most organic influences, such as burrowing, boring, and root penetration, generally are limited to a few meters or less, and most organic decomposition and gas evolution are also likely to be accomplished at shallow depths. In the low-lying terrane of temporarily emergent carbonate deposits and in areas of flat supratidal surfaces that are only occasionally inundated, the effective range of these and other eogenetic processes probably is mainly in the uppermost few meters of the sediment, or perhaps is in a thickness comparable to the "tidal" range. Unfortunately, information is scanty on processes operating more than a meter or two below modern low-lying surfaces of Holocene carbonates, such as in western Andros, Bahamas (Roehl, 1967; Shinn *et al.*, 1965), and on carbonate sabkhas such as those described by Illing *et al.* (1965).

A problem in determining the lower limit of the eogenetic zone is related to the circulation of fluids at depth, which could cause solution, cementation, replacement (including dolomitization), or other diagenetic effects. If reflux of heavier brines occurred only in a shallow zone of sediments below the depositional interface, it would be classified as eogenetic. But if reflux

extends to depths of hundreds of meters, as inferred for the Capitan Reef complex in the pioneering paper of Adams and Rhodes (1960), should all this be considered eogenetic? Or if a freshwater lens is present in newly deposited strata below an oceanic islet, does the eogenetic zone include the entire lens, which may extend many tens of meters below other surface-related processes? These unanswered questions demonstrate the difficulty of applying a single simple classification across the broad range of places and processes involved in carbonate deposition and diagenesis, but hardly prove that the concept of an eogenetic zone or process is without merit.

Although the time of eogenesis may be geologically brief, and the zone thin, eogenetic processes can be of extreme importance in diagenesis and in porosity evolution. The processes that effect these changes or the environments in which they occur are varied, and it is commonly useful to denote them more specifically; hence such terms as "freshwater," "subaerial," or "submarine eogenesis," or more explicit terms such as "vadose eogenetic solution," "submarine eogenetic cementation," or "eogenetic sabkha dolomitization." Very significant porosity evolution may occur during eogenesis of carbonate facies and retain its identity in ancient carbonates. In unconsolidated carbonate sediments, eogenetic porosity can be created by burrowing, sediment shrinkage, sediment distension caused by gas evolution from decomposing organic matter, or root penetration and subsequent decomposition. In more rigid carbonates, boring and root penetration, aided by solution, can create and modify porosity. Eogenetic solution of carbonate or evaporite minerals from a less soluble host, particularly selective solution of aragonite by fresh water, is probably the most important process creating porosity in this zone. However, the major change in the eogenetic zone probably is not creation of new or additional porosity, but reduction of porosity, chiefly through cementation by carbonate or, less commonly, by evaporite minerals. Even the creation of molds from aragonite constituents, though it adds new pores, may reduce porosity either by introduction of cement from another source or by reprecipitation of $CaCO_3$ derived from aragonite in the less dense form, calcite (*cf.* Land, 1967). Internal sedimentation, a porosity-reducing process, most generally occurs in the eogenetic zone. The relation between cement and internal sediment can help in diagnosis of eogenetic cementation, but in many carbonates eogenetic and mesogenetic cementations are difficult or impossible to differentiate.

Mesogenetic stage, mesogenetic porosity.— The term *mesogenetic* is here proposed for the time interval or stage in which the sediments or rocks are buried at depth below the major influence of processes directly operating from or closely related to the surface. It constitutes the entire time between the geologically brief early stage of burial and a final phase of imminent erosion. *Mesogenetic porosity* is that created during the mesogenetic stage. Mesogenetic also applies to the processes occurring within the mesogenetic stage and to the zone in which they occur (Fig. 1).

Porosity changes in sedimentary carbonates within the zone of mesogenesis can be presumed to be extensive. Cementation is probably the major process affecting porosity in the mesogenetic zone, whereas solution is probably minor. Both processes commonly begin in the eogenetic stage. Porosity obliteration may persist through much of mesogenesis. Filling of the innermost parts of formerly larger pore spaces by mosaics of coarsely crystalline calcite may reflect long-continued mesogenetic cementation in rock becoming progressively less permeable. Although many carbonate facies show little evidence of compaction (Beales, 1965; Pray, 1961), marked physical compaction and pressure-solution effects probably can be related to the higher pressures of the mesogenetic zone.

Subdivision of the broad realm of mesogenesis would be desirable, and may become more feasible as future research provides more interpretive leverage. The evolution of the mineral assemblages or of the fabrics undoubtedly will be useful.

Telogenetic stage, telogenetic porosity.—The term *telogenetic* is here proposed for the time interval or stage during which long-buried carbonate rocks are influenced significantly by processes associated with the formation of an unconformity. *Telogenetic porosity* is that formed during the telogenetic stage, and the term can be applied to processes operating at that time, or to the zone influenced by these late-stage processes. The term applies specifically to the erosion of old rocks, in contrast to erosion of newly deposited sediments or rocks during temporary interruptions of a long period of deposition. The prefix "telo-," from the Greek *telos* meaning end or final, is used to denote a final or very late effect in contrast to the early effects connoted by "eo-" (Greek *eos*,

dawn or early). Telogenetic porosity is unconformity-developed porosity, but not all porosity associated with an unconformity is of this type. The upper limit of the telogenetic zone is the subaerial or subaqueous erosional interface. The lower boundary is gradational and is placed at the depth at which the erosional processes become insignificant or unrecognizable. The depth of the telogenetic zone and the sharpness of the lower boundary can range widely, depending on the nature of the erosional processes, the environment of erosion, and the nature of the substrate. Although the zone can range in thickness up to hundreds of meters in high-standing areas of karst topography, it is generally a thin zone in the geologic record. In some areas of low relief or of marine planation across massive, nonporous carbonates, it may be less than a meter, and beneath many unconformities no telogenetic zone is detectable.

The lower limit of the telogenetic zone extends to or somewhat below the water table. The telogenetic zone thus encompasses the vadose zone below subaerial surfaces and may include rock affected by phreatic solution associated with the water table. The water table commonly appears to serve as an effective lower limit of many weathering processes including solution. Although Davis (1930) and Bretz (1942) have shown the importance of phreatic solution in cavern development, fortunately for the purpose of locating a practical geologic boundary, most phreatic solution may occur not far below the water table (Thrailkill, 1968).

Solution by meteoric water is undoubtedly the major porosity-forming process of the telogenetic zone. Processes other than solution that create porosity in the telogenetic zone are many, but minor. Borings into a subaqueous erosion surface and fracture and breccia porosity consequent upon solution-collapse may be locally important. Porosity-reduction processes are largely those of filling by (1) internal sedimentation and (2) precipitation from solution in either the vadose zone below a subaerial surface or the subaqueous zone beneath a submarine erosion surface.

In ancient carbonates a variety of features can be used to identify the telogenetic zone. The criteria of fabric selectivity, discussed in Part 1, are very useful in distinguishing telogenetic secondary pore systems from eogenetic pore systems. If the pore boundaries are not fabric selective, the porosity is likely to be telogenetic. Features suggestive of the vadose zone below subaerial erosion surfaces include typical cave deposits, the subtler but distinctive forms of internal sediment (Dunham, 1963), dedolomitization structures shown to be products of weathering (Evamy, 1967), and cementing minerals such as limonite and goethite whose presence similarly reflects oxidizing conditions.

It was long believed that much porosity in carbonates formed by solution below major unconformities. Without doubt, some important petroleum reservoirs and aquifers were created in this manner. The oil fields of the "Golden Lane" in the El Abra Limestone of Mexico (Bonet, 1952) are excellent examples of spectacular porosity (cavern) development associated with an unconformity. But the importance commonly attributed to this late-stage porosity development (*e.g.,* Levorsen, 1967; Murray, 1930) seems overrated. Telogenetic porosity influence on petroleum reservoir quality seems much better demonstrated in the significant enhancement of permeability by fracturing and subsequent solution enlargement than in the development of large volumes of new pore space.

As the length of the mesogenetic stage diminishes, both the distinction between telogenesis and eogenesis and the usefulness of trying to make this distinction diminish. Telogenesis grades into eogenesis somewhat as unconformities grade into diastems. How much older must the eroded strata be than the erosion surface to qualify for telogenesis? Where the age difference spans geologic periods or epochs, the usual diagnosis would be telogenesis; for shorter intervals of time the decision is commonly more arbitrary. Elements besides actual age difference that might be pertinent in distinguishing temporary eogenetic erosion from telogenetic erosion could be the amount of uplift, the amount of eroded strata, or the degree of mineral stabilization or cementation. We would classify as eogenetic the zones of minor erosion and temporary uplift that are common in each of a series of cycles. Thus the intertidal to supratidal cycles described by Laporte (1967) and Roehl (1967) would represent eogenetic erosion, and not telogenesis. The erosion surface that separates Pleistocene from Holocene carbonates in south Florida and the Bahamas could be telogenetic or eogenetic, depending on one's purpose in classification.

PART 3. CLASSIFICATION OF
CARBONATE POROSITY

Classifications of porosity in sedimentary carbonates, like most systems of ordering natural phenomena, vary in objectives, emphasis, and detail. No single published classification we know of has the major goal of aiding the geologic interpretation of porosity, or is structured to permit the succinct recording of both physical and genetic characteristics. The literature bearing on the classification of porosity in carbonates can be grouped into two general types, one primarily concerned with the physical properties of principal utility for evaluating or exploiting the fluid content of the rocks, and the other with more geologic or genetic emphasis.

Several classifications in the petroleum geology literature focus on purely descriptive, physical properties of pore systems—the volume percent porosity or other physical properties such as size, shape, and distribution of pores. The main objective of these classifications is correlation of these physical properties with such petrophysical properties as permeability, relative permeability, capillary pressure, fluid saturation, and electrical resistivity. Classifications of this type include those of Teodorovich (*in* Chilingar, 1957; Aschenbrenner and Chilingar, 1960), Archie (1952), Stout (1964), and Jodry (1966).

Classifications of carbonate porosity with more geologic or genetic emphasis are of various types. Some of the earlier published articles relating rock textures or structures to porosity are the very generalized classifications of Howard (1928), Murray (1930), and Howard and David (1936), and the more detailed classification of Imbt and Ellison (1946). A detailed system with particular emphasis on fracture openings is that of Waldschmidt *et al.* (1956). Although the literature on carbonate-rock classification has increased significantly in the past decade, in most of it porosity classification has been ignored or treated only incidentally. Thus, of the articles in a symposium volume on carbonate rock classification edited by Ham (1962), only those by Leighton and Pendexter, Powers, and Thomas consider porosity in any detail. The treatment by Thomas is the most detailed and genetic. It provides illustrations and some discussion of a variety of types of porosity, and also calls attention to the effect of carbonate matrix sorting on porosity, a consideration generally overlooked. More recent classifications of carbonate rocks, however, treat porosity briefly and in general terms (*e.g.,* Sander, 1967; Todd, 1966).

Some of the most valuable recent literature on porosity of sedimentary carbonates is concerned primarily with geologic interpretation and not with problems of classification as such. Thus von Engelhardt's (1960) treatise on porosity in sedimentary rocks affords useful insight on carbonate porosity but does not give a detailed classification. Other articles that add to an understanding of porosity, but emphasize the geologic characteristics, occurrence, and origin of pore space rather than classification, are by Illing *et al.* (1967), Lucia (1962), Lucia and Murray (1967), R. C. Murray (1960), R. C. Murray and Lucia (1967), Roehl (1967), and Schmidt (1965). The general approach in these articles is well expressed by Murray's statement (1960, p. 61) that the ". . . general categories [of porosity] by no means form a suggested classification, but only provide a framework for examining processes and mechanisms of porosity formation and destruction." A recent article on carbonate reservoir rocks by Harbaugh (1967) uses with only slight modification the "general categories" of Murray (1960).

There long has been a need for a comprehensive geologic classification of porosity in sedimentary carbonates—a classification specific enough to permit detailed description, yet genetically oriented enough to foster and guide the kinds of observations needed to understand the origins and modifications of porosity. The system we propose has these goals.

Our approach is to identify porosity with other sediment or rock constituents, textures, and structures, focusing on those features to which the origin and later evolution of pores and pore systems seem most commonly related. In taking this approach we have drawn heavily on current terminology and concepts. The result is a broadly applicable system which is sufficiently "open" to allow the incorporation of other descriptive or interpretive terms. The classification was designed primarily for use in porosity study of hand specimens and cores, but also is adaptable to both microscopic and field studies.

The four main elements of the proposed classification are shown in Figures 2 and 3. These elements include what we call "basic porosity types" (the principal group of elements), and three sets of porosity modifiers that concern (1) the time of porosity origin and the process and direction or stage of porosity modification, aspects we designate with genetic modifiers, (2) pore size (and shape), and (3) pore abundance. The modifiers may be used singly or in combinations, either with a basic porosity type, or with the more general designations of

pore or porosity. These features provide much of the descriptive and interpretive value of the classification and adapt it for different levels of detail.

Basic Porosity Types

A principal element of the proposed classification is the characterization of a given pore or pore system as one or more of several basic porosity types. Each type is simply a physically or genetically distinctive kind of pore or pore system that can be defined by such attributes as pore size, pore shape, genesis, and position or association relative to either particular constituents or overall fabric.

We recognize 15 basic types of porosity which are listed in the summary chart of Figure 2 and are defined in the glossary. Most of them are illustrated in Figures 4 through 12. Other basic types could be recognized, but these 15, in combination with the other elements of the classification, permit detailed geologic characterization of almost all porosity in sedimentary carbonates. Recognition of these 15 types appears to be the most practical way to cope with the extreme physical and genetic diversity of pore systems in carbonates and still use current terms.

The 15 basic types vary considerably in volumetric abundance and commonness of occurrence. Seven of them are extremely common and volumetrically important, probably forming the bulk of pore space in most sedimentary carbonates. These types are interparticle, intraparticle, intercrystal, moldic, fenestral, fracture, and vug porosity. The rest appear to be less abundant, although some are common (*e.g.*, shelter porosity), and their separate designation and recognition can be useful for porosity characterization and facies interpretation.

Most of the basic types recognized here have been identified and named by previous workers, and their names conform as closely as possible to current usage and generally identify the main characteristics. Definitions of some types, particularly vug, channel, and growth framework, have been restricted or modified from current ill-defined, broad, and/or variable usage, both to make them more meaningful as porosity terms and to integrate them better into the system.

The attributes that characterize the 15 basic porosity types, such as size, shape, genesis, or position with respect to fabric elements of the rock, merit further attention to clarify the nature of these types. Table 2 summarizes the main attributes involved in the definitions. The single element in defining three porosity types —interparticle, intraparticle, and intercrystal —is the position of the pore with respect to the fabric elements; pore size, shape, and origin are involved either secondarily or not at all in the definitions. One basic type, cavern porosity, is defined solely on the basis of size. Others such as moldic, boring, and shrinkage are defined solely on the basis of origin. Still others such as vug, channel, and various minor types are more complexly defined on the basis of several attributes.

Determining which of the basic porosity types are present in a sediment or rock is not only a matter of identification and interpretation; it also involves judgments as to which of the types best serve the classifier's needs. Several of the porosity types are not mutually exclusive. Thus, the porosity within a pellet composed of aragonite crystals may be interparticle porosity with reference to the component crystals, but on a larger scale it is intraparticle porosity. In Figure 8F the porosity of the sediment within the gastropod shell is primary interparticle porosity, but is also part of the intraparticle porosity in the gastropod. Likewise, dolomitized sediment in a burrow may contain intercrystal porosity that could be designated as burrow porosity, as intercrystal porosity, or as both. Some of the basic types of porosity are little more than physical or genetic varieties of other basic types; for example, fenestral, shelter, and breccia are all varieties of interparticle porosity. Clearly, classification cannot be separated from one's objectives. Deciding which basic porosity types are to be used relates to one's purpose.

The interrelations of the basic porosity types with the time of their origin relative to final deposition and with their mode of origin are summarized in Table 3. It is important to recognize that many of the types can be created at different times and by different processes. For example, although interparticle porosity commonly forms during the process of final deposition of the carbonate sediment, some can form prior to final deposition. Of more significance, interparticle porosity can also form after deposition by selective solution of matrix particles from between larger particles. Thus, the practice of equating the interparticle (intergranular) porosity of carbonates with primary or depositional porosity (*e.g.,* Levorsen, 1967, p. 113) is an unfortunate simplification, though it may be satisfactory for most sandstones. The complexity introduced into the interpretation of carbonate porosity by multiple modes and times of origins is a prime reason for using genetic modifiers with basic porosity types.

Compound and gradational basic porosity types.—Many carbonate facies contain two or more basic types of porosity that are easily differentiated. *Compound* pore systems are those composed of two or more basic types of pores, each type physically somewhat discrete and easily distinguishable. Common examples are those composed of both interparticle and intraparticle porosity, of moldic and intercrystalline porosity, or of any fabric-selective type of porosity combined with fracture porosity (Fig. 12).

Gradational pores or pore systems cannot be clearly differentiated physically and/or genetically. They may be intermediate in characteristics between two basic types; or they may intergrade in very short distances within a thin section, hand specimen, or small part of an exposure; or they may interconnect in a manner that makes separate recognition difficult. As an example, fracture porosity commonly grades both spatially and genetically into breccia porosity, a situation approximated in Figure 11A and B. In some sucrose dolomites where depositional texture is poorly preserved, the larger intercrystal porosity may grade into, and be indistinguishable from, that of small molds or vugs. As another example, carbonates may have some porosity that is both interparticle and moldic, but much of the porosity may not be resolvable into one or the other type; their porosity is gradational.

Gradational porosity also may be designated in the many instances in which fabric-selective porosity becomes nonselective within very short distances. For example, a pore of channel shape may have margins that are locally fabric selective; the channel may have begun to form by solution enlargement of interparticle voids, some of whose edges are preserved along its margins.

Another type of gradation of basic types occurs between interparticle and shelter porosity or interparticle and fenestral porosity. Shelter and fenestral are varieties of interparticle porosity, and distinguished from it partly by the larger size of the pore in relation to the associated particles. As pore size diminishes in relation to these fabric elements, the distinctions also diminish and pores can be classified as of either type or as gradational between them.

Fabric selectivity of basic porosity types.—

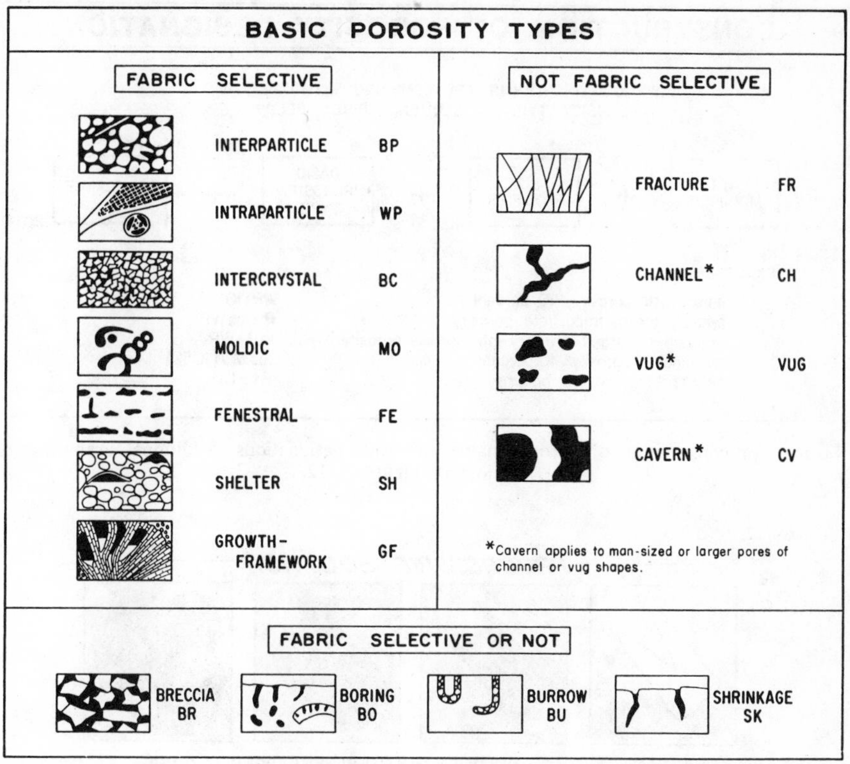

BASIC POROSITY TYPES

FABRIC SELECTIVE

INTERPARTICLE	BP
INTRAPARTICLE	WP
INTERCRYSTAL	BC
MOLDIC	MO
FENESTRAL	FE
SHELTER	SH
GROWTH-FRAMEWORK	GF

NOT FABRIC SELECTIVE

FRACTURE	FR
CHANNEL*	CH
VUG*	VUG
CAVERN*	CV

*Cavern applies to man-sized or larger pores of channel or vug shapes.

FABRIC SELECTIVE OR NOT

BRECCIA BR	BORING BO	BURROW BU	SHRINKAGE SK

MODIFYING TERMS

GENETIC MODIFIERS

PROCESS

SOLUTION	s
CEMENTATION	c
INTERNAL SEDIMENT	i

DIRECTION OR STAGE

ENLARGED	x
REDUCED	r
FILLED	f

TIME OF FORMATION

PRIMARY	P
pre-depositional	Pp
depositional	Pd
SECONDARY	S
eogenetic	Se
mesogenetic	Sm
telogenetic	St

Genetic modifiers are combined as follows:

PROCESS + DIRECTION + TIME

EXAMPLES:

solution-enlarged	sx
cement-reduced primary	crP
sediment-filled eogenetic	ifSe

SIZE* MODIFIERS

CLASSES			mm†
			256
MEGAPORE	mg	large	lmg
			32
		small	smg
			4
MESOPORE	ms	large	lms
			1/2
		small	sms
			1/16
MICROPORE	mc		

Use size prefixes with basic porosity types:

mesovug	msVUG
small mesomold	smsMO
microinterparticle	mcBP

*For regular-shaped pores smaller than cavern size.

†Measures refer to average pore diameter of a single pore or the range in size of a pore assemblage. For tubular pores use average cross-section. For platy pores use width and note shape.

ABUNDANCE MODIFIERS

percent porosity	(15%)
or	
ratio of porosity types	(1:2)
or	
ratio and percent	(1:2) (15%)

FIG. 2.—Geologic classification of pores and pore systems in carbonate rocks.

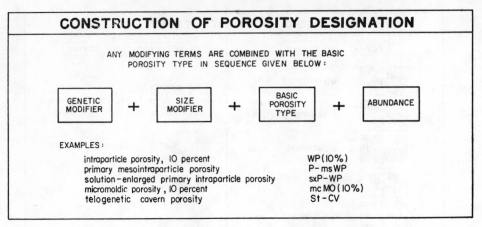

FIG. 3.—Format for construction of porosity name and code designations. Additional examples are shown in captions of Figures 5–12.

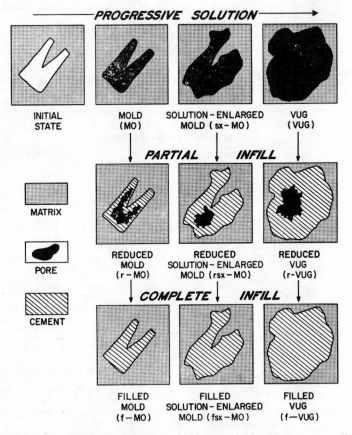

FIG. 4.—Common stages in evolution of one basic type of pore, a mold, showing applications of genetic modifiers and classification code. Starting material is crinoid columnal (top left). It, and matrix adjoining it, then may be dissolved in varying degrees. Depending on extent of solution (top row), resulting pore is classed as mold, solution-enlarged mold, or vug if precursor's identity is lost. Filling by cement could occur after each solution stage.

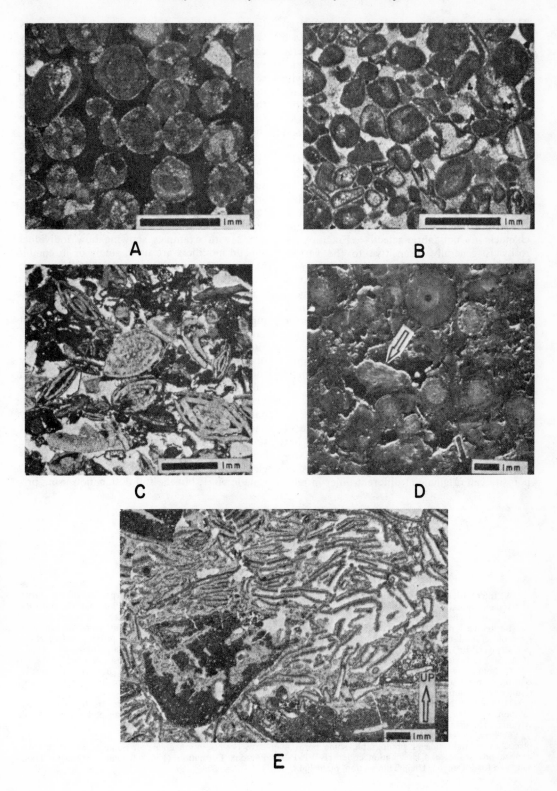

The basic porosity types can be characterized usefully on the basis of fabric selectivity (see Fig. 2 and discussion in Part 1), a property which stresses relations between pore space and other constituents. The two fabric-selectivity criteria of pore position and pore-boundary configuration help both in identifying basic porosity types and in interpreting their times of origin. Interparticle, intercrystal, moldic, and fenestral pores have both their positions and their boundaries determined by the fabric elements, hence are fabric selective. Most intraparticle porosity also is fabric selective and is so classed in Figure 2. Some nonselective intraparticle porosity may be present, however, such as a vug within a clast. By definition, vugs and channels are not fabric selective. Fracture porosity is generally insensitive to the smaller scale features of the rock, and hence is considered not fabric selective. But where pore systems that would be classified as vugs, channels, or fractures on the basis of their indiscriminate position relative to fabric elements show fabric selectivity along part or all of their boundaries, they may have formed before complete cementation of the rock. Thus, the abnormal fabric selectivity of some basic pore types has genetic significance.

Genetic Modifiers

Genetic information is implicit in some of the designations of basic porosity types, but other basic-type terms supply little or no genetic information (Table 2). Many types of porosity can originate at different times in relation to sediment deposition or burial, and by several processes. And, once created, porosity can be modified by various processes. These processes, and the direction and extent of porosity evolution, are significant descriptive and interpretive elements. The genetic modifers in this classification provide a way to designate such elements. They can be used either with the basic porosity types or independently.

We recognize 13 genetic modifiers of three types which denote (1) the *time* of origin of the porosity, (2) the *process* involved in its subsequent modification, and (3) the *direction* and extent of such modification(s), herein referred to simply as the "direction." The three types are listed in the summary diagram of Figure 2 with examples showing how individual genetic modifiers are used, singly or in combinations. The complete genetic-modifier term coupled with the basic porosity type provides a definitive porosity characterization (Fig. 3).

Time modifiers.—The seven modifers relating to time of origin consist of the two most general time terms, *primary* and *secondary,* and five more detailed time terms that are subdivisions of the two general terms. Specifically these are *predepositional* and *depositional,* both subdivisions of primary; and *eogenetic, mesogenetic,* and *telogenetic,* all subdivisions of secondary. These terms are defined in the glossary and discussed in Part 2. The five more explicit time terms can be combined directly with the basic porosity type (*e.g.,* depositional interparticle porosity, eogenetic moldic porosity, or telogenetic vug), but the full designation using pri-

←〿

FIG. 5.—Examples of interparticle porosity

A. Interparticle porosity in oölitic grainstone. Grainstone is well sorted and free of interparticle matrix. Little of its depositional porosity (black) has been filled. Classification: primary depositional interparticle porosity (Pd-BP). Ste. Genevieve Limestone (Mississippian), Bridgeport field, Illinois. Thin section, cross-polarized light.

B. Reduced primary interparticle porosity (black) in oölitic grainstone. Calcite cement, some as syntaxial rims on crinoid columnals, has filled most pore space. Classification: cement-reduced primary interparticle porosity (crP-BP). Remaining voids are classified as small mesopores (sms) in contrast to large mesopores (lms) of **A.** Ste. Genevieve Limestone (Mississippian), Bridgeport field, Illinois. Thin section, cross-polarized light.

C. Solution interparticle porosity in foraminiferal packstone. Pores are white. Note irregular, erratically distributed pores and finely particulate matrix (dark gray) within and between forams. Porosity appears to have resulted from solution of matrix. Tertiary, Libya. Thin section, plane light.

D. Solution interparticle porosity in crinoid-fusulinid packstone. Pores (black) were created largely by solution of matrix, in places with partial corrosion of large particles (arrow). Classification code: s-BP. Pennsylvanian, Hulldale field, Texas. Polished core surface.

E. Primary and reduced primary interparticle and intraparticle porosity in phylloid algal grainstone. In places, as on right side of photograph, some pores may have been solution enlarged. Some algal plates have trapped fine sediment. Classification code: rP-WP/P-BP. Paradox Formation (Pennsylvanian), Honaker Trail, San Juan River Canyon, Utah. Thin section, plane light.

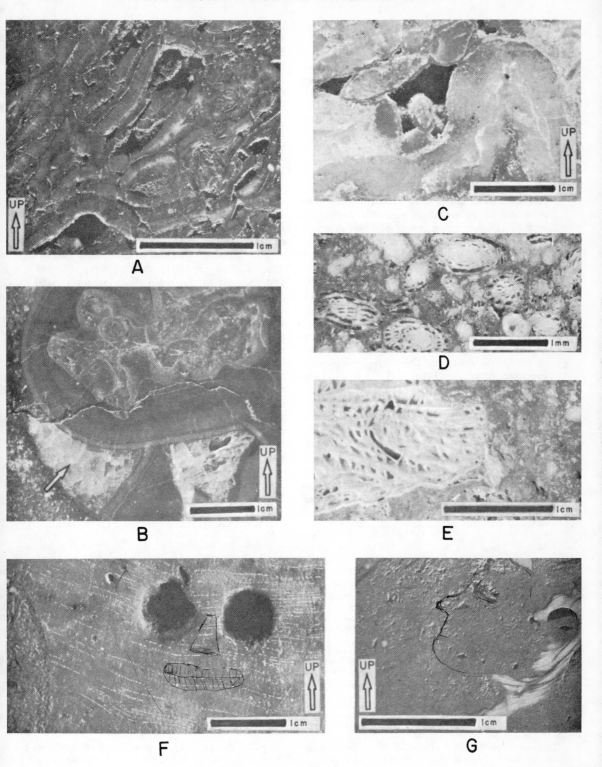

mary or secondary together with the more explicit terms may be desirable (*e.g.,* primary depositional or secondary eogenetic).

Modification process and direction.—Six of the 13 genetic modifiers relate to the processes by which pores are modified, and to the direction(s) taken by modifications. An example of some of the possible modification effects is shown diagrammatically in Figure 4 for a crinoid mold.

Of a variety of modification processes, *solution, cementation,* and *internal sedimentation* are recognized in this classification. *Solution* processes both create and modify pores. The main use of "solution" as a genetic modifier is to note solution enlargement of basic types of porosity and to designate a solution origin for those basic types that designate position in a fabric, namely interparticle and intercrystal. The designation of solution is not required for moldic porosity, a basic type defined as solution created. As solution normally is assumed to have been the genetic mechanism in vug, channel, and cavern porosity, with these terms it need not be specified. *Cementation,* used here in the broad sense for the filling of voids by precipitation of mineral matter from solutions, probably accounts for most of the wholesale reduction of porosity from newly deposited sediments to ancient rocks. The reduction process can be noted specifically by the modifier term "cementation." The quantitative importance of internal sedimentation as a porosity-reducing process in carbonates is still being debated, but the process is being recognized increasingly as a useful indicator of special postdepositional

events, such as vadose circulation (Dunham, 1963). Normally it occurs as particle-by-particle deposition within the interstices of a porous sediment or rock. Processes of mass sediment injection associated with limestone clastic dikes (Pray, 1964) also may eliminate some porosity.

The porosity of some carbonates may be reduced by changes in packing consequent upon physical compaction. This is not provided for in our system, because it is believed to be uncommon and is difficult to recognize or record on the basis of pore characteristics. Other processes of porosity modification, such as gas distension or mineral-volume change, likewise are not considered feasible to note for the purpose of this classification.

The direction or extent of the porosity modification is noted by three modifiers, *enlarged* and *reduced* as the main direction terms, and *filled* for the commonly encountered end stage of porosity reduction. These are used best with the notation of process, but can be used independently. The modifier "enlarged" normally is used to denote enlargement by solution. It is applied only to modifications that do not obliterate the identity of the original pore. "Reduced" is used for stages of porosity reduction between the initial state and the end stage of "filled." In view of the almost universal reduction of pores by some cementation or other form of filling, the modifier "reduced" is used, as in "reduced primary interparticle porosity," normally only if the volumetric reduction is appreciable, perhaps 30–50 percent or more. Examples of reduced porosity are shown in

←‹‹‹‹‹

FIG. 6.—Examples of intraparticle, boring, and shelter porosity.

A. Shelter porosity (SH), a type of interparticle porosity, in algal packstone. Large pores (black) were sheltered from sediment beneath "umbrellalike" phylloid algae. Paradox Formation (Pennsylvanian), Ratherford field, Utah. Polished core surface.

B. Primary (depositional) shelter porosity below reef framework (megabreccia clast) virtually filled by white sparry calcite cement. Classification: cement-filled depositional shelter porosity (cfPd-SH). Upper Bone Spring Limestone (Permian), Guadalupe Mountains, Texas. Polished surface.

C. Shelter porosity between coarse stromatoporoid fragments in coarse-textured part of fine-grained, nearly nonporous packstone. Loosely packed, relatively coarse debris prevented infilling by finer contemporaneous sediment (white). Leduc Formation (Devonian), Redwater field, Alberta, Canada. Polished core surface.

D. Intraparticle porosity within fusulinids. Classification: primary mesointraparticle porosity (P-msWP). Lansing Group (Pennsylvanian), Kansas. Polished core surface.

E. Intraparticle porosity in horn coral. Pennsylvanian, Hulldale field, Texas. Polished core surface.

F. Boring porosity (BO) of large-mesopore size which truncates growth laminations (accented by retouching on photo) in massive stromatoporoid. Matrix at left is fine-grained packstone. Leduc Formation (Devonian), Redwater field, Alberta, Canada. Polished core surface.

G. Boring in thick-shelled pelecypod. Note partial filling by internal sediment, which suggests that shell was bored before its final deposition. Classification: sediment-reduced, predepositional boring porosity (irPp-BO). Matrix surrounding shell and internal sediment are porous, dolomitic, bioclastic packstone. Tertiary, Libya. Polished core surface.

FIG. 7.—Intercrystal porosity in dolomites.

A. Microcrystal porosity (black) in sucrose dolomite of very fine texture and high porosity (37 percent). Micropores are well connected and form very permeable pore system. Classification code: mcBC (37%). Ste. Genevieve Formation (Mississippian), Bridgeport field, Illinois. Thin section, cross-polarized light.

B. Broken surface of rock shown in A, illustrating finely sucrose texture as highlighted by small reflecting crystal surfaces.

C. Mesointercrystal porosity (black) in sucrose dolomite. Apparent "diameters" of pores that look discrete in two dimensions range from about 0.02 to about 0.1 mm, but are dominantly of small-mesopore sizes. Note that photos A and C are at same scale. Porosity is 14 percent. Classification code: smsBC (14%). Madison Group (Mississippian), Oregon Basin field, Wyoming.

Figures 5B, 8E, and 10C. If greater detail is needed, the amount of reduction can be stated, as in "reduced 40 percent" or "reduced one half," and a corresponding code notation of "$r_{40\%}$" or "$r_{1/2}$" can be used. The designation "filled" is commonly very useful in description and interpretation of the porosity evolution of nonporous carbonate rocks, which are much more common than porous carbonates. It also permits treatment of obliterated voids in rocks retaining some porosity. Filled former voids may involve more than half the volume of the rock!

The direction term *incomplete* can be useful for designating incompletely formed molds, but for simplicity and because the term is not as widely applicable as the others, it is not a formal part of the classification.

Pore Size and Pore-Size Modifiers

The size of pores in sedimentary carbonates is an important descriptive parameter, but one difficult to treat. The distinction has been made between pores and pore throats or interconnections. Some quantitative visual characterization of pore size generally can be made without undue difficulty, but determination of pore-throat size by direct observation is generally difficult or impossible. Pore-throat size can be determined indirectly by observation in those unusual carbonates that consist of grains of uniform size, shape, and packing; but uncemented, well-sorted oölites and their textural analogs are rare! The vast preponderance of ancient carbonates and most modern carbonate sediments require capillary-pressure measurements combined with other mass-response petrophysical data to characterize pore-throat size quantitatively. Such characterizations, though important for an understanding of reservoir behavior, are outside the scope of this classification; here we are concerned primarily with pore-system attributes that can be directly and readily observed. How can the size of the pores, as differentiated from pore throats, best be characterized? What level of precision is feasible for most geologic description and interpretation? Our system is summarized in Figure 2.

Several factors make it difficult or impossible to be precise in a visual characterization of pore size. One is that the physical boundaries of an individual pore are arbitrary if, as is normal, the pore is part of a continuous pore system. A second limiting factor is the difficulty (and even impossibility) of observing the three-dimensional shape of pores. Shapes generally must be visualized from a two-dimensional surface in an opaque rock. A third factor is the irregular shape of pores. But the main control on useful precision relates, not to these difficulties in determining the size of an individual pore, but to the normal range in sizes and shapes of all the pores in a reservoir, outcrop, hand specimen, or even thin section. The common need for geologic description is

an expression of average size or average size range as determined by quick visual inspection. Practicality thus dictates a need for broad size (and shape) classes. If size is expressed by a diameter measure, the question of which diameter is somewhat academic if many pores are considered. A pore-size grade scale as detailed as the Wentworth scale for grain sizes, utilizing a class interval ratio of two, or even of four (Todd, 1966), is usually much too refined for carbonate porosity.

Some need for expressing pore size in carbonates can be eliminated by careful lithologic description, coupled with a notation of the basic porosity type. Thus, the interparticle porosity in a slightly cemented, well-sorted, medium-grained oölite rarely needs a direct pore-size description. Likewise, the description, "fusulinid moldic porosity," may convey adequately both size and shape of pore. Another way of simplifying pore-size expressions is to describe the pore size of each porosity type individually, rather than the whole pore-size spectrum collectively.

To designate pore size quantitatively, pore shape first must be considered, and in carbonates the shapes can be extremely diverse. We divide pore shapes into two broad categories: *regular*, with shapes that can be characterized by one-, two-, or three-diameter measures, and *irregular*, with shapes so complex they cannot be described adequately by a few measurements. It is impractical to subdivide the many possible shapes of irregular pores. Regular pores, however, can be classified on the basis of their diameters and pore shapes: *equant, tubular,* and *platy.* Tubular and platy pores are notably elongate in one or two directions or diameters, in comparison to the short diameter. The equant class includes pores whose three diameters are about the same and pores that are not so distinctly elongate in one or two dimensions as to be called tubular or platy. The range in shape of closely associated pores makes unnecessary much concern with precise boundaries between these three regular-shape categories.

For size classification, equant pores can be characterized adequately by a single measure, an average diameter. Sizes of tubular and platy pores can be characterized adequately by an average cross-section diameter or width. In this pore-size classification, if shape is not specified, it can be assumed that essentially equant-shaped pores are referred to. Shape should be specified explicitly where pores are tubular or platy, unless shape is implicit in the porosity-

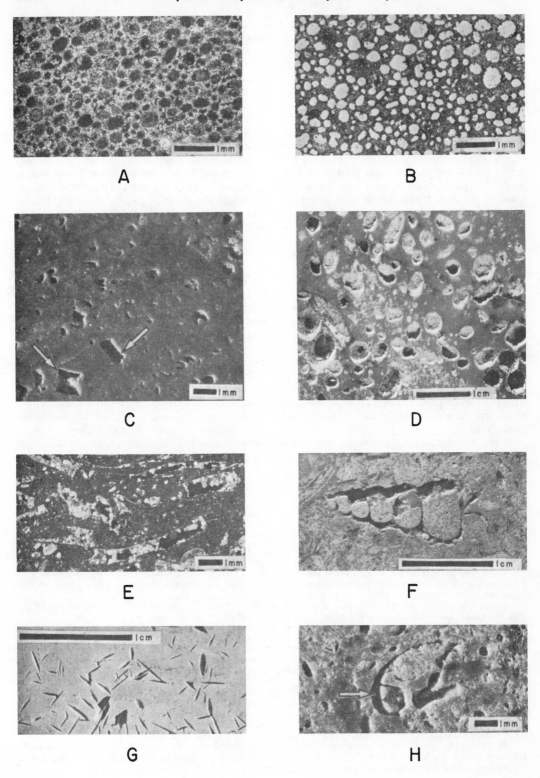

type term, such as fracture porosity where measurement could be assumed to mean width. In practice, size classification is made easier by the fact that average diameters of equant pores and cross-section diameters of tubular and platy openings are the most easily observed measures.

The pore-size classification is shown in the bottom part of Figure 2. We propose three main size classes for regular-shaped pores smaller than cavern size (diameter exceeds 256 mm): *micro-* for pores smaller than 1/16 mm, *meso-* for pores 1/16–4 mm, and *mega-* for pores larger than 4 mm. These class terms are used as prefixes to the word "pore" itself (*e.g.*, micropore or megapore) if only size is to be designated, or as prefixes to the basic porosity type if this is designated (*e.g.*, micromoldic, mesointercrystal, or megavug).

Two subdivisions of the mega- and meso-size ranges are useful, based on subclass interval ratios of eight. Subdivision of micropores is more difficult and has limited value in visual work. Subdivisions of the meso- size are *small* (1/16–½ mm) and *large* (½–4 mm). The two subclasses of megapores are likewise *small* (4–32 mm) and *large* (32–256 mm). Openings larger than about 256 mm (roughly "man size") in average diameter, cross section, or width are classified simply as "caverns" (see glossary).

There are significant advantages of such a grade scale permitting size prefixes to be com-bined with the word "pore" to form a complete size term, as in "micropore," "mesopore," or "megapore." Size characterization can be independent of judgments as to type of porosity. The term "vug" can be restricted more readily to the geologically more meaningful sense proposed in this classification, and terms like "micropore" and "small mesopore" can be used to replace the ill-defined and loosely used term "pinpoint" (see glossary).

Choices of boundaries for the size classes were guided in part by the natural selection or geologic breaks they achieve, and the manner in which the porosity can be observed. Micropores can be assessed only with a hand lens or microscope. Mesopores are normally observable in hand specimens and subsurface cores, and megapores are so large that generally they can be observed and described only in outcrop, or inferred from tool drops during the drilling of wells. These broadest size categories have significance as geologic fences across the wide range of pore sizes in carbonates. Porosity in chalks and earthy dolomites is dominantly microporosity. As shown by Archie (1952), carbonates of chalky or earthy texture generally differ significantly from coarser pore systems in such petrophysical attributes as porosity-permeability characteristics, fluid saturations, capillary-pressure behavior, or electrical resistivity. Most of the intraparticle, moldic, and fenestral porosity and the coarser interparticle and intercrystal porosity in limestones and dolomites are

---

←⦗⦗⦗

Fig. 8.—Examples of moldic porosity.

A. Moldic porosity in pellet packstone. Many molds (black) are incomplete. Paradox Formation (Pennsylvanian), Ismay field, Utah. Thin section, cross-polarized light.

B. Moldic porosity in dolomitized pellet packstone. Molds (white) are dominantly of small mesopore sizes. Classification: small mesomoldic porosity (smsMO). Smackover Limestone (Jurassic), Texas. Thin section, plane light.

C. Moldic porosity in dolomite due largely to solution of calcitic crinoid columnals. Madison Group (Mississippian), Oregon Basin field, Wyoming. Polished core surface.

D. Fusulinid moldic or fusumoldic porosity in dolomitized wackestone. Some fusulinids were incompletely dissolved. San Andres Formation (Permian), Andrews Co., Texas. Polished core surface.

E. Reduced moldic porosity in phylloid algal wackestone. Molds of fragmented platy algae have been filled partly to completely by sparry calcite. Classification: cement-reduced moldic porosity (cr-MO). Paradox Formation (Pennsylvanian), Ismay field, Utah. Thin section, cross-polarized light. From Choquette and Traut (1963).

F. Gastropod mold in dolomitic packstone. Shell has been dissolved, leaving intraparticle filling of internal sediment and coarse calcite. Internal sediment and surrounding packstone matrix contain compound interparticle and intercrystal (in dolomitized micrite) porosity. Tertiary, Libya. Polished core surface.

G. Gypsum crystal molds in unfossiliferous, microcrystalline dolomite. Greenfield Formation (Silurian), Ohio. Polished surface. Specimen courtesy of C. H. Summerson (see Summerson, 1966).

H. Pelecypod (arrow) in dolomite containing abundant moldic porosity. Precursor responsible for molds can be noted by symbols such as MO_{pe} for this example; MO_{fu} for example in D; MO_{ga} for F; MO_{gy} for G; *etc.* Tertiary, Libya. Polished core surface.

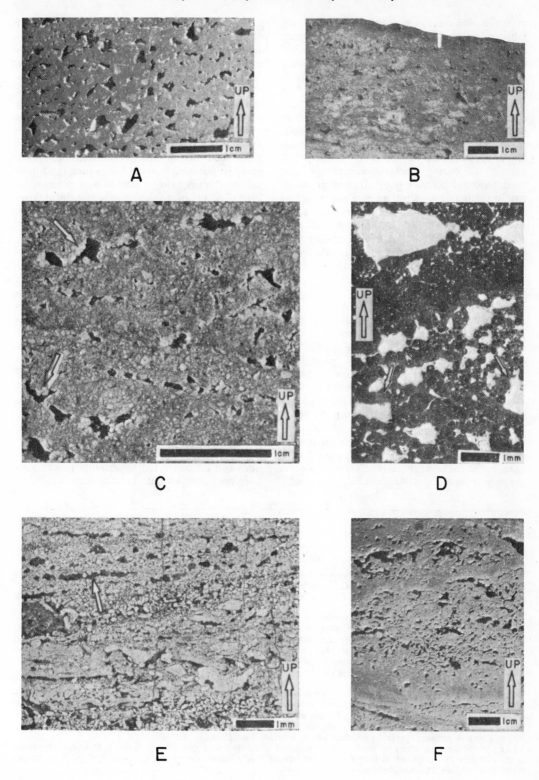

in the mesopore range. Most mesopores are fabric-selective types of pores, whereas many of the megapores represent types that are not fabric selective (channels, vugs, and caverns) and were formed by solution beneath erosion surfaces in the telogenetic zone.

Subclass boundaries within the mesopore range also correspond in part to natural groupings. The interparticle porosity of many pisolitic limestones, much moldic porosity due to solution of bioclastic debris, much interparticle porosity of coarse bioclastic limestones, and most fenestral porosity generally are predominantly in the large-mesopore size range ($\frac{1}{2}$–4 mm). Pore sizes in most oölitic limestones and significant amounts of the intercrystal pore space in sucrose dolomites that is coarser than microporosity ($<1/16$ mm) are in the small-mesopore size range ($1/16$–$\frac{1}{2}$ mm).

Porosity Abundance

Porosity abundance is a useful descriptive parameter that is hard to determine visually with accuracy. Thus, there is much use of qualitative terms such as "fair," "good," and "excellent," with varied amounts of porosity qualifying for each, depending on the perspective or purpose of the observer. This approach no doubt will continue. Our concern, however, is with more quantitative ways to express porosity abundance. Accurate visual estimation of porosity abundance is difficult with most porous carbonates, for several reasons: very large pores commonly cause sampling problems; a multi-

plicity of porosity types and complexities of size and shape make estimates inaccurate; and micropore systems, such as those found in many marls, chalks, and very finely crystalline dolomite, are more difficult to estimate than porosity of rocks with mesopores. Study of thin sections impregnated with colored plastic helps in determining porosity abundance in uniform types of mesopore and micropore systems. Experience with rocks for which porosity values have been determined by conventional core analysis, porosity analysis by gamma ray attenuation (Evans, 1965; Harms and Choquette, 1965), or other mass methods is helpful, particularly if the rocks are of the same facies as those being estimated. Suites of porosity reference standards for various rock types may permit direct visual comparison of measured porosity samples with "unknowns."

Porosity abundance normally is expressed as the percentage of the total sample volume occupied by pore space. In the notation of this classification (Fig. 2), abundance is stated in a percentage which follows the designation of the porosity type. If more than one basic type of porosity is present, the abundance of each may be useful. It can be noted as a percentage of each type or as a simple ratio of relative abundances of the two or more types, or as both a ratio and the total percent porosity abundance. Relative-abundance ratios are easy to make by quick visual inspection. Moreover, ratio estimates made in routine sample descriptions can be converted to absolute percentages once core-analysis data are available.

Fɪɢ. 9.—Examples of fenestral porosity.

A. Fenestral porosity in pisolitic wackestone dolomite. These fenestral pores, like those of examples **B-F,** are probably of secondary eogenetic origin. Pore sizes are dominantly in large-mesopore range. Classification: eogenetic, large mesofenestral porosity (SE-lmsFE). Tansill Formation (Permian), Guadalupe Mountains, New Mexico. Polished surface.

B. Fenestral porosity in irregularly laminated algal-mat dolomite. Mission Canyon Formation (Mississippian), North Dakota. Polished core surface.

C. Fenestral porosity in poorly laminated dolomitic packstone. Note large pore size in relation to grain size, and multigranular margins of pores (arrows), a distinctive and diagnostic feature of fenestral porosity. Phosphoria Formation (Permian), Cottonwood Creek field, Wyoming. Polished core surface.

D. More magnified thin-section view of rock shown in **C,** illustrating more clearly the multigranular roofs, walls, and floors of fenestral openings.

E. Completely filled former fenestral pores ("birdseyes") in laminated, pellet-intraclast limestone. Multigranular roofs characterized long former pores (arrow). Clear sparry calcite cement has filled pores. Classification: cement-filled fenestral porosity (cf-FE). To this characterization could be added descriptors noting pore size, inferred time of porosity origin, and even inferred time of cement filling. McLish Formation (Ordovician), Oklahoma. Polished surface. Specimen courtesy of W. E. Ham (see Ham, 1954).

F. Well-connected fenestral porosity in laminated pellet-intraclast dolomite packstone. Complex shapes of pores could be characterized as irregular (Ir) to equant (Eq). Tansill Formation (Permian), Guadalupe Mountains, New Mexico. Polished surface.

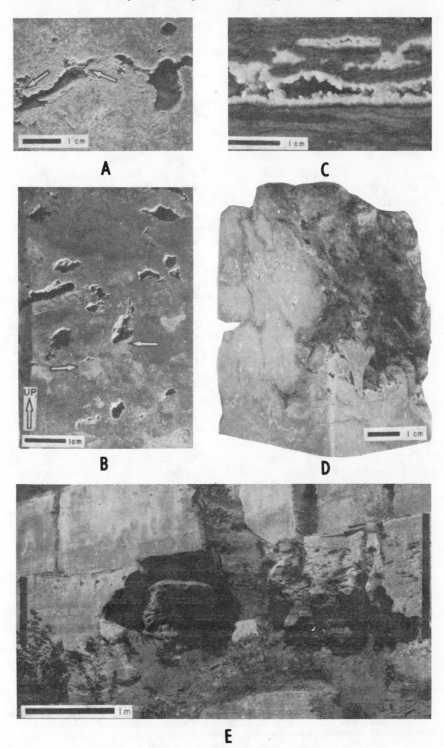

Porosity Descriptions and Code

A complete porosity description using the elements of this classification includes a designation of basic porosity type(s) and one or more accessory modifying terms relating to genesis, size (and shape), and abundance. The sequence in which these terms may be combined is shown in Figure 3, with examples illustrating various levels of descriptive detail. It is further illustrated in the captions of Figures 5 through 12.

Mnemonic letter symbols for the basic porosity types and most porosity modifiers, coupled with percentages and/or ratios for abundance, adapt this classification for brief porosity notation or coding for field or wellsite descriptions (Fig. 2). The symbols suggested in Figure 2 have proved easy to learn and useful.

The code symbols use upper case letters for the basic porosity types and the modifying terms "primary" (P) and "secondary" (S). Symbols of most modifying terms use lower case letters. The derivation of the symbols are apparent, except for the three porosity types, interparticle, intraparticle, and intercrystal, whose letter construction makes a direct mnemonic notation difficult. Code letters for these three basic types are the initial letters W for "within" (intra-) and B for "between" (inter-); thus the letter symbols are BP, WP, and BC, respectively. Vug is not abbreviated.

It can be useful to record pore-shape information directly, in place of or in addition to pore-size information, though in our experience shape modifiers are commonly unneeded. Pore shape can be expressed by the following symbols enclosed in parentheses: (Eq) for equant, (Tb) for tubular, (Pl) for platy, and (Ir) for ir-regular. In a code notation the shape modifier is placed just to the left of the pore-size modifier or basic porosity type symbol. Examples are (Eq)MO and (Tb)mgCH.

For some purposes it is desirable simply to record the size, abundance, or some genetic information about porosity without designating the basic porosity type. The symbol PO is used for porosity or pore, as in mcPO for micropores, S-PO for secondary pores, or PO(15%) for 15 percent porosity.

Compound and gradational porosity name and code designations involve the same basic construction as in Figure 3. To designate *compound* pore systems (Fig. 12), the individual porosity type and its modifying terms should be separated by the word "and." The most abundant porosity type should be listed last and followed by the porosity-abundance parameters; for example, "reduced moldic and reduced primary interparticle porosity (15%) (1:4)." For the porosity code, separate the individual porosity-type terms (and their modifier terms, if used) by a slash mark, so that the example just given would be represented as r-MO/rp-BP (15%) (1:4). *Gradational* porosity types (Fig. 11B) are separated by the word "to" if described in words, as in the description "solution-enlarged interparticle to channel porosity," and are separated by a long dash in code form, as in FR—CH.

Study of the illustrated examples of porosity and their code designations (Figs. 4–12), and some practice with actual rock specimens suffice to show the descriptive and interpretive leverage of the system, and the ease of learning it. For very detailed porosity characterizations, additional parameters can be added to

---

←≪≪

FIG. 10.—Examples of vug and channel porosity.

A. Channel pore system (CH) in dolomite. Large openings at left and right are interconnected in three dimensions. In places (see arrows) intercrystal porosity connects and is gradational with channel porosity. Leduc Formation (Devonian), Big Valley field, Alberta. Polished core surface.

B. Vug porosity in microcrystalline dolomite. A few vugs have been filled partly to completely by internal sediment (small arrows) prior to dolomitization. Vugs are mostly mesovugs (VUG). Leduc Formation (Devonian), Big Valley field, Alberta, Canada. Polished core surface.

C. Reduced channel porosity in dolomite. Channels of elongate to platy shapes that parallel lamination have been reduced or filled by cementation. Cement is coarsely crystalline dolomite. Classification code: cr-CH. Trenton Formation (Ordovician), Scipio field, Michigan. Polished core surface.

D. Irregular surface of non-fabric-selective megapore in dolomite. Distinction between large-scale channels and vugs in relatively small rock samples may not be possible. Devonian, Alberta. Two polished core surfaces.

E. Solution-developed megapores (cavern, solution-enlarged fractures, channels, and vugs) in bioclastic "lime" grainstone. Cavern is about 3½ m across. Solution development of cavern was selective to very permeable zone of primary interparticle porosity (interval shown by vertical bars) where fractures intersected this zone. Salem Limestone (Mississippian), quarry near Oolitic, Indiana.

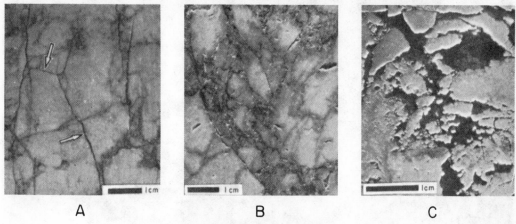

FIG. 11.—Examples of fracture and breccia porosity.

A. Fracture porosity in stylolitic "lime" mudstone. Dark gray patches are caused by oil stain. Madison Group (Mississippian), Oregon Basin field, Wyoming. Polished core surface.

B. Fracture porosity grading to breccia porosity (FR—BR) in microcrystalline dolomite. Porosity along microfractures is shown by oil stain (darker gray). Leduc Formation (Devonian), Big Valley field, Alberta. Polished core surface.

C. Solution-enlarged breccia porosity (sx-BR) in microcrystalline dolomite. Leduc Formation (Devonian), Big Valley field, Alberta. Polished core surface.

suit one's purpose. But for many uses, we find that simple combinations of only two or three of the parameters are satisfactory. The major advantage which the classification system provides is not, however, that of providing an easy method of characterizing porosity in sedimentary carbonates, but that of forcing more critical observations of the pores in relation to the enclosing rock. Use of the classification system should result in more accurate genetic interpretations.

CONCLUSIONS

1. The origin and modification of porosity are important for understanding sedimentary carbonates, and in exploring for and exploiting their fluids. A genetically oriented system of porosity nomenclature and classification helps to develop the requisite understanding.

2. Modifications in porosity are a major and commonly the predominant diagenetic process in most sedimentary carbonates. The vast reduction in porosity from the initial sediment to the negligible porosity of most ancient carbonates is accomplished largely by cementation. The volume of cement filling former pores approaches or exceeds the volume of the framework in many carbonate rocks.

3. Even though most porosity in limestones and dolomites can be related to primary features, many pores form after deposition (secondary).

4. Porosity in carbonate rocks is normally physically complex, genetically diverse, and distinct from that of other sedimentary rocks. Carbonate porosity generally differs significantly from that of sandstone (Table 1), with which it commonly is compared, in that the amount of pore space is ordinarily smaller; interparticle porosity is less important and intraparticle, intercrystal, moldic, and other types much more important; pore size and shape can be much more varied; and both the pre- and postdepositional periods are more important in forming and modifying porosity.

5. Pore space which reflects by its position and boundaries the depositional or diagenetic fabric elements of a sediment or rock is termed "fabric selective." Porosity formed early in diagenesis is commonly fabric selective, in contrast to much of the porosity formed later when unstable carbonate minerals and most or all former pore space has been eliminated. Much carbonate porosity is fabric selective.

6. The time of final deposition and burial provides a practical basis for subdividing the porosity history of sedimentary carbonates into three main stages: *predepositional, depositional,* and *postdepositional. Primary* porosity forms during the first two stages, and *secondary* porosity forms during the last one. The use of all these terms is independent of lithification.

7. Much postdepositional creation and modification of porosity occur either very early or

A

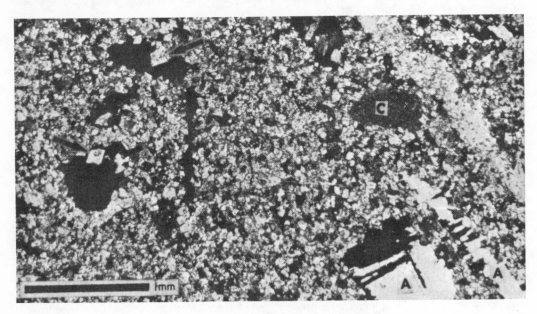

B

FIG. 12.—Examples of compound porosity types.

A. Mesopores (black) in skeletal packstone. Larger interparticle voids show evidence of solution enlargement. Some nummulitid forams contain small intraparticle mesopores (arrows). Notice partial pore fillings of calcite overgrowths on echinoderm debris, seen best in central part of photo. Classification code: smsWP/sx-lmsBP (1:10). Tertiary, Libya. Thin section, cross-polarized light.

B. Moldic and intercrystal porosity in sucrose dolomite. Molds (large black areas) have been filled in part by dolomite rhombs (arrows) and large anhydrite crystals, A. Several undissolved calcitic echinoderm fragments, C, are visible. Simple classification code representation would be cr-MO/BC; more complete designation would be cr-lmsMO/smsBC(1:12). Madison Group (Mississippian), Oregon Basin field, Wyoming. Thin section, cross-polarized light.

Table 2. Attributes Used to Define Basic Porosity Types

(Main attributes are indicated by "X" and attributes of lesser importance by "x."
Detailed definitions are given in glossary)

Basic Porosity Type	Size	Shape	Position in Fabric	Mode of Origin	Fabric Selective	Example (Fig. No.)
Boring		x		X	Variable	6F, G
Burrow		x	X	X	Yes	
Breccia			X		Variable	11C
Cavern	X			x^1	Uncommonly	10E
Channel		X		x^1	No	10A, C
Fenestral	x^2	x	X	x	Yes	9A–F
Fracture		x		X	Uncommonly(?)	11A, C
Growth framework			X	X	Yes	
Intercrystal			X	X^3	Yes	7A–C, 12B
Interparticle			X		Yes	5A–E, 12A
Intraparticle			X		Yes	6D, E, 12A
Moldic				X	Yes	8A–H, 12B
Shelter	x^2		X	X	Yes	6A, B
Shrinkage				X	Variable	
Vug		X		x^1	No	10B, D, E

[1] Solution is the dominant process, but interpretation of process is not required for the definition.
[2] The size implication is that pore size is large in relation to the normal size of interparticle fabric elements.
[3] Intercrystal porosity applies largely to carbonate rocks composed of dolomite.

very late in burial history, when the sediment or rock is influenced significantly by surface-related processes. Therefore, it is useful to subdivide the postdepositional period into three main burial stages (Fig. 1): (a) the *eogenetic* stage, when newly deposited and/or recently buried deposits are subjected to processes operating from or related to a deposition surface or a surface of intraformational erosion; (b) the *telogenetic* stage, when long-buried rocks are affected by processes at or just below an erosion surface; and (c) the *mesogenetic* stage, or intermediate time of burial at depths below sig-

nificant influence by surficial processes. These three terms also can be used to designate the porosity formed in each stage, the processes acting during each stage, or the corresponding burial zones.

8. Current porosity nomenclature can be improved by adding a few new terms and by sharpening or restricting the definitions of current terms. Key elements of the nomenclature we suggest are: (a) definition of primary and secondary and predepositional, depositional, and postdepositional as major porosity time terms; (b) recognition of the eogenetic, meso-

Table 3. Times[1] and Modes of Origin of Basic Porosity Types

(Letter symbols denote dominant, D; subordinate, s; and rare, r)

Basic Porosity Type	Time of Origin Relative to Time of Final Deposition			Mode of Origin			
	Before	During	After	Framework Accretion	Sorting, Packing	Organic or Physical Disruption	Solution, Decomposition, or Replacement
Boring	r^2	s	D			D	
Breccia	r^2	s	D		s	D	
Burrow	r^2		D			D	
Cavern		r	D			r	D
Channel	r^2		D			r	D
Fenestral	r^2	s	D	s?	s?	D	
Fracture	r^2		D			D	
Growth framework	r^2	D		D			
Intercrystal	r^2	s	D^3				D^3
Interparticle	r^2	D	s	s	D		s
Intraparticle	D	r	s	s	s		s
Moldic	r^2		D				D
Shelter	r^2	D			D		
Shrinkage	r^2		D			D	
Vug	r^2		D				D

[1] Exclusive of porosity of recycled extraformational rock fragments.
[2] This relates to porosity of individual particles, including intraformational clasts, that subsequently were moved to the site of final deposition.
[3] Intercrystal porosity of dolomites is of chief interest for purposes of this table.

genetic, and telogenetic time stages and corresponding burial zones; (c) restriction of "vug" and "channel" to pores of contrasting shape that are not fabric selective (see glossary); and (d) proposal of a size grade scale for porosity, the terms for which can be used as prefixes either to a porosity-type term (*e.g.*, micromold, mesovug) or to "pore" (*e.g.*, micropore, mesopore). A glossary with discussion of most porosity terms is appended to this article.

9. The geologic classification of porosity we propose incorporates most current nomenclature and the modifications cited, and is summarized in Figure 2. Its main elements are 15 basic porosity types defined by physical and/or genetic features. Of these types seven (interparticle, intraparticle, intercrystal, moldic, fenestral, vug, and fracture) are the dominant forms in sedimentary carbonates. Each basic type can be used independently or combined with modifying terms that give information about genesis, size, and abundance of porosity. Genetic modifiers pertain to the time of porosity origin, the process of porosity modification (solution, cementation, or internal sedimentation), and the direction or stage of porosity modification (enlarged, reduced, or filled). These genetic modifiers give the classification much of its interpretive value.

As a better understanding of porosity in sedimentary carbonates is developed, it undoubtedly will prove desirable to build more elaborate or different classifications of porosity, and an entirely new nomenclature may prove feasible for general and specialized purposes. Perhaps the system advocated here will speed these developments. In the interim we hope this article will help to focus more attention on the useful geologic information available from scrutinizing pores in relation to their carbonate host.

References Cited

Adams, J. E., 1953, Non-reef limestone reservoirs: Am. Assoc. Petroleum Geologists Bull., v. 37, p. 2566–2569.
—— and H. N. Frenzel, 1950, Capitan barrier reef, Texas and New Mexico: Jour. Geology, v. 58, p. 289–312.
—— and M. L. Rhodes, 1960, Dolomitization by seepage refluxion: Am. Assoc. Petroleum Geologists Bull., v. 44, p. 1912–1920.
American Geological Institute, 1960, Glossary of geology and related sciences with supplement: Washington, D.C., Am. Geol. Inst. Pub. 501, 397 p.
Archie, G. E., 1952, Classification of carbonate reservoir rocks and petrophysical considerations: Am. Assoc. Petroleum Geologists Bull., v. 36, p..278–298.

Aschenbrenner, B. C., and G. V. Chilingar, 1960, Teodorovich's method for determining permeability from pore-space characters of carbonate rocks: Am. Assoc. Petroleum Geologists Bull., v. 44, p. 1421–1424.
Bathurst, R. G. C., 1959, The cavernous structure of some Mississippian *Stromatactis* reefs in Lancashire, England; Jour. Geology, v. 67, p. 506–521.
—— 1964, The replacement of aragonite by calcite in the molluscan shell wall, *in* J. Imbrie and N. Newell, eds., Approaches to paleoecology: New York, John Wiley & Sons, p. 357–376.
—— 1966, Boring algae, micrite envelopes and lithification of molluscan biosparites: Geol. Jour., v. 5, pt. 1, p. 15–32.
Beales, F. W., 1958, Ancient sediments of Bahaman type: Am. Assoc. Petroleum Geologists Bull., v. 42, p. 1845–1880.
—— 1965, Diagenesis in pelletted limestones, *in* L. C. Pray and R. C. Murray, eds., Dolomitization and limestone diagenesis—a symposium: Soc. Econ. Paleontologists and Mineralogists Spec. Pub. 13, p. 49–70.
Beales, F. W., and A. E. Oldershaw, 1969, Evaporite-solution brecciation and Devonian carbonate reservoir porosity in western Canada: Am. Assoc. Petroleum Geologists Bull., v. 53, p. 503–512.
Behrens, E. W., 1965, Environment reconstruction for a part of the Glen Rose Limestone, central Texas: Sedimentology, v. 4, p. 65–111.
Black, M., 1933, The algal sedimentation of Andros Island, Bahamas: Royal Soc. London Philos. Trans., ser. B, v. 222, p. 165–192.
Boekschoten, G. J., 1966, Shell borings of sessile epibiotic organisms as paleoecological guides (with examples from the Dutch coast): Palaeogeography, Palaeoclimatology, Palaeoecology, v. 2, p. 333–379.
Bonet, F., 1952, Urgonian facies of the middle Cretaceous in the region of Tampico: Asoc. Mexicana Geólogos Petróleros Bol., v. 8, p. 389–488.
Boyd, D. W., 1958, Observations on the Phosphoria reservoir rock, Cottonwood Creek field, Washakie County, Wyoming: Am. Assoc. Petroleum Geologists, Rocky Mountain Sec., Petroleum Inf., Geol. Rec., p. 45–53.
Bretz, J H., 1942, Vadose and phreatic features of limestone caverns: Jour. Geology, v. 50, p. 675–811.
Chilingar, G. V., 1957, A short note on types of porosity in carbonate rocks: Compass, v. 35, p. 69–74.
——H. J. Bissell, and K. H. Wolf, 1967, Diagenesis in carbonate rocks, *in* G. Larsen and G. V. Chilingar, eds., Diagenesis in sediments: Developments in Sedimentology, Amsterdam, Elsevier Pub. Co., v. 8, p. 179–322.
Choquette, P. W., and J. D. Traut, 1963, Pennsylvanian carbonate reservoirs, Ismay field, Utah and Colorado, *in* R. O. Bass, ed., Shelf carbonates of the Paradox basin: Four Corners Geol. Soc., p. 157–186.
Cloud, P. E., Jr., 1960, Gas as a sedimentary and diagenetic agent: Am. Jour. Sci. (Bradley vol.), v. 258-A, p. 34–45.
Davis, W. M., 1930, Origin of limestone caverns: Geol. Soc. America Bull., v. 41, p. 475–628.
Dunham, R. J., 1962, Classification of carbonate rocks according to depositional texture, *in* W. E. Ham, ed., Classification of carbonate rocks—a symposium: Am. Assoc. Petroleum Geologists Mem. 1, p. 108–121.
—— 1963, Early vadose silt in Townsend mound

(reef) in New Mexico (abs.): Am. Assoc. Petroleum Geologists Bull., v. 47, p. 356.

——— 1965, Vadose pisolite in the Capital Reef (abs.): Am. Assoc. Petroleum Geologists Bull., v. 49, p. 338.

Engelhardt, W. von, 1960, Der Porenraum der Sedimente: Berlin, Springer-Verlag, 207 p.

Etienne, J., 1963, Rock impregnation by colored resins for studying porosity in thin section: Inst. Français Pétrole Rev., v. 18, no. 4, p. 611–623.

Evamy, B. D., 1967, Dedolomitization and the development of rhombohedral pores in limestones: Jour. Sed. Petrology, v. 37, p. 1204–1215.

Evans, H. B., 1965, GRAPE—A device for continuous determination of material density and porosity: 6th Ann. Soc. Prof. Well Log Analysts Symposium Trans., Dallas, v. 2, p. B1-B25.

Fairbridge, R. W., 1967, Phases of diagenesis and authigenesis, in G. Larsen and G. V. Chilingar, eds., Diagenesis in sediments: Developments in Sedimentology, Amsterdam, Elsevier Pub. Co., v. 8, p. 179–322.

Fay, A. H., 1920, A glossary of the mining and mineral industry: U.S. Bur. Mines Bull. 95, 754 p.

Fischer, A. G., 1964, The Löfer cyclothems of the Alpine Triassic, in Symposium on cyclic sedimentation: Kansas Geol. Survey Bull. 169, p. 107–150.

——— and R. E. Garrison, 1967, Carbonate lithification on the sea floor: Jour. Geology, v. 75, p. 488–496.

Folk, R. L., 1959, Practical classification of limestones: Am. Assoc. Petroleum Geologists Bull., v. 43, p. 1–38.

Fraser, H. J., 1935, Experimental study of the porosity and permeability of clastic sediments: Jour. Geology, v. 43, p. 910–1010.

Friedman, G. M., 1965, Occurrence and stability relationships of aragonite, high-magnesian calcite, and low-magnesian calcite under deep-sea conditions: Geol. Soc. America Bull., v. 76, p. 1191–1196.

Gebelein, C. D., 1967, Origin and growth rates of subtidal algal stromatolites, Bermuda (abs.): Geol. Soc. America Prog. Ann. Mtg., New Orleans, p. 75; 1968, Geol. Soc. America Spec. Paper 115, p. 75.

Ginsburg, R. N., 1956, Environmental relationships of grain size of Florida carbonate sediments: Am. Assoc. Petroleum Geologists Bull., v. 40, p. 2384–2427.

——— ed., 1964, South Florida carbonate sediments: Geol. Soc. America Ann. Mtg. Field Trip Guidebook No. 1, Miami, Florida, 72 p.

——— E. A. Shinn, and J. H. Schroeder, 1967, Submarine cementation and internal sedimentation within Bermuda reefs (abs.): Geol. Soc. America Prog. Ann. Mtg., New Orleans, p. 78–79; 1968, Geol. Soc. America Spec. Paper 115, p. 78–79.

Ham, W. E., 1954, Algal origin of the "birdseye" limestone in the McLish Formation: Oklahoma Acad. Sci. Proc., v. 33, p. 200–203.

——— ed., 1962, Classification of carbonate rocks—a symposium: Am. Assoc. Petroleum Geologists Mem. 1, 279 p.

——— and L. C. Pray, 1962, Modern concepts and classifications of carbonate rocks, in W. E. Ham, ed., Classification of carbonate rocks—a symposium: Am. Assoc. Petroleum Geologists Mem. 1, p. 2–19.

Harbaugh, J. W., 1960, Petrology of marine bank limestones of Lansing Group (Pennsylvanian), southeast Kansas: Kansas Geol. Survey Bull. 142, pt. 5, p. 189–234

——— 1967, Carbonate oil reservoir rocks, in G. V.

Chilingar, H. J. Bissell, and R. W. Fairbridge, eds., Carbonate rocks, Pt. A, Origin, and classification: Developments in Sedimentology, Amsterdam, Elsevier Pub. Co., v. 9A, p. 349–398.

Harms, J. C., and P. W. Choquette, 1965, Geologic evaluation of a gamma-ray porosity device: 6th Ann. Soc. Prof. Well Log Analysts Symposium Trans., Dallas, v. 2, p. C1-C37.

Harris, W. H., and R. K. Matthews, 1967, Subaerial diagenesis of aragonitic carbonate sediments, Barbados, West Indies: Efficiency of the solution-reprecipitation process (abs.): Geol. Soc. America Prog. Ann. Mtg., New Orleans, p. 91–92; 1968, Geol. Soc. America Spec. Paper 115, p. 91–92.

Hohlt, R. B., 1948, The nature and origin of limestone porosity: Colorado School Mines Quart., v. 43, no. 4, 51 p.

Holmes, A., 1920, The nomenclature of petrology, with references to selected literature (1st ed.): London, Thomas Murby & Co., 284 p.

Howard, J. H., 1967, A classification of subsurface bodies of fragmented rocks: Am. Assoc. Petroleum Geologists Bull., v. 51, p. 945–951.

Howard, W. V., 1928, A classification of limestone reservoirs: Am. Assoc. Petroleum Geologists Bull., v. 12, p. 1153–1161.

——— and M. W. David, 1936, Development of porosity in limestones: Am. Assoc. Petroleum Geologists Bull., v. 20, p. 1389–1412.

Illing, L. V., 1954, Bahaman calcareous sands: Am. Assoc. Petroleum Geologists Bull., v. 50, p. 1–95.

——— 1959, Deposition and diagenesis of some upper Paleozoic carbonate sediments in Western Canada: 5th World Petroleum Cong. (New York) Proc., Sec. I, p. 23–52.

——— A. J. Wells, and J. C. M. Taylor, 1965, Penecontemporary dolomite in the Persian Gulf, in L. C. Pray and R. C. Murray, eds., Dolomitization and limestone diagenesis—a symposium: Soc. Econ. Paleontologists and Mineralogists Spec. Pub. 13, p. 89–111.

——— G. V. Wood, and J. G. C. M. Fuller, 1967, Reservoir rocks and stratigraphic traps in non-reef carbonates: 7th World Petroleum Cong. Proc., Mexico City, v. 2, p. 487–499.

Imbt, W. C., and S. P. Ellison, 1946, Porosity in limestone and dolomite petroleum reservoirs: Am. Petroleum Inst. Drilling and Production Practice, p. 364–372.

Ireland, H. A., 1951, Insoluble residues, in L. W. Leroy, ed., Subsurface geologic methods: Colorado School Mines, p. 140–156.

Jodry, R. L., 1966, Pore geometry of carbonate rocks (abs.): Am. Assoc. Petroleum Geologists Bull., v. 50, p. 619

Krynine, P. D., 1948, The megascopic study and field classification of sedimentary rocks: Jour. Geology, v. 56, p. 130–165.

Land, L. S., 1967, Diagenesis of skeletal carbonates: Jour. Sed. Petrology, v. 37, p. 914–930.

——— F. T. MacKenzie, and S. J. Gould, 1967, Pleistocene history of Bermuda: Geol. Soc. America Bull., v. 78, p. 993–1006.

Laporte, L. F., 1967, Carbonate deposition near mean sea-level and resultant facies mosaic: Manlius Formation (Lower Devonian) of New York State: Am. Assoc. Petroleum Geologists Bull., v. 51, p. 73–101.

Lees, A., 1964, The structure and origin of the Waulsortian (lower Carboniferous) "reefs" of west-central Eire: Royal Soc. London Trans., v. 247, p. 483–531.

Leighton, M. W., and C. Pendexter, 1962, Carbonate

rock types, in W. E. Ham, ed., Classification of carbonate rocks—a symposium: Am. Assoc. Petroleum Geologists Mem. 1, p. 33–61.

Levorsen, A. I., 1967, Geology of petroleum (2d ed.): San Francisco, W. H. Freeman & Co., 724 p.

Lindstrom, M., 1963, Sedimentary folds and the development of limestone in an Early Ordovician sea: Sedimentology, v. 2, p. 243–275.

Lucia, F. J., 1962, Diagenesis of a crinoidal sediment: Jour. Sed. Petrology, v. 32, p. 848–865.

—— and R. C. Murray, 1967, Origin and distribution of porosity in crinoidal rock: 7th World Petroleum Cong. (Mexico City) Proc., v. 2, p. 409–423.

Matthews, R. K., 1966, Genesis of recent lime mud in southern British Honduras: Jour. Sed. Petrology, v. 36, p. 428–454.

Milliman, J. D., 1966, Submarine lithification of carbonate sediments: Science, v. 153, p. 994–997.

Monty, C., 1965, Recent algal stromatolites in the windward lagoon, Andros Island, Bahamas: Soc. Géol. Belgique Annales, v. 88, Bull. no. 5–6, p. 269–276.

Murray, A. N., 1930, Limestone oil reservoirs of the northeastern United States and of Ontario, Canada: Econ. Geology, v. 25, p. 452–469.

Murray, R. C., 1960, Origin of porosity in carbonate rocks: Jour. Sed. Petrology, v. 30, p.. 59–84.

—— 1964, Preservation of primary structures and fabrics in dolomite, in J. Imbrie and N. D. Newell, eds., Approaches to paleoecology: New York, John Wiley & Sons, p. 388–403.

—— and F. J. Lucia, 1967, Cause and control of dolomite distribution by rock selectivity: Geol. Soc. America Bull., v. 78, p. 21–35.

—— and L. C. Pray, 1965, Dolomitization and limestone diagenesis, an introduction, in L. C. Pray and R. C. Murray, eds., Dolomitization and limestone diagenesis—a symposium: Soc. Econ. Paleontologists and Mineralogists Spec. Pub. 13, p. 1–2.

Muskat, Morris, 1949, Physical principles of oil production: New York, McGraw-Hill, 922 p.

Nuss, W. F., and R. L. Whiting, 1947, Technique for reproducing rock pore space: Am. Assoc. Petroleum Geologists Bull., v. 31, p. 2044–2049.

Pettijohn, F. J., 1957, Sedimentary rocks: New York, Harper & Brothers, 526 p.

Powers, R. W., 1962, Arabian Upper Jurassic carbonate reservoir rocks, in W. E. Ham, ed., Classification of carbonate rocks—a symposium: Am. Assoc. Petroleum Geologists Mem. 1, p. 122–192.

Pray, L. C., 1961, Compaction in calcilutites (abs.): Geol. Soc. America Bull., v. 71, p. 1946.

—— 1964, Limestone clastic dikes in Mississippian bioherms, New Mexico (abs.): Geol. Soc. America Spec. Paper 82, p. 154.

—— 1965, Limestone clastic dikes and marine cementation, Mississippian bioherms, southern New Mexico (abs.): Soc. Econ. Paleontologists and Mineralogists, Permian Basin Sec., Prog. Ann. Mtg., Midland, Texas, p. 21–22.

—— and P. W. Choquette, 1966, Genesis of carbonate reservoir facies (abs.): Am. Assoc. Petroleum Geologists Bull., v. 50, p. 632.

—— and J. L. Wray, 1963, Porous algal facies (Pennsylvanian) Honaker Trail, San Juan Canyon, Utah, in R. O. Bass, ed., Shelf carbonates of the Paradox basin: Four Corners Geol. Soc., p. 204–234.

Purdy, E. G., 1963, Recent calcium carbonate facies of the Great Bahama Bank. I. Petrography and reaction groups: Jour. Geology, v. 71, p. 334–355.

Rice, C. M., 1955, Dictionary of geological terms: Ann Arbor, Michigan, Edwards Brothers, 465 p.

Rittenhouse, G., 1959, There is a reason, in Reports and minutes of the 33rd Annual Meeting of the Society of Economic Paleontologists and Mineralogists: Jour. Sed. Petrology, v. 29, p. 289–291.

Robinson, R. B., 1966, Classification of reservoir rocks by surface texture: Am. Assoc. Petroleum Geologists Bull., v. 50, p. 547–559.

Roehl, P. O., 1967, Stony Mountain (Ordovician) and Interlake (Silurian) facies analogs of recent low-energy marine and subaerial carbonates, Bahamas: Am. Assoc. Petroleum Geologists Bull., v. 51, p. 1979–2032.

Rooney, L. F., 1966, Evidence of unconformity at top of Trenton Limestone in Indiana and adjacent states: Am. Assoc. Petroleum Geologists Bull., v. 50, p. 533–546.

Sander, N. J., 1967, Classification of carbonate rocks of marine origin: Am. Assoc. Petroleum Geologists Bull., v. 51, p. 325–336.

Schmidt, V., 1965, Facies, diagenesis, and related reservoir properties in the Gigas Beds (upper Jurassic), northwestern Germany, in L. C. Pray and R. C. Murray, eds., Dolomitization and limestone diagenesis—a symposium: Soc. Econ. Paleontologists and Mineralogists Spec. Pub. 13, p. 124–168.

Seilacher, A., 1964, Biogenic sedimentary structures, in J. Imbrie and N. D. Newell, eds., Approaches to paleoecology: New York, John Wiley & Sons, p. 296–316.

Shinn, E. A., 1964, Recent dolomite, Sugarloaf Key, in R. N. Ginsburg, ed., South Florida carbonate sediments: Geol. Soc. America Ann. Mtg. Field Trip Guidebook No. 1, Miami, Florida, p. 62–67.

—— 1968, Practical significance of birdseye structures in carbonate rocks: Jour. Sed. Petrology, v. 38, p. 221–224.

—— R. N. Ginsburg, and R. M. Lloyd, 1965, Recent supratidal dolomite from Andros Island, Bahamas, in L. C. Pray and R. C. Murray, eds., Dolomitization and limestone diagenesis—a symposium: Soc. Econ. Paleontologists and Mineralogists Spec. Pub. 13, p. 112–123.

Stanton, R. J., Jr., 1966, The solution brecciation process: Geol. Soc. America Bull., v. 77, p. 843–848.

Stout, J. L., 1964, Pore geometry as related to carbonate stratigraphic traps: Am. Assoc. Petroleum Geologists Bull., v. 48, p. 329–337.

Summerson, C. H., 1966, Crystal molds in dolomite: their origin and environmental interpretation: Jour. Sed. Petrology, v. 56, p. 221–224.

Taft, W. H., and J. W. Harbaugh, 1964, Modern carbonate sediments of southern Florida, Bahamas, and Espíritu Santo Island, Baja California—A comparison of their mineralogy and chemistry: Stanford Univ. Pubs. Geol. Sci., v. 8, no. 2, 133 p.

Tebbutt, G. E., C. D. Conley, and D. W. Boyd, 1965, Lithogenesis of a distinctive carbonate fabric: Wyoming Univ. Contr. Geology, v. 4, no. 1, 13 p.

Thomas, C. M., 1965, Origin of pisolites (abs.): Am. Assoc. Petroleum Geologists Bull., v. 49, p. 360.

Thomas, G. E., 1962, Grouping of carbonate rocks into textural and porosity units for mapping purposes, in W. E. Ham, ed., Classification of carbonate rocks—a symposium: Am. Assoc. Petroleum Geologists Mem. 1, p. 193–223.

Thrailkill, J., 1968, Chemical and hydrologic factors in the excavation of limestone caves: Geol. Soc. America Bull., v. 79. p. 19–46.

Todd, T. W., 1966, Petrogenetic classification of carbonate rocks: Jour. Sed. Petrology, v. 36, p. 317–349.

Waldschmidt, W. A., P. E. Fitzgerald, and C. L. Lunsford, 1956, Classification of porosity and fractures in reservoir rocks: Am. Assoc. Petroleum Geologists Bull., v. 40, p. 953–974.

Waring, W. W., and D. B. Layer, 1950, Devonian dolomitized reef, D-3 reservoir, Leduc field, Alberta, Canada: Am. Assoc. Petroleum Geologists Bull., v. 34, p. 295–312.

APPENDIX A

Glossary of Porosity Terms

In this Glossary most of the terms that have been used in the past few decades to characterize porosity in sedimentary carbonates are defined and/or discussed. The listing of terms is alphabetic. A usage is suggested for each term which either reflects prevailing usage as we understand it, or seems desirable in view of present knowledge about carbonate rocks. For some of the terms, the glossary gives the original definition and reviews significant subsequent usage. But for most terms, particularly the older ones and those which have evolved gradually and somewhat haphazardly from a nontechnical usage into more precise usage, details of the evolution of the term have little relevance.

The discussions of many terms not only consider definitions and usage, but briefly treat the geologic occurrence and/or the origin of the porosity features.

Birdseye, birdseye fabric, birdseye porosity.—In sedimentary carbonates, the term "birdseye" commonly is used for conspicuous, somewhat lens-shaped or globular masses of sparry carbonate cement a few millimeters to 1 cm or more in size. Although the term normally refers to either the sparry carbonate features themselves or to the carbonate rock containing them (Folk, 1959; Ham, 1954; Illing, 1959), it has also been applied to voids of like sizes and shapes; hence, the expression "birdseye porosity." Most birdseye features appear to be identical to what has been termed more recently "fenestral" (Tebbutt et al., 1965). We recommend adoption of "fenestral" (q.v.) for the individual features whether open or infilled, and for the fabric of the rocks containing such features. The use of "fenestral" achieves more precision than "birdseye" and avoids possible confusion arising from the use of "birdseye" for lenslike or "augen" features of varied origins in nonsedimentary rocks.

Borings, boring porosity.—Openings created in relatively rigid constituents or rock by boring organisms. A rigid host is the feature which distinguishes borings from burrows; the latter form in unconsolidated sediment. Porosity created by boring organisms is not abundant in most ancient carbonate rocks, but borings constitute a distinctive and commonly genetically important minor type of porosity (Fig. 6F, G). Borings can be formed by a variety of organisms in a wide array of depositional or eogenetic environments and also can be formed in the telogenetic zone (Fig. 1). Recognition of borings (whether as porosity or as infilled openings) can be important in environmental and stratigraphic analysis. Discussions on borings in carbonate rocks and particles have been given by Ginsburg (1956), Behrens (1965), Bathurst (1964, 1966), Matthews (1966), and Boekschoten (1966).

Breccia porosity.—The type of interparticle porosity in a breccia. Breccias are rather common in many carbonate facies, but breccia porosity is only locally of quantitative importance. Carbonate breccias are of diverse origins (Howard, 1967). Some form by deposition of angular clasts. These depositional breccias may retain some primary porosity in the ancient geologic record if they were well sorted initially and were composed of relatively large particles; but typically, the more poorly sorted, matrix-rich depositional breccias, such as carbonate debris flows, retain negligible porosity. Postdepositional breccias form by fracturing of previously deposited sediment or rock. These can be termed "fracture breccia" and any associated porosity "fracture-breccia porosity." If the process responsible for fracturing is known, the fracture breccias can be identified more specifically as collapse breccias (Stanton, 1966), fault breccias, tectonic breccias, etc. Any associated breccia porosity can be designated similarly. Fracture-breccia porosity commonly intergrades with fracture porosity. We differentiate the two on the basis of the amount of displacement or chaos created by the fracturing process. If there has been rupture causing porosity by simple opening along a fracture, this is considered fracture porosity. But where there has been rupture and appreciable rotation or jumbling, resulting in chaotic rearrangement of the rock fragments, any resulting porosity is considered "fracture-breccia porosity." Illustrations of several rocks with breccia and fracture porosity are given in Figure 11. Beales and Oldershaw (1969) presented an excellent discussion of breccia-moldic porosity created by solution in Devonian oil reservoirs of western Canada.

Burrows, burrow porosity.—Features created by organic burrowing in relatively unconsolidated sediment, in contrast to borings, which formed in rigid sedimentary particles or rock. Porosity representing discrete burrows is relatively uncommon in ancient carbonate rocks, because most burrows collapse, become filled by sediment, or are backfilled by the burrow-forming organism itself. However, other types of porosity, such as interparticle porosity, may occur within burrow fillings in carbonate facies. In somewhat muddy facies, burrow fillings may have more permeability than the host sediment. Commonly these structures, perhaps because of higher permeability, appear to have localized dolomitization (Beales, 1958). In some carbonates the porosity is largely in dolomitized burrows. Features that aid in the recognition of burrows may be found in articles by Seilacher (1964) and Behrens (1965).

Cavern porosity.—A pore system characterized by large openings, or caverns. Although much cavernous porosity is of solution origin, the term is descriptive and not genetic. The term "cavern" or "cavernous" has been widely applied to porosity in carbonate rocks and reservoirs, and the only confusion in the use of the term is the size of opening large enough to warrant this designation. A practical lower size limit of "cavern" for outcrop studies is about the smallest opening an adult person can enter. Where the rock unit is known only from drilling, a practical lower size limit is that large enough to cause an easily recognizable drop of the drilling bit (a half meter or so). Cavern porosity is too large to be identified in subsurface cores of the usual diameters of only 7–12 cm.

Cellular porosity.—This term has diverse meanings. It appears to have been applied first in a technical sense to carbonate-rock porosity by Howard and David (1936, p. 1406), who used it for solution-formed molds and other generally equidimensional solution vugs, as opposed to more elongate channel-like openings. The term "cellular" also has been applied to organically created intraparticle openings within fossils, particularly chambered organisms such as corals or bryozoans. "Cellular" is little used currently to designate porosity. In view of its infrequent use, its diverse connotations, and the availability of more explicit terms, it seems best to abandon the term (see *intraparticle*).

Chalky, chalky porosity.—"Chalky" is a widely used surface-texture term denoting the distinctive dull and earthy character of many chalks, marls, and other minutely structured porous carbonates. We recommend continued use of the descriptive term "chalky" for such surface texture, as advocated by Ireland (1951, p. 146) and Archie (1952, p. 280). The term "chalky" also can be applied to the porosity of such very finely textured rocks. It is useful where a more specific size or porosity-type designation, such as "micropore," "microintraparticle," or "micromold," is not warranted. Chalky texture and chalky porosity are important in petroleum geology. Under low capillary pressures, chalky carbonates can have high water saturations and low oil saturations, and may form reservoir seals for petroleum. However, under extremely high capillary pressures, such as those in the upper part of an oil column several thousands of meters thick in the Asmari limestone of Iran, they can form productive reservoirs (Illing *et al.*, 1967, p. 490).

Channel, channel porosity.—A type of pore or pore system, here defined on the basis of its shape and origin. We propose that "channel" be used for markedly elongate pores or irregular openings with a marked elongation or continuity in one or two dimensions relative to a third dimension, and that it be applied only to such pores and openings which show by their boundaries or continuity that they have developed indiscriminately with respect to texture or fabric elements in the host rock. Thus, "channel" is a shape category of pore which does not display fabric selectivity. "Markedly elongate" is used to mean shapes whose lengths are 10 times or more their cross-section diameter or width. Channel pores or pore systems less than 1/16 mm in cross section or thickness are termed "microchannels." Most channels originate by indiscriminate solution along fracture systems or by lateral coalescence, through enlargement, of other types of pores.

The term "channel" normally does not connote the full range of elongate shapes or openings to which it is applied in the foregoing definition. But it has been used for similarly shaped pores in sedimentary carbonates. Howard and David (1936, p. 1403–1406) used "channel" specifically for solution-created porosity of an elongate or "continuous" nature in contrast to their "cellular" and "equisolution" porosity. Their discussions and illustrations indicate that some "channels" were tubelike or planar. Powers (1962, p. 140) used the term in a similar shape sense, noting that ". . . channels in some aphanitic limestones are commonly 0.5 mm wide and can be traced continuously along an irregular path for 10 to 20 mm." If a more specific shape connotation is desired than simply that of continuity, "channel" can be modified to denote more specifically various cross-sectional shapes along the direction(s) of elongation such as "tubular" or "platy." Examples of channel porosity are shown in Figure 10.

Channels constitute a basic type of porosity closely related to vugs by our definition (see *vug*). The two terms are contrasting shape end members. The more discrete, somewhat equant or equant-elongate voids are classed as vugs; the more markedly elongate pores or pore systems are channels. Channels, as defined heretofore, may grade into other porosity types. Gradations of channel and vug porosity are common. Other types of gradational porosity involving channel as one type are channel-to-fracture porosity, or combinations of solution-enlarged moldic or fenestral porosity with channel porosity. Although channels are classified as not showing fabric selectivity, indiscriminate solution may enlarge or cause coalescence of former pores and pore interconnections in a manner that creates large irregular pores of channel shape, but leaves at least part of the boundary showing fabric-selective relations to the host rock.

Compact.—A surface-texture term applied to rocks that break along smooth to conchoidal faces and generally have little or no porosity. The term was advocated in a classification of carbonate reservoir rocks by Archie (1952, p. 280) and currently has rather wide usage in this sense. "Compact" is useful as a gross indicator of low matrix porosity in a finely textured rock, and seems preferable to the somewhat synonymous term "dense," as it avoids connotations of mass.

Constructional void porosity.—See *growth-framework porosity*.

Continuous porosity.—A term proposed by A. N. Murray (1930) for systems of interconnected pores, in contradistinction to isolated or "discontinuous" porosity. The terms "continuous" and "discontinuous," though easily understandable, are little used now, and we see no reason to advocate their use. Other porosity terms also imply degree of continuity without needing a specific designation of "continuous" or "discontinuous." Somewhat related and more widely used terms are "effective" and "noneffective" porosity.

Dense.—See *compact*, the preferred term.

Discontinuous porosity.—Poorly connected or isolated pore chambers (Murray, 1930). See discussion of continuous porosity.

Disrupted porosity.—A general term proposed by Powers (1962, p. 140) for voids in some aphanitic limestones which are ". . . of irregular shape and result from diverse but unknown causes . . ." such as "burrowing organisms, entrapped gas, incomplete buckling and tearing of semiconsolidated mud, and slumping." Though little used by subsequent workers, it perhaps has utility as a "wastebasket" term. We prefer more specific porosity terms, such as "shrinkage" or "fenestral," where possible.

Earthy.—This is a widely used surface-texture term, with usage commonly like that of "chalky" (Archie, 1952, p. 280), denoting the dull, unreflective, finely textured appearance of many porous chalks, marls, carbonaceous micrites, and microcrystalline dolomites. The term "earthy" has been applied more restrictively by Thomas (1962, p. 194) to slightly argillaceous carbonates, and commonly implies porosity values as well as particle sizes similar to those of rocks with chalky textures. The term "earthy porosity" is useful if rock examination is made with the unaided eye or at low magnification and observable detail is insufficient to allow a more specific identification of porosity types.

Effective porosity.—The "intercommunicating void space of a rock" (Muskat, 1949, p. 114). As it is usually the effective and not the total porosity that is measured in standard core-analysis procedures, in petroleum engineering practice the term "porosity" normally means "effective porosity" (Muskat, 1949, p. 114).

Eogenetic stage, eogenetic porosity.—"Eogenetic stage" (Greek *eos*: dawn, early), a term herein proposed, applies to the time interval between final deposition and the time when the newly deposited sediment or rock is buried below the depth of significant modification by processes that either operate from the surface, or whose effectiveness is dependent upon proximity to the surface. Eogenetic porosity is that formed in the eogenetic stage. (See discussion in Part 2.)

Fenestra, fenestral fabric, fenestral porosity.—The term "fenestra" (pl. fenestrae) was proposed by Tebbutt et al. (1965, p. 4) for a ". . . primary or penecontemporaneous gap in rock framework, larger than grain-supported interstices." They specifically applied the term "fenestra" both to the void and to the feature resulting from partial to complete infilling of the original void. "Fenestra," "fenestral fabric," and "fenestral porosity" are broadly equivalent to the widely used terms "birdseye," "birdseye fabric," and "birdseye porosity" of most carbonate literature (e.g., Folk, 1959; Ham, 1954; Illing, 1959). We prefer "fenestra(e)" and "fenestral" to "birdseye," partly to recognize the contribution made by Tebbutt et al. in defining the critical aspect of these types of features in carbonates—namely that the opening is larger than the grain-supported interstices—and partly because many geologists use "birdseye" in other connotations. The only modification we suggest in the Tebbutt et al. definition is application of "fenestra(e)" and "fenestral" to both mud-supported and grain-supported fabrics, provided the opening is larger than normal interparticle openings.

Fenestrae, fenestral fabrics, and fenestral porosity, illustrated in Figure 9, are important and distinctive features in sedimentary carbonates and warrant specific recognition. They run the entire textural gamut of clastic carbonates from carbonate mudstones to grainstones and some boundstones (textural rock classification terms of Dunham, 1962). Petroleum reservoirs formed of rocks containing fenestral porosity are a distinctive and important type of "specific reservoir facies" (Pray and Choquette, 1966) in strata of many ages. Many distinctive fabrics or pore systems in ancient carbonate facies interpreted as algal mat during the past decade are of fenestral nature.

Fenestrae occur as somewhat rounded features of spherical, lenticular, or more irregular shapes; their large size in comparison to normal interparticle openings and their multigranular roofs, floors, and other margins are key characteristics (Fig. 9D). Fenestrae are commonly somewhat flattened parallel with the laminae or stratigraphic planes of the rock. However, they may be round or very irregular, and some are elongate in a vertical dimension. Although isolated fenestrae occur in sedimentary carbonates, it is more common to find many in close association. They are most abundant along obscure partings or laminae in the rock. Such fabrics are termed "laminoid fenestral" by Tebbutt et al. (1965, p. 4). Rock with a well-developed fenestral porosity paralleling lamination normally has greater horizontal than vertical permeability.

Fenestral porosity is almost certainly polygenetic. A detailed discussion of its origin is given by Tebbutt et al. (1965, p. 11–13), who suggested numerous mechanisms of formation, chiefly involving decay of sediment-covered algal mats, shrinkage during drying, and accumulation of pockets of gas or water. Well-developed fenestral fabrics in Triassic backreef facies of Austria have been described by Fischer (1964), who emphasized a sediment-shrinkage origin and suggested the term "löferite" for rock fabrics "riddled with shrinkage pores" (fenestrae). Pores formed by gas bubbles in Holocene sediment cores described by Cloud (1960) closely resemble fenestrae. Features identical to many fenestrae of ancient rocks can be formed in carbonate sand and mud samples in the laboratory by acidizing the solution to generate small amounts of gas. We believe most fenestrae form by gas evolution and sediment distension shortly after deposition, an interpretation supported by recent observations by Shinn (1968).

Although fenestral porosity and fenestral fabrics need not be restricted to any particular environment, concentrations of fenestrae along laminae are usually interpreted, perhaps correctly, as indicators of high intertidal or supratidal algal-mat sedimentation. However, caution is needed in interpreting environments on the basis of these distinctive features of fabrics. Well-developed fenestral fabric is also prominent in many calcareous spring deposits (travertine), and certainly the generation of gas within a sediment need not be restricted to supratidal or intertidal environments. For a further sampling of geologic literature regarding fenestral fabrics of both Holocene and ancient deposits, see Black (1933), Boyd (1958), Shinn (1964), and Shinn et al. (1965).

Fracture porosity.—Porosity formed by fracturing. "Fracture porosity" generally is used for porosity occurring along breaks in a sediment or rock body where there has been little mutual displacement of the opposing blocks. Fracture porosity grades into breccia porosity with increasing dislocation or "chaos" (see Fig. 11; *breccia porosity*). In carbonate rocks, fractures and hence fracture porosity may originate in diverse ways, such as by collapse related to solution, slumping, or various kinds of tectonic deformation. A detailed geometric classification of fractures in reservoir rocks is given by Waldschmidt et al. (1956).

Growth-framework porosity.—Primary porosity created by the in-place growth of a carbonate rock framework. "Growth-framework porosity," as herein defined, is reserved specifically for the pore space of rock frameworks known or inferred to have grown in place as rigid or semirigid fabrics. It applies to "boundstones" rather than to "clastic carbonates" in Dunham's (1962) terminology. Growth-framework porosity can form by organic and/or inorganic processes. It may consist of a variety of geometric or genetic subtypes. The most important of these is "growth intra-framework porosity," which designates such openings as the internal chambers of colonial framework organisms. "Growth interframework porosity" is created where elements of the growth structure, such as the platy arms of the colonial coral Acropora palmata or irregular sheets of the alga Lithoporella or Archaeolithothamnium intergrow in such a manner as to isolate voids from sedimentation. Unusual types of growth-framework porosity occur in travertine and in pisolitic caliches (Dunham, 1965; Thomas, 1965).

Porosity occurring in "rigid or semirigid . . . sediment frameworks" was one of three general categories of primary porosity in carbonate rocks discussed by R. C. Murray (1960, p. 61), who used the term "constructional void porosity" for the "primary porosity of carbonate frameworks." Our definition of growth-framework porosity is drawn from Murray's concept of constructional void porosity, but is more restrictive in that we exclude intraparticle openings of any individual organisms or particles that were clastic components of the rock.

Although growth-framework porosity as applied to the primary porosity of in-place carbonate deposits may seem conceptually distinct from the primary intraparticle porosity of clastic limestones, the distinction may not be sharp, and differentiation in a specific carbonate rock can be arbitrary and troublesome. How large must the growth unit be to qualify as a growth framework or boundstone? Frameworks can range in scale from microscopic tests of individual organisms, through the size of oncolites or clams, to the massive organic growth frameworks of barrier reefs. The answer must be varied to fit the purpose of the classifier. We find it practical to restrict the use of "growth-framework porosity" to rock of hand-specimen or larger size in which the boundstone origin can be inferred.

Quantitatively, growth-framework porosity is a relatively minor type of primary porosity in ancient carbonate facies. This scarcity reflects not only the vast preponderance of clastic carbonates in the geologic record, but also the fact that even in facies interpreted as growth frameworks, such as true reefs, the porosity of intimately associated clastic carbonates commonly may exceed that of the framework itself.

Intercrystal porosity.—Porosity between crystals. Although this simple definition could apply in a strict sense to almost all porosity in carbonates, "intercrystal" (or "intercrystalline") normally is restricted to the porosity between individual crystals of somewhat equant and equal size, as in many porous dolomites (Fig. 7). Intercrystal porosity may be of either primary or secondary origin. The primary porosity of depositional fabrics composed of crystals such as halite and other evaporites that have grown in place is an intercrystal type.

Intergranular porosity.—Porosity between grains (cf. interparticle porosity). "Intergranular" is the most commonly used term for between-grain porosity in clastic sandstones and carbonates alike. Occasionally, but unfortunately, it has been considered synonymous with primary porosity; for example, the porosity classification of Fraser (1935), adopted for petroleum reservoir rocks by Levorsen (1967, p. 113), recognized two major categories, primary or intergranular porosity and secondary or intermediate porosity. It seems preferable to use "intergranular" to designate only the position of the porosity with respect to grains, independent of the time of its formation.

"Intergranular porosity" is used more commonly than the broader term, "interparticle porosity." If "intergranular" is used, we suggest it be restricted to between-grain porosity of carbonates whose particles are coarse enough to be considered "grains." The lower size limit of "grains" ranges from 0.004 to 0.06 mm in the major carbonate rock classifications (Ham, 1962).

Interparticle porosity.—Porosity between particles (cf. intergranular porosity). Interparticle porosity denotes position and not genesis. In clastic carbonates, interparticle porosity is generally of depositional (primary) origin, as illustrated in Figures 5A, B, and E, 6A-C, and 12A. But it also can form by several postdepositional processes of which the predominant mechanism is selective solution of finer textured matrix or micrite from between larger particles. Examples of solution interparticle porosity in carbonate packstones are shown in Figure 5C and D. The discrimination, if possible, between a primary depositional origin and a secondary origin is important and commonly difficult. Interparticle porosity is the dominant type of porosity in most carbonate sediments; it is important in some carbonate rocks but is unimportant in others.

We advocate the term "interparticle porosity" as the general name for between-particle porosity in sedimentary carbonates, in preference to the more widely used "intergranular porosity." "Interparticle" is being adopted increasingly following its use by R. C. Murray (1960). "Interparticle" is the broader of the two terms because "particle" has no lower size limit, unlike the term "grain" as defined in some modern carbonate

rock classifications (Ham, 1962). Thus, "interparticle porosity" can be used for "lime muds" or micrites as well as for coarser clastic carbonates. In a strict sense, neither "grain" nor "particle" is satisfactory, as etymologically both imply small size. Yet current sedimentologic usage dating at least from Krynine (1948) recognizes no upper size limit to grains, and the same seems warranted for particles or clasts.

Many specialized geometric and genetic types of interparticle porosity can be recognized. Some related porosity types are fenestral and shelter porosity and some types of breccia and growth-framework porosity (q.v.).

Intracrystal porosity.—Porosity within individual crystals, pores in large crystals of echinoderms, and fluid inclusions form most of this category of porosity.

Intragranular porosity.—Porosity within individual grains. Despite wide usage of "intragranular," we prefer to use "intraparticle" as the general term.

Intraparticle porosity.—Porosity within individual particles or grains (see interparticle porosity). "Intraparticle porosity" as used here is a physical, positional, not a genetic porosity type. It is abundant in carbonate sediments and can be an important part of the preserved porosity in carbonate rocks. In spite of its importance, it has been neglected in comparison to other major types of carbonate porosity. Much intraparticle porosity in carbonates forms before final deposition of the sedimentary particle or grain (predepositional porosity); some forms during or after final deposition. Internal chambers or other openings within individual or colonial skeletal organisms are the most commonly recognized intraparticle pores. However, an appreciable amount of the primary intraparticle porosity in carbonate sediments consists of pore space within individual pellets, intraclasts, oöids, and other nonskeletal grains. It may be pertinent to designate specific types of intraparticle porosity as "intrabiotic," "intracoral," "intrapellet," etc. Intraparticle porosity of postdepositional origin forms chiefly by solution and borings. Examples of types of intraparticle porosity are shown in Figures 6 and 12A.

Matrix porosity.—The porosity of the matrix or finer portion of a carbonate sediment or rock, in contrast to porosity associated with the coarser particles or constituents; or the porosity of "blocks" of the rock in contrast to the porosity of the fractures.

Megapore, megaporosity.—Size terms herein proposed for large pores. Megapore is the largest of three pore-size classes (see pore-size discussion; mesopore and micropore). The "mega-" size designation is used for equant to equant-elongate pores whose average diameter is larger than 4 mm, and for tubular or platy pores whose average cross-sectional diameter or thickness, respectively, is larger than 4 mm. "Mega-" can be combined with "pore" as in "megapore," or with the basic porosity type as in "megamold" or "megamoldic porosity."

Mesogenetic.—A term herein proposed to designate the postdepositional stage between the time when newly buried deposits are acted upon chiefly by processes related to the depositional interface, and the time when long-buried deposits are acted upon primarily by processes operating from the erosional interface. The term also can be used to designate porosity formed in this stage, processes acting during this stage, or the burial zone in which they operate. (See discussion in Part 2.)

Mesopore, mesoporosity.—Size terms herein proposed for intermediate-size pores (see pore-size discussion; *megapore* and *micropore*). The "meso-" size designation is used for equant to equant-elongate pores whose average diameter is between 4 and 1/16 mm, and for tubular or platy pores whose average cross-sectional diameter or least diameter, respectively, is between 4 and 1/16 mm. "Meso-" can be combined with "pore" as in "mesopore" or with the basic porosity type, as in "mesomold" or "mesomoldic porosity."

Micropore, microporosity.—Size terms herein proposed for microscopic pores. Micropore is the smallest of three pore-size classes (see pore-size discussion; *mesopore* and *megapore*). The "micro-" designation is used for equant to equant-elongate pores whose average diameter is less than 1/16 mm and for tubular or platy pores whose average cross-sectional diameter or least diameter, respectively, is less than 1/16 mm. "Micro-" can be combined with "pore" as in "micropore" and "microporosity," or with the basic porosity type, as in "micromold" or "micromoldic porosity."

Mold, moldic porosity.—A mold is a pore formed by the selective removal, normally by solution, of a former individual constituent of the sediment or rock such as a shell or oölith. The resulting porosity is moldic. In general geologic usage, a mold is a "negative" of a former feature and two types, mold cavities and mold impressions, long have been recognized in sedimentary rocks. The terms "mold porosity" and "moldic porosity" have been used sporadically for many years by insoluble-residue workers (1946 Residue Conference reported *in* Ireland, 1951). But the use of "moldic" (or "mold") as a general name for a class of porosity in carbonate literature during the past decade has been meager. The term deserves wider usage. Molds are extremely abundant in many porous carbonate rocks. Many of the so-called "vugs" of petroleum reservoir facies are molds and should be so designated. Molds and moldic porosity are identified on the basis of shape, size, wall ornamentation, or relict features.

Most molds in sedimentary carbonates are created by the selective solution of various types of carbonate depositional particles. Especially common in limestones are molds of primary aragonitic constituents, notably oölites and molluscan shells. Molds in dolomite commonly have formed by selective solution of either aragonite or calcite primary constituents, and less commonly by solution of anhydrite (Murray, 1960, p. 80), gypsum (Summerson, 1966), or halite. A complex genesis of molds by dedolomitization has been documented by Evamy (1967). Decomposition of organic matter, such as that in the plant roots, stalks, or twigs, forms molds. Figure 13 portrays diagrammatically the origins of most molds in carbonate rocks, and examples of moldic porosity are shown in Figures 8 and 12B.

An unusual type of moldic porosity, apparently formed by organic decay and known in ancient rocks largely from features now completely filled by cement, is interpreted to have formed some of the types of structures loosely termed "Stromatactis" in the lower Carboniferous "reef knolls" of England and Ireland. The former cavities are believed (Bathurst, 1959; Lees, 1964) to record the presence of an unknown type of a somewhat rigid-bodied, noncalcareous organism that did not decay until at least partial cementation of the host sediment had occurred. Cavities like these may be more widespread in ancient carbonates than generally has been recognized. The oncolite biscuits described in Holocene carbonates of Florida (Ginsburg, 1964), the Bahamas (Monty, 1965), and Bermuda (Gebelein, 1967) could easily form a related type of moldic porosity.

If the identity of the mold is known, it can be added to the porosity term, a long-established practice with terms like "oömold" or "oömoldic" and "dolomold" or "dolomoldic" (Ireland, 1951, p. 146). A few other

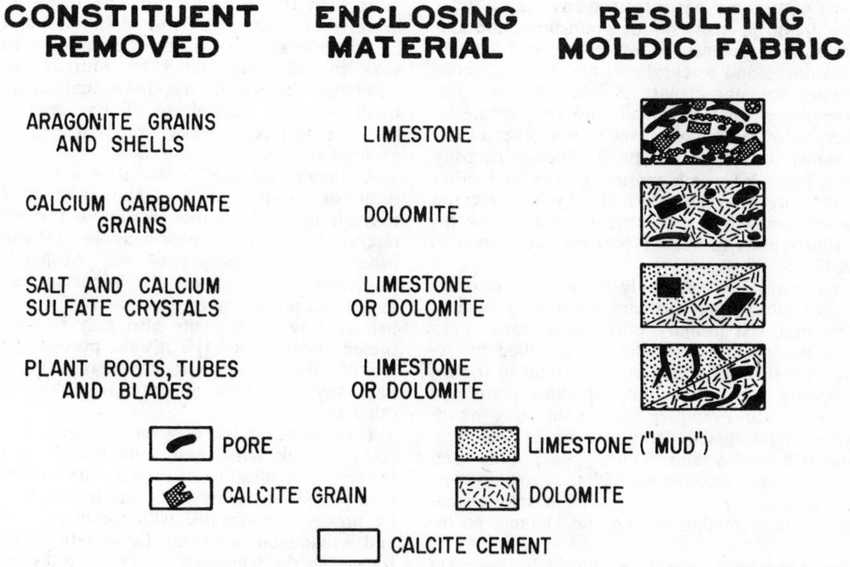

CONSTITUENT REMOVED ENCLOSING MATERIAL RESULTING MOLDIC FABRIC

CONSTITUENT REMOVED	ENCLOSING MATERIAL	RESULTING MOLDIC FABRIC
ARAGONITE GRAINS AND SHELLS	LIMESTONE	
CALCIUM CARBONATE GRAINS	DOLOMITE	
SALT AND CALCIUM SULFATE CRYSTALS	LIMESTONE OR DOLOMITE	
PLANT ROOTS, TUBES AND BLADES	LIMESTONE OR DOLOMITE	

PORE   LIMESTONE ("MUD")

CALCITE GRAIN   DOLOMITE

CALCITE CEMENT

FIG. 13.—Common forms of moldic porosity in carbonate rocks.

examples that we have found useful are "pelmoldic" (pellets), "fusumoldic" (fusulinids), and "crimoldic" (crinoids). See breccia-moldic porosity of Beales and Oldershaw (1969).

Pinpoint porosity.—A wastebasket term for very small pores in carbonate rocks. This term has been used almost exclusively in the petroleum industry, usually in a semitechnical sense. It has no genetic implications. Pore sizes to which "pinpoint" has been applied range from a few hundredths of a millimeter to about a millimeter in diameter. Most commonly, "pinpoint" has been used to designate pores that are barely discernible to the unaided eye (about 0.1 mm in diameter). The term has been used most commonly for rocks with much less porosity than chalks or earthy dolomites.

The term "pinpoint" is most useful for simple, nontechnical, characterizations of pore size. For detailed characterization we prefer to note both size and type of porosity more specifically, either by giving dimensions and pore type directly or by using the size grade scale terms proposed in this article. Most pores of pinpoint sizes are micropores or small mesopores of moldic or intercrystal porosity types.

Primary porosity.—Porosity formed during final sedimentation or present within sedimentary particles at the time of deposition. The term "primary porosity" includes all predepositional and depositional porosity of a particle, sediment, or rock. It also applies to any remnant of the primary porosity (see Part 2).

Saccharoidal.—A textural term, essentially synonymous with "sucrose," referring to a textural resemblance to common table sugar (see *sucrose*).

Secondary porosity.—Porosity formed in a sediment or rock subsequent to final deposition. The term "postdepositional porosity" is essentially synonymous with "secondary porosity" as defined here (see Part 2).

Shelter porosity.—A type of primary interparticle porosity, proposed herein, created by the sheltering effect of relatively large sedimentary particles which prevent the infilling of pore space beneath them by finer clastic particles. Shelter porosity is a common and important type of primary porosity in many clastic limestones. It is found in many oölitic grainstones containing coarse shell fragments or intraclasts, and in carbonate packstones and wackestones and some carbonate mudstones containing platy skeletal particles. Excellent examples of shelter porosity are the "umbrella-like" structures of Harbaugh (1960), and other examples are shown by Dunham (1962). Shelter porosity also can be formed beneath marine grasses and other decomposable organic materials and may be preserved if rigidity was created by cementation prior to decomposition. Illustrations of shelter porosity are shown in Figure 6A-C.

As shelter pores are commonly larger than most of the associated interparticle primary pores, they tend to be sites of preserved primary porosity in many rocks whose finer interparticle pores have been filled by cementation. This tendency has been important in the favorable porosity and permeability of some petroleum reservoir facies, for example, those containing abundant phylloid algae in the Pennsylvanian of the Paradox basin (Choquette and Traut, 1963; Pray and Wray, 1963). Large shelter pores enhance rock permeability and may partly localize subsequent solution enlargement in the formation of vug and channel porosity.

Shrinkage porosity.—Porosity produced by sediment shrinkage. Drying commonly produces shrinkage porosity, but other processes can create contraction cracks (shrinkage porosity) in aqueous environments. Although most shrinkage porosity is a specialized type of fracture porosity, it can be formed by shrinkage of individual sedimentary particles (Schmidt, 1965).

Sucrose, sucrosic.—"Sucrose" and the common variant, "sucrosic," have been used in both a semitechnical and a technical sense to describe carbonate rocks that have appreciable intercrystal pore space and are composed dominantly of somewhat equant, uniformly sized, euhedral to subhedral crystals. Sucrose texture implies appreciable intercrystal pore volume, relatively uniform crystal size, and enough free planar surfaces on the crystals to create a host of reflecting surfaces. Many porous dolomites have a sucrose texture; aggregates of calcite crystals having sucrose texture are very uncommon. We prefer to use "sucrose" as a textural term and not as a porosity term (*cf.* Harbaugh, 1967). Examples of dolomites with sucrose texture are shown in Figure 7.

The terms "sucrose," "sucrosic," and "saccharoidal" are derived from the textural resemblance to common table sugar. The analogy to cube or lump sugar is particularly close. Some geologists follow the standard English-language dictionaries (Oxford, Webster's Unabridged, or Random House) and use "saccharoidal" as the textural term, reserving "sucrose" for the chemical disaccharid compound of common sugar. British geologists appear to have followed this usage more carefully than American geologists. Despite the dictionary authority, the word "sucrose" has had much more extensive usage than "saccharoidal" as a textural term for carbonate rocks (*e.g.*, Archie, 1952; Illing *et al.*, 1967; Levorsen, 1967; Murray, 1960). "Sucrose" seems too firmly entrenched to be eliminated, and as it is the simpler of the two terms we recommend it.

The crystal sizes of what have been termed "sucrose" dolomites range from that of common table sugar (normally 0.1–0.5 mm) to much smaller. Crystal sizes coarser than 0.5 mm are very unusual. Murray (1960, p. 67) states that the crystal size of sucrose dolomite ". . . ranges from less than 5 μ to more than 100 μ, with 25 to 50 μ being very common in reservoir rocks." Sucrose dolomites of interbedded carbonate-evaporite facies commonly have crystal sizes in the range cited by Murray. Most porous dolomites in which the individual crystals are so small as to be difficult to discern even with a hand lens are termed "chalky" or "earthy" by American geologists.

Although "sucrose" is useful as a textural term, the term "sucrose porosity" (*cf.* Harbaugh, 1967) has questionable merit, for although sucrose texture implies intercrystal porosity, many sucrose dolomites contain other types of porosity as well. Moldic porosity, in particular, is a common and important contributor to many sucrose dolomite reservoir rocks, and vug, channel, or fracture porosity also may be significant. We prefer to designate explicitly the porosity between crystals of sucrose carbonates as intercrystal, and to designate any associated porosity as moldic, fenestral, or other basic types.

Telogenetic stage, telogenetic porosity.—Telogenetic stage (Greek *telos:* end, completion), a term herein proposed, applies to the time interval during which long-buried carbonate rocks are influenced significantly by processes associated with weathering and subaerial and subaqueous erosion. Telogenetic porosity is that formed in the telogenetic stage. (See discussion in Part 2.)

Total porosity.—The designation for all the porosity of a rock, regardless of whether it is interconnected or isolated (*cf. effective porosity*).

Vug, vug porosity.—"Vug" and its derived forms, "vuggy" and "vugular," are probably the most commonly used carbonate porosity terms, and also have had the most widely varied definitions and usages. We define "vug" as a pore that (1) is somewhat equant, or not markedly elongate, (2) is large enough to be visible with the unaided eye (diameter greater than 1/16 mm), and (3) does not specifically conform in position, shape, or boundaries to particular fabric elements of the host rock (*i.e.*, is not fabric selective). Solution is the dominant process in formation of vugs as we use the term, but an interpretation of process is not essential to our definition. Most vugs may represent solution enlargement of fabric-selective pores to such an extent that the identity of the precursor cannot be discerned, and at a stage in diagenesis when solution is apparently indiscriminate of fabric elements. The evolution of vugs from molds, which undoubtedly are common precursors of vugs, is illustrated diagrammatically in Figure 4.

The definition of "vug" proposed here, involving size, shape, and the absence of fabric selectivity, is more restrictive than most earlier definitions and usages. It permits the recognition of an important type of porosity that was not specifically differentiated heretofore but was used in a broader sense by many geologists. The new definition also permits integration of vug with the other basic types of porosity in our classification (Part 3).

In our terminology, vugs and channels are similar in that neither is fabric selective. They differ in shape, however; "vug" is used for the more equidimensional pores and "channel" is used for pores more markedly elongate or continuous in one or more dimensions. We arbitrarily separate the two shape categories at a ratio of length to average cross-sectional diameter of about 10:1. Because of the complex shapes of pores in carbonate rocks that might qualify as vugs or channels, actual diameter ratios rarely are calculated; precision generally is not practical or necessary. The compound term "vug-channel" can be useful for pore systems displaying a range of shapes across this boundary. If practical, vug shapes that are somewhat elongate (diameter ratios 3:1 to 10:1) can be differentiated from the more equant forms.

In our usage, vugs, like other basic porosity types, can be designated more specifically as to size by terms such as "mesovug" (1/16–4 mm), "small mesovug" (1/16–½ mm), or "megavug" (4–256 mm). Those relatively few pores that are smaller than 1/16 mm but otherwise fit our definition of "vug" can be termed "microvugs." The practice of indiscriminately calling any visible pore a vug, whether or not it can be identified more exactly or informatively, can be abandoned in favor of combining a size and/or shape designation with the word "pore," as in "mesopore" or "platy megapore." If terminologic anarchy persists in the usage of "vug," a new term should be coined for the porosity here designated as "vug."

The widespread use of "vug," its importance in the classification system we propose, and its varied usage justify more discussion than has been accorded most of the other terms in this glossary. "Vug" seems to have been derived from the Cornish word, *voogha*, meaning underground chamber. Holmes (1920, p. 238) used "vug" or "vugh" as a mining term for ". . . an unfilled cavity . . . generally with a mineral lining of different composition from that of the immediately surrounding ore." Fay (1920) cited "a cavity in the rock, usually lined with a crystalline incrustation," and noted the alternate spellings, "voog," "vough," and "vugg." Rice (1955, p. 444) cited the definitions of both Holmes and Fay. Pettijohn (1957, p. 217) defined vugs differently as "solutional structures" that are ". . . irregular openings related in origin to the 'phreatic' passages produced by ground water action . . . common in carbonate rocks." The AGI Glossary (1960, p. 317) cited Holmes and Fay, but added the more specialized usage of "vug" by many petroleum geologists for " . . . any opening from the size of a small pea to the size of a boulder." Applied to carbonate porosity, "vug" usually connotes "large" size and a somewhat equant shape, as implied in the quoted AGI definition. Two points of difference among geologists are "what size?" and whether "vug" should be applied to any type of porosity of the requisite size and shape regardless of the nature of the porosity. Moreover, some geologists seem to designate all visible pore spaces as "vugs," making "vug" synonymous with "pore."

A few examples in recent literature further illustrate the use of "vug." Murray (1960, p. 61, 81, Figs. 17, 18) used the term in a sense essentially synonymous with "pore" and applied it to a variety of specific types of porosity, many of a fabric-selective type, as in "primary constructional vugs," "anhydrite mold vugs," and "intercrystal vugs." Likewise, Thomas (1962, Pls. 1–3) illustrated interparticle (intraparticle), intrabiotic, intercrystal, and birdseye (fenestral) types of vugs. Others differentiate vugs from interparticle and intercrystal pores (Illing *et al.*, 1967, p. 488; Waring and Layer, 1950, p. 310). Vugs are generally differentiated from more elongate or continuous openings such as channels (*e.g.*, Powers, 1962, p. 140–141; Rooney, 1966, p. 540). Though some use "vug" only for pores of a "pea to boulder size," others apply it to pores as small as ¼-1 mm in diameter or less (*e.g.*, R. C. Murray, 1960, Figs. 17, 18; Robinson, 1966, p. 550; Shinn *et al.*, 1965, Fig. 7a, b; Thomas, 1962, Pls. 1, 2; Waring and Layer, 1950, Fig. 13).

The examples cited are exceptions, however, to the more general practice of indiscriminately lumping porosity of many basic types, sizes, and shapes into a wastebasket category termed "vug." This practice clearly has resulted in the loss of information that might have helped in identifying and interpreting pores in carbonates. The definition of "vug" proposed here, involving size, shape, and restriction to pores that are not fabric selective, is suggested to encourage more critical observations and descriptions of porosity in carbonate facies, without abandoning the term itself.